The Yoga Sūtras of Patañjali

The Yoga Sūtras of Patañjali

Nature of the mind, the universe, and the true self.

B. Ravikanth

Sanskrit Works

www.sanskritworks.com

Published by Sanskrit Works.
Email: info@sanskritworks.com
Phone: 510-400-4825
Web: www.sanskritworks.com

Patañjali.

Yoga Sūtras of Patañjali: Nature of the mind, the universe, and the tue self. / B. Ravikanth
1st ed.
Sanskrit Works, 2012.
7.5" x 9.25" (19.1 cm. x 23.5 cm.)
English and Sanskrit
Summary: A translation and interpretation of Patañjali's Yoga Sūtras. Explains Sāṅkhya and Yoga philosophies.

1. Yoga Sūtras of Patañjali. 2. Yoga — Early works to 1800. 3. Patañjali. Yogasūtra. II. Title: Yoga Sūtras of Patañjali: Nature of the mind, the universe, and the tue self. II. Title.
ISBN 13: 978-0-9882515-0-2
ISBN 10: 0988251507

BISAC:
OCC010000 BODY, MIND & SPIRIT / Meditation
PHI033000 PHILOSOPHY / Hindu
HEA025000 HEALTH & FITNESS / Yoga

विद्या (*Vidyā,* Knowledge)[1]

māteva rakṣati piteva hite niyuṅkte

kānteva cābhiramayatyapanīya duḥkham ।

kīrtiṁ ca dikṣu vitanoti tanoti lakṣmīṁ

kiṁ kiṁ na sādhayati kalpalateva vidyā ॥

Like a mother, it protects you.
Like a father, it engages you in wellbeing.
Like a beloved, it enchants you, taking away your sorrow.
It spreads your name in all directions and extends your wealth and beauty.
What is it that the wish fulfilling vine of knowledge cannot accomplish?

1 The deity depicted is Goddess Sarasvatī, the symbol of knowledge in Hindu tradition. Art work printed with permission from Marehalli Parasad.

ॐ

May the mind hold auspicious thoughts (Śivasaṅkalpa-sūkta)

यज्जाग्रतो दूरमुदैति दैवं तदु सुप्तस्य तथैवैति।
दूरङ्गमं ज्योतिषां ज्योतिरेकं तन्मे मनः शिवसङ्कल्पमस्तु ॥1॥
येन कर्माण्यपसो मनीषिणो यज्ञे कृण्वन्ति विदथेषु धीराः।
यदपूर्वं यक्षमन्तः प्रजानां तन्मे मनः शिवसङ्कल्पमस्तु ॥2॥
यत्प्रज्ञानमुत चेतो धृतिश्च यज्जोतिरन्तरमृतं प्रजासु।
यस्मान्न ऋते किञ्चन कर्म क्रियते तन्मे मनः शिवसङ्कल्पमस्तु ॥3॥
येनेदं भूतं भुवनं भविष्यत्परिगृहीतममृतेन सर्वम्।
येन यज्ञस्तायते सप्तहोता तन्मे मनः शिवसङ्कल्पमस्तु ॥4॥
यस्मिन्नृचः साम यजूꣳषि यस्मिन् प्रतिष्ठिता रथनाभाविवाराः।
यस्मिँश्चित्तꣳ सर्वमोतं प्रजानां तन्मे मनः शिवसङ्कल्पमस्तु ॥5॥
सुषारथिरश्वानिव यन्मनुष्यान्नेनीयतेऽभीशुभिर्वाजिन इव।
हृत्प्रतिष्ठं यदजिरं जविष्ठं तन्मे मनः शिवसङ्कल्पमस्तु ॥6॥

–*Yajurveda 34.1 - 6*

1. That mind which wanders in the waking state as well as in sleep, the far-wanderer, that which is the one and only illuminator of knowledge, may that mind of mine hold auspicious thoughts.
2. That mind, by the help of which men who are well-versed in a variety of knowledge perform sacred sacrificial fire ceremonies, which is unique and is the inner power of all people, may that mind of mine hold auspicious thoughts.
3. That mind which is embodied with knowledge, consciousness, and steadfastness, that which is the inner light and ambrosia of the people, that without which no action can be performed, may that mind of mine hold auspicious thoughts.
4. That immortal one with which the past, present, and future are grasped, that by which the sacred fire ritual is performed by the seven priests, may that mind of mine hold auspicious thoughts.
5. That mind in which the knowledge of *Ṛg*, *Sāma*, and *Yajur Vedas* is placed like the spokes in a chariot wheel, which is intertwined with the minds of all people, may that mind of mine hold auspicious thoughts.
6. That mind which leads men to discover their inner immortal self in the heart like a good charioteer leads horses, which is quick and most speedy, may that mind of mine hold auspicious thoughts.

To my dad.

Table of Contents

Preface

I've always been fascinated with ancient Indian scriptures. I wanted to study, understand, and make use of the wealth of knowledge contained in them. At the age of fourteen, I got hold of a translation of the *Yoga Sūtras* from my grandfather's collection of books. As I was reading, I found many concepts and terms difficult to understand. At the time, I assumed that this confusion was due to my poor command of Telugu (a language spoken in southern India). But, over the years, I've attempted to study other translations (in both Hindi and English), and I found them equally difficult to comprehend. This led me to think that the only way to fully understand the scriptures was to learn the language in which they were originally written — Sanskrit.

In my study of Sanskrit I met with great scholars like Dr. Ram Karan Sharma and Acharya Ananda Prakash. After studying the *Yoga Sūtras* with their help, I realized that the difficulty in understanding was largely not due to the language itself, but rather to the many Sāṅkhya terms used in the text that were not explained in the translations I had come across. It was only after I was introduced to the concepts of Sāṅkhya that I could fully understand the *Yoga Sūtras*. The verses that I had previously found boring or pointless became filled with profound insights into the workings of the mind and the world around us (*prakṛti*).

The hurdles I faced and the difficulty in understanding the material made me think that there is a need for a more accessible way to present the *Yoga Sūtras*. I find that when I can visualize a concept, I understand it better. Following that, I've tried to visually illustrate the difficult-to-understand concepts found in Sāṅkhya and Yoga philosophies. Pictures can act as mnemonics while recalling a topic or an idea, and this can be very helpful while presenting the *Yoga Sūtras* to others. As such, I hope that both students and teachers of Yoga can benefit from the explanations and illustrations presented in this book.

Any suggestions to make this book more accessible or easier to understand will be greatly appreciated. Suggestions can be sent to info@sanskritworks.com.

Acknowledgements

I'm extremely indebted to my Sanskrit teachers – Dr. Ram Karan Sharma, Acharya Ananda Prakash, and Indira Devi. Without their teaching, I wouldn't have even conceived of writing this book. Dr. Ram Karan Sharma, and Acharya Ananda Prakash have taught me everything that I know about Sāṅkhya and Yoga. Likewise, the creation of this book would have not succeeded without the mentorship of Les Morgan, a fine author, whose proficiency in Sanskrit and English has helped tremendously throughout the editing process. We analyzed each verse of this book from the view point of my previous works on the subject. His book-building skills have made the item you hold in your hands a lot more presentable than I ever could have managed on my own.

Many thanks to Dr. Matthew Ritchie for his meticulous editing. To Mariann Clark for proofreading under exacting time constraints. To my very good friend Vinay Doma and to my brother Srikanth for going through the first scribbling of my writing and giving me many valuable suggestions. I'm very grateful to my friends Kieth Lazuka and Anthony Biduck for their extreme generosity in going through the book and suggesting valuable changes. I have learned a lot through the many philosophical discussions I had with them. And to Nathan Clark, for getting the project started by helping me with the initial document.

Special thanks go to my illustration team, Ronaldo Florendo, Chakkaratana Dhamma, Sagar Niyogi, Juan Carlos Acland and Marco Baccioli, for their fine illustrations. Last but not least, I'm grateful for the support I received from my friends – Sreenivasa Paidi, Shanta Bulkin, Khwan Biduck, Becky Horch and Howard Clein, John Marino, Jon Miller and Ann Milner, and Jorge Cal.

Transliteration and Pronunciation

Transliteration

This book includes text in Devanāgarī, one of the Indian writing systems used for Sanskrit.[1]

अ	a	आ	ā	इ	i	ई	ī	उ	u
ऊ	ū	ए	e	ऐ	ai	ओ	o	औ	au
ऋ	ṛ	ॠ	ṝ	ऌ	ḷ				
				ँ	m̐	ं	ṁ	ः	ḥ
क	ka	ख	kha	ग	ga	घ	gha	ङ	ṅa
च	ca	छ	cha	ज	ja	झ	jha	ञ	ña
ट	ṭa	ठ	ṭha	ड	ḍa	ढ	ḍha	ण	ṇa
त	ta	थ	tha	द	da	ध	dha	न	na
प	pa	फ	pha	ब	ba	भ	bha	म	ma
		य	ya	र	ra	ल	la	व	va
		श	śa	ष	ṣa	स	sa	ह	ha
				क्ष	kṣa	त्र	tra	ज्ञ	jña

Pronunciation

The Sanskrit language is most often written in the Devanāgarī writing system, which has more letters than English. The sounds are arranged in a system in which vowels combine with consonants to form syllables. Long vowels (*ā*, *ī*, *ū*, *ṝ*, *ḹ*) are held for a longer duration than short vowels (*a*, *i*, *u*, *ṛ*, *ḷ*). The following examples are based on "standard" American English pronunciations, but are only the closest approximations. For an understanding of the proper pronunciation of

1 This section on Transliteration and Pronunciation is adapted with permission from Les Morgan, Croaking Frogs: A Guide to Sanskrit Metrics and Figures of Speech (Pacifica, California: Mahodara Press, 2011), xix-xxiv.

Sanskrit, study with a specialist of the language is invaluable.

Vowels and aftersounds

a	अ	like the *a* in *about* or the *u* in *but* or *sum*.
ā	आ	like the *a* in *father* or *tar*, held twice as long as short *a*.
i	इ	like the *i* in it or *pin* or *bit*.
ī	ई	like the *i* in *pique* or *police* or *magazine*, or the *ee* in *week*, held twice as long as short *i*.
u	उ	like the *u* in *push* or *bush*.
ū	ऊ	like the *u* in *rule* or *rude* or the *oo* in *fool*, held twice as long as short *u*.
ṛ	ऋ	sonorous "r" sound, not exactly but similar to both *r* sounds in *error*. Some pronounce it as "ri" while others pronounce it as "ru."
ṝ	ॠ	held twice as long as short *ṛ*.
ḷ	ऌ	no good English equivalent, but like the *lry* in *revelry* or the *le* in *table*, but in some regions more like *lree* and in other regions more like *lruu*.
e	ए	like the *e* in *they* or *prey*, or like the *a* in *made*. This is a dipthong.
ai	ऐ	like the *ai* in *aisle*, or the *i* in *bite*. This is a single dipthong, not two vowels.
o	ओ	like the *o* in *go* or *home*. This is a dipthong.
au	औ	like the *ow* in *cow*, or the *ou* in *found*, or the *au* sounds in *sauerkraut*. This is a single dipthong, not two vowels.
ḥ	ः	*visarga* is a final whispering unvoiced *h* sound, uttered in the articulating position of the preceding vowel and echoing that vowel. *Gajaḥ* (गजः elephant) sounds like "*gajaha*," *guruḥ* (गुरुः teacher) sounds like "*guruhu*."
ṁ	ं	*anusvāra* indicates that the vowel is pronounced with a resonant nasal aftersound. The sound is influenced by whatever consonant follows the *anusvāra*.
m̐	ँ	*anunāsika* (*candrabindu*) is a type of nasal sound following a vowel like the *n* in the French word *bon*.

Twenty-five consonants fall into five groups based on the part of the mouth in which the sound is produced. These groups begin at the throat (guttural consonants), and move forward to end at the lips (labial consonants). Further, Sanskrit has both aspirated and unaspirated consonants. Aspirated consonants (*kh, gh, ch, jh, ṭh, ḍh, th, dh, ph, bh*) are pronounced with a slight expulsion of air accompanying the consonant.

Gutturals are pronounced with the sound coming from the throat

k	क्	like the *ck* in *tick* or *clack.*
kh	ख्	like the *kh* in *Eckhart* or *workhorse.*
g	ग्	like the *g* in *tag* or *fog.*
gh	घ्	like the *gh* in *dog-house.*
ṅ	ङ्	like the *n* in *sink.*

Palatals are pronounced with middle of the tongue close to the palate

c	च्	like the *ch* in *chair* or *chill* or *church.*
ch	छ्	like the *ch* in *staunch heart.*
j	ज्	like the *j* in *joy* or *jump.*
jh	झ्	like the *dgeh* in *hedgehog* or *lodgehouse.*
ñ	ञ्	like the *n* sound in *bunch.* Commonly pronounsed like the *ny* in *canyon,* or the Spanish *ñ* in *piñata.*

Cerebrals are pronounced with the tip of the tongue touching the roof of the mouth in a retroflex position

ṭ	ट्	like the *t* in *got,* but with the tongue more retroflex.
ṭh	ठ्	like the *t* in *light hearted,* but with the tongue more retroflex.
ḍ	ड्	like the *d* in *sod* or *rod,* but with the tongue more retroflex.
ḍh	ढ्	like the *d* in *red hot,* but with the tongue more retroflex.
ṇ	ण्	like the *n* in *tint* or *under,* or in *rna* [prepare to say the *r* and say *na*] , but with the tongue more retroflex.

Dentals are pronounced with the tip of the tongue touching behind the teeth

t	त्	like the *th* in *Earth* but with the tip of tongue touching behind the teeth (and unaspirated).
th	थ्	like the *t* in *bath-house,* but with the tip of the tongue touching behind the teeth.
d	द्	like the *the* in *bathe* but with the tip of the tongue touching behind the teeth.
dh	ध्	like the *th-h* in *breath heavy* but with the tip of tongue touching behind the teeth.
n	न्	like the *n* in *nut* or *no* but with the tongue touching behind the teeth.

Labials are pronounced with lips first closed and then open

p	प्	like the *p* in *sip* or *lap.*
ph	फ्	like the *ph* in *uphill,* but sometimes more like *pharmacy.*
b	ब्	like the *b* in *rib* or *nab.*
bh	भ्	like the *bh* in *abhor* or *rub hard.*
m	म्	like the *m* in *mother* or *mum.*

Semivowels

y	य्	*y* as in *yes* or *yellow.*
r	र्	*r* as in *run* or *rum.*
l	ल्	*l* as in *light* or *love* or *lug.*
v	व्	*v* as in *vine* or *vote.*

Sibilants

ś	श्	*sh* as in *shoot* or *shove*, or the German word *sprechen*, but with the tongue in a palatal position.
ṣ	ष्	*sh* with a curved retroflex tongue, as with the cerebral consanants above. There is no good match in English, but a *sh* after a back vowel as in *crashed* comes close.
s	स्	*s* as in *such* or *suit*.

Aspirate

h	ह्	*h* as in *home* or *hope*.

Introduction and Concepts

Introduction

Healing Through Knowledge

Welcome to the readers who are inquisitive about the workings of life. This quest invariably leads to the inquiry of the mind and the universe around us which is the subject of this book.

The ultimate goal of all spiritual pursuit is to eliminate every kind of misery, and to experience our true self. The desire to attain bliss is innate to our souls. Many of our anxieties and frustrations result from misunderstandings about our mind, body, and true self. We don't understand the boundaries between the functionings of our body, of our mind, and of our core self. Instead, we often superimpose one over the other. In the simple act of raising a hand, the body carries out many intricate functions. When the arm moves, it is actually the muscles at the root of the arm — the muscles of the entire upper quadrant of that side of the body, in fact — that act to produce the effect. Simultaneously, the entire body responds to the movement in order to maintain equilibrium and poise as the arm moves. Almost all of this is completely unconscious, part of the hidden machinery of an action that seems very simple.

Likewise, during the acts of thinking, planning, and striving in the pursuit of our well-being, the mind carries out many actions that we are not aware of, and so take for granted. Knowing how the consciousness, mind, and body function gives us new perspectives and mindsets for dealing with our experiences, situations, and relationships. This can result in a productive change in our behavior — helping us to experience our own true self and the nature around us.

The *Yoga Sūtras* of Patañjali presents this knowledge of the mind and of the self in a succinct body of aphorisms. These passages can be an invaluable tool for self-analysis and personal development, and can help us pursue our goals in a healthy manner without falling prey to frustrations. I hope that you benefit from reading the *Yoga Sūtras*, and I wish you great success and peace.

How to read this book

To fully understand all the concepts present in this book, it might be necessary to read this book more than once. Due to the sheer number of concepts introduced in this book, it is very possible to ignore a few of them in the first reading.

Sanskrit Words

Important Sanskrit words used in this book are marked in italic font to make them easy to track. Note that it is not necessary to memorize them. They are only for advanced readers who wish to continue their study with other branches of eastern philosophy. They may come handy when you are having a conversation with an expert in the field. A few Sanskrit words that are essential to understanding the *Yoga Sūtras* are listed in the section "Terminology" at the end of the chapter "Concepts and Terminology." Very common words like Yoga, Sāṅkhya, yogī, and karma are not italicized.

The word Yoga (with capital "Y") is used to refer to Yoga as one of the six schools of Indian philosophy which is explained in the coming sections. When used in every other sense (like in "the practice of yoga"), it is not capitalized.

Background of the Yoga Sūtras

Purpose of the Yoga Sūtras and Darśanas

The purpose of the *Yoga Sūtras* is to eliminate human misery by means of knowledge of the self and the universe. This goal of eliminating misery is shared by each of the six Indian spiritual sciences, called *darśanas*. The *Yoga Sūtras* of Patañjali is one of them, and is also known as "*Yoga-darśana*." In ancient India, *darśana* is synonymous with science. The word derives from the root *dṛś*, which means to see. A *darśana* helps one see that which is not previously seen or recognized, much as a periscope or telescope lets one see things that are obstructed or far away.

In modern times, the six *darśanas* are more popularly known as "the six systems of Indian philosophy." Six different rishis propounded these, and are their founding teachers. These teachings do not compete with one another, nor are they mutually exclusive — each addresses a separate topic, but there is overlap.

Misery (*duḥkha*) is classified into three kinds:

- *Ādhyātmika*: Suffering caused by one's own body and mind — for example, depression, trauma, and frustration.
- *Ādhibhautika*: Suffering caused by other beings, such as a bite from a snake or dog.
- *Ādhidaivika*: Suffering caused by natural calamities, such as earthquakes, floods, and tornadoes.

The highest goal of human pursuit is to completely eliminate these three kinds of misery. This goal and the effort to achieve it is called *puruṣārtha*. The objective of all *darśanas* is to help us in achieving that goal. There are four *puruṣārthas* — right conduct, earning wealth, fulfilling physical and mental desires, and liberation from all misery. Liberation is one of the main topics of *darśanas*.

The Six Darśanas

Each of the *darśanas* addresses a different topic.

- *Sāṅkhya*: The distinction between consciousness and nature which will be discussed in this book. The great sage Kapila is considered the founder of this philosophy.
- *Yoga*: The control of the mind that enables this distinction between consciousness and nature (and the overall goal of Sāṅkhya). Patañjali codified this body of knowledge into the *Yoga-darśana*.
- *Nyāya*: Methods of investigating the truth (reality), and discussion of proof. Gautama is the author of the *Nyāya-darśana*.

- *Vaiśeṣika*: The discussion of various categories of substances, entities found in the universe, and atomic theory, and also discussion of proof. This work was developed by Kaṇāda.
- *Pūrva Mīmāṁsā* (also called *Dakṣiṇa Mīmāṁsā*): The discussion of virtuous conduct and the interpretation of ancient texts called *Vedas* (and associated rituals), which will be introduced in the coming sections. Sage Jaimini was the composer of this work.
- *Vedānta* (also called *Uttara Mīmāṁsā*, or *Brahmasūtras*): The discussion of the nature of God (*Brahman*). This *darśana* is attributed to Sage Bādarāyaṇa.

What is Yoga?

The word *yoga* comes from the root "*yuj*," meaning "a deep state of meditation." Yoga is a state in which a person's inner core, the consciousness, remains in its own true form without being influenced by the impressions, thoughts, and dispositions of the mind. This is attained by restraining the operations of the mind — in such a state, a person is free from all misery. The word yoga also refers to a system of practices used to reach that state. There are eight "limbs" of yoga, as described by Patañjali.

What is a Sūtra?

A *sūtra* is a highly-condensed, succinct principle — short enough to be easily memorized and passed on to others, as though it were a seed of knowledge. The word sūtra literally means "thread," referring in this sense to a collection of aphorisms that are strung together like beads on a thread. The word sūtra can refer to an individual aphorism, or to the collection of aphorisms. Because sūtras are so concise, they can be hard to understand without additional clarification. Many commentaries have been written to help understand Patañjali's *Yoga Sūtras*. The interpretation in this book is based largely on famous commentaries by Vyāsa and Vācaspati Miśra.

Other Meanings of the Word Yoga

The word *yoga* also has other meanings — for example, sometimes the word simply means "spiritual practice." Here are a few contexts in which the word yoga is used:

1. *Rāja-yoga* (*rāja* = royal) sometimes refers to any type of meditation, because control of the mind is essential to any yogic practice. Often, *rāja-yoga* is used as a synonym for yogic practice as described by Patañjali.
2. *Haṭha-yoga* (*haṭha* = force) involves physical practices intended to aid in spiritual practice. *Haṭha-yoga* also includes meditation practices. In popular language today, the word yoga often refers to the exercises associated with *haṭha-yoga* postures (*āsanas*) and various breathing practices (prāṇāyāma).
3. *Jñāna-yoga* (*jñāna* = knowledge) emphasizes study and intellectual insight to achieve self-realization.
4. *Bhakti-yoga* (*bhakti* = devotion) emphasizes devotion to God as the primary means to attain self-realization.

5. *Karma-yoga* (*karma* = action) is the art of "right action," performing actions because it is the right thing to do, without being attached to the results.
6. *Kriyā-yoga* (*kriyā* = activity) has two meanings. Patañjali defines *kriyā-yoga* as consisting of three practices — austerity, self-study and introspection, and devotion to God (sūtra 2.1). It is also the name of some specific yoga practices that are popular in the West.

Who can Practice Yoga, and When?

Yoga can be practiced by anyone, in any stage of life. Ancient Indians recognized four stages (*āśrama*) of human life:

1. Bachelorhood (Brahmacarya āśrama)

The term *brahmacarya* refers to the conduct of a religious student, a *Brahman*. The term also means "chastity," because people of that age were traditionally expected not to engage in sexual activity. This is a stage of growth and learning — one gains spiritual knowledge and learns worldly trades, which are later used to support oneself and society. Yoga can be practiced in this stage of life to enhance the ability to learn, and to grow strong physically, mentally, and spiritually.

2. Household life (Gṛhastha āśrama)

The term *gṛhastha* means "householder." In this stage, people work to sustain themselves and society. One cannot take care of anybody without taking care of oneself. People take on different professions during this stage of life, protecting the nation as soldiers, raising crops and animals, performing services, or joining the priesthood. Many are engaged in childbearing and raising a family. Since considerable time is spent in day-to-day activities, a subset of yogic practices called *kriyā-yoga* was recommended for those with less time to devote.

3. Pre-renouncement (Vānaprastha āśrama)

The term *vānaprastha* means "heading toward the forest." Originally, people literally went into the forest (*vana*) to continue their spiritual practices. This stage of life puts more emphasis on spiritual learning. A person gains expertise, and may begin to teach in this phase of life. In today's society, we must recognize that we can do this anywhere.

4. Renouncement (Saṁnyāsa āśrama)

Saṁnyāsa means "letting go," in the sense of abandoning the things of this world. It is associated with a growing awareness that nothing in life can be kept forever. Traditionally, this meant a renunciation of all worldly attachments — in ancient times, individuals changed their names and cut off contact with relatives. The world became their family. Some become the leaders of teaching communities (*gurukulas*).

The Place of the Yoga Sūtras in Indian Spiritual Literature

In ancient India, it was believed that all forms of knowledge were derived from a series of texts called the *Vedas*, from the Sanskrit word *veda* for "knowledge." There are four *Vedas*: *Ṛg*, *Yajur*, *Sāma*, and *Atharva*. They are thought to be divinely inspired, not of human origin. Traditionally, the *Vedas* were communicated orally, and so are also called *śruti*, "that which is heard." It is believed they were originally revealed to holy seers (*Ṛṣi*), who shared them through chants in a language now known as Vedic Sanskrit. Later, the chants were transcribed into writings.

The word Sanskrit (*Saṁskṛt*), which means "refined," comes from two words: *sam* ("well") and *kṛt* ("made" or "prepared"). Sanskrit has been the language of religion, philosophy, science, and art in India for many centuries. The *Yoga Sūtras* is written in Classical Sanskrit, a later, more systematized form of Vedic Sanskrit.

The *Vedas* are a body of hymns chiefly concerned with how people should interact with the world, with one another, and with the divine. All later spiritual literature in India pays respect to, and is influenced by, the *Vedas*. Some of the salient works that evolved from the *Vedas* include the following:

- The *Vedāṅgas*, the six limbs of the *Vedas*, are Phonetics (*śikṣā*), Grammar (*vyākarana*), Etymology (*nirukta*), Poetic rhythm (*chandas*), Rituals and Duties (*kalpa*), and Mathematics, which includes astronomy (*jyotiṣa*), algebra, trigonometry, and so on. These six limbs are essential to understanding the *Vedas*.
- The *Upavedas*, the four "sub-Vedas," consist of Medicine (*āyurveda*), Musicology (*gāndharvaveda*), the science of warfare (*dhanurveda*), and Economics and Commerce (*arthaveda*).
- The *Brāhmanas* and *Āranyakas* are multiple bodies of texts that explain Vedic hymns. Some are lost to history, while others remain available today.
- The *Upaniṣads* contain explanations of specific topics that occur in the *Vedas*. These were written to be easily understood by everyone.
- The *Darśanas* are the six spiritual sciences, as explained earlier.

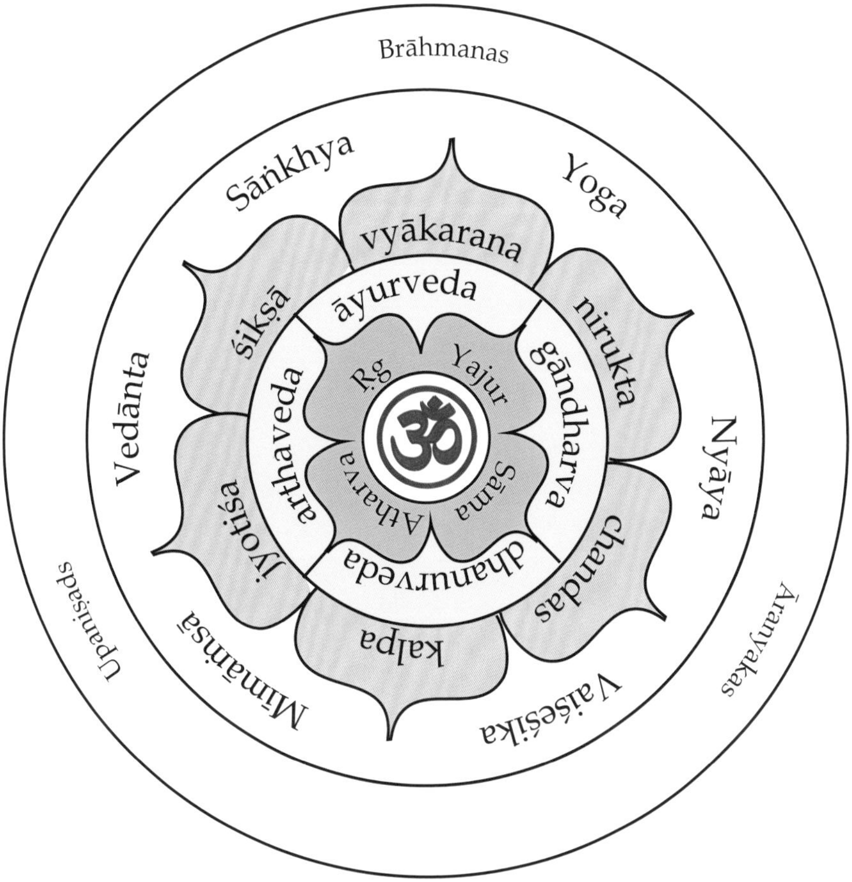

Vedas, the source of Sanskrit language and spiritual literature of India

Unity and Coexistence of the Six Darśanas

Traditional Indian culture is deeply invested in the concepts of unity and mutual endorsement. Strong evidence for this is found in *Mahābhārata* (and *Bhagavadgītā*).

> एकं साङ्ख्यं च योगं च यः पश्यति स तत्त्ववित्
>
> ekaṁ sāṅkhyaṁ ca yogaṁ ca yaḥ paśyati sa tattvavit - *Mahābhārata 12.304.4*
>
> "The knowers of truth see that Sāṅkhya and Yoga are one."

> नास्ति साङ्ख्यसमं ज्ञानं नास्ति योगसमं बलम्
>
> nāsti sāṅkhyasamaṁ jñānaṁ nāsti yogasamaṁ balam - *Mahābhārata 12.304.2*
>
> "There is no knowledge like Sāṅkhya and no power like Yoga."

> साङ्ख्ययोगौ पृथग्बालाः प्रवदन्ति न पण्डिताः।
> एकमप्यास्थितः सम्यगुभयोर्विन्दते फलम्॥
>
> sāṅkhyayogau pṛthagbālāḥ pravadanti na paṇḍitāḥ ।
> ekamapyāsthitaḥ samyagubhayorvindate phalam ॥ *Bhagavadgītā 5.4* ॥
>
> "Children speak of Sāṅkhya and Yoga as different, not the wise. He who is well established in one gains the fruit of both."

On the different causes of creation mentioned in the six *darśanas*, the pioneering Vedic scholar Maharshi Swami Dayananda Saraswati says the following:

> Just as multiple different causes take part in the formation of a pot — application, time, clay, intellect, labour (required for mixing or separating different materials), the properties of matter, and the potter himself — similarly, six different causes of the world have been discussed by the six *śāstras*. Thus, application is discussed by the *Mīmāṁsā*, time by the *Vaiśeṣika*, material cause by the *Nyāya*, the two-fold purpose of *puruṣa* by the Yoga, the primordial elements and the gradual formation of the different substances of the world from them by the Sāṅkhya, and the efficient cause of God by the *Vedānta*.
>
> - Satyarthaprakash. New Delhi: Vijaykumar Govindram Hasanand, 2000.

Much as many painters will stand on different scaffoldings while painting the same house, the six *darśanas* use different logical and technical artifacts to explain the reality that we experience. As such, while there may be differences in the terminology and methods, the core philosophy remains the same. In this way the six *darśanas* complement and corroborate each other in explaining Vedic philosophy.

Mahābhārata and Bhagavadgītā

The *Mahābhārata*, listed as the source of some of the citations, is one of the two great epics of India. The *Mahābhārata* is the story of the sons of half-brothers Pāṇḍu and Dhṛtarāṣṭra, events said to have taken place five thousand years ago. The five Pāṇḍava brothers were the sons of Pāṇḍu, and the hundred Kaurava brothers were the sons of Dhṛtarāṣṭra. A great war ensued between the Pāṇḍavas and Kauravas to gain possession of their ancestral kingdom of Bhārata. Apart from being a historical account, this epic contains many colorful anecdotes and fables that teach philosophy and *dharma* (virtuous action) in an engaging fashion. A part of the *Mahābhārata*, called the *Bhagavadgītā*, consists of eighteen chapters that teach a practical philosophy called the "yoga of action" (karma-yoga). It is a revered text in Hinduism, much like the Bible or the Quran.

Patañjali, Vyāsa, and Vācaspati Miśra

Very little is known about Patañjali, the author of the *Yoga Sūtras*, who is dated to have lived anywhere between 200 BCE to 500 CE. There was another Patañjali, the author of the great work of grammar entitled *Mahābhāṣya*, which is a commentary on Pāṇini's *Aṣṭādhyāyī*. Some believe that the two Patañjalis are the same, but most modern scholarship concludes that they are in fact different persons.

Vyāsa (circa 500 CE) is the first known commentator on the *Yoga Sūtras*, and all later commentaries depend heavily on his. A prominent example of these is Vācaspati Miśra's *Tattvavaiśāradī* (850 CE). Most of what we know today of the *Yoga Sūtras* comes from these two commentaries, and this book is based on them. Other invaluable commentaries that contribute to this book include *Bhāsvatī* by Hariharānanda Āraṇya, *Yogasūtra-bhāṣya-vivaraṇa* by Śaṅkara, *Yogavārttika* by Vijñānabhikṣu, *Raja Yoga* by Swami Vivekananda, and *Rājamārtāṇḍa* by Bhojarāja.

Many Vyāsas

Vyāsa, the first known commentator of the *Yoga Sūtras* is different from the Vyāsa who is known to be the author of *Mahābhārata*. There is another Vyāsa, also known as Bādarāyaṇa, who is the author of *Vedānta-darśana*. The name is so common that some consider Vyāsa to be a class of scholars or a degree attained by some scholoars.

Concepts and Terminology

Patañjali's *Yoga Sūtras* consists of only 195 lines. They are very concise, based on a much older philosophical system called Sāṅkhya. The *Yoga Sūtras* assumes prior knowledge of Sāṅkhya, and also some concepts and terminology that were prevalent in those times. In this book, I will present these essential concepts and terminology, and the philosophy of Sāṅkhya, before examining the *Yoga Sūtras*.

Mind, Body and Soul: Introducing the Subtle Body

In this section I will discuss popular beliefs relating to the mind, the body, and the soul, and show how Sāṅkhya and Yoga differ from them. Although the words "spirit," "soul," "self," and "consciousness" may mean different things to different people, I will use them as synonyms for one another throughout this book.

Many people believe that the human body is made up of matter, and that consciousness inside the body originates from this matter. This approach treats consciousness as an "emergent effect" of matter — that is, if you have no matter, you cannot have consciousness.

Others believe that the soul or consciousness is a separate entity from the physical, material body. In this view, the functions of the mind — such as thoughts, emotions, and ego — are part of this separate, non-physical entity.

Sāṅkhya and Yoga agree with the second perspective, that the soul or consciousness is a separate entity from the gross material body. In addition, they offer that there is an internal body called the "subtle body," distinct from our external gross body. The mind which is the container of thoughts, emotions, and ego is part of this subtle body. The soul, however, is separate from both the gross body and the subtle body. The important thing to note is that the subtle and gross bodies are both made of matter while the soul is not composed of matter. It is an entirely different entity.

This distinction is important, because it leads to the concept of the "Self" that I will use in this book. This Self is the soul, the indescribable core self of a person that is different from your physical body, different from what you know, even different from your personality, your impulses, and everything else that you might think makes you who you are. The Self is something deeper than all of those things, the core consciousness of a person. Our gross material body has the "brain," while our subtle body has the "mind." The Self is external to both of them. The benefit of practicing Patañjali's yoga is that, by realizing that your Self is really in charge and distinct from your mind, you are freed from the miseries that come from attachment with mind and body. In fact, the *Yoga Sūtras* states that all misery comes from our identification with the mind and the body. The following picture shows a schematic representation of the gross body, subtle body, and consciousness.

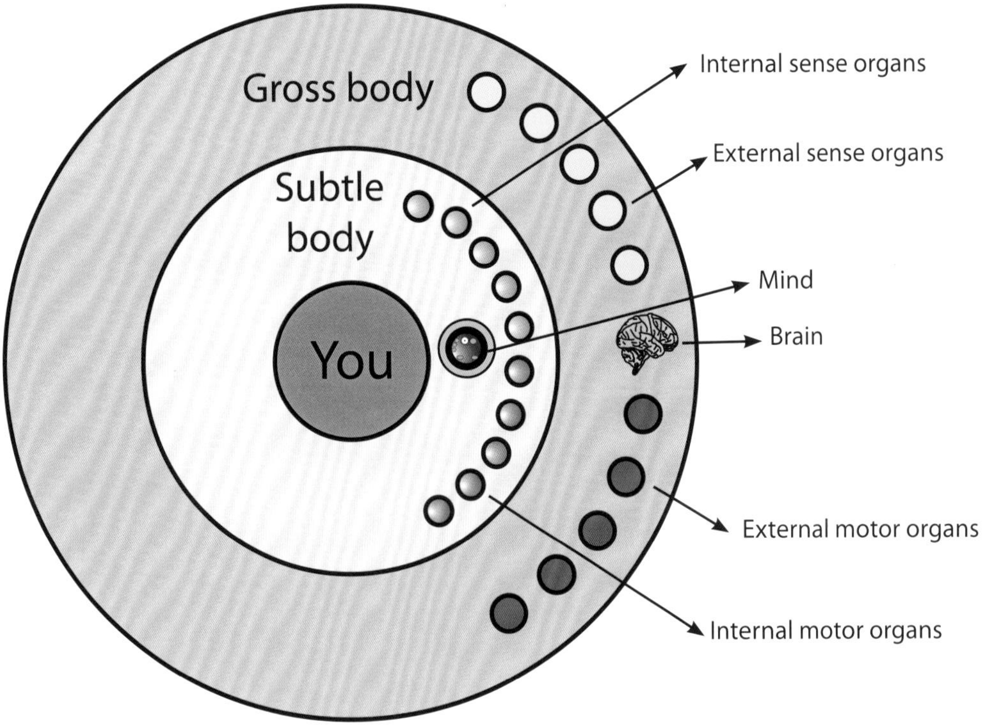
Gross body
Subtle body
You
Internal sense organs
External sense organs
Mind
Brain
External motor organs
Internal motor organs

The Subtle Body and the Gross Body

The subtle body consists of the following components:

- *Buddhi*, or intellect, aids in judgment and decision-making.
- *Ahaṅkāra*, or ego, is the faculty responsible for the idea of "I," "me," and "mine."
- *Manas* is the coordinator of the sense and motor organs, and is also the instrument of desire and impulse.
- The five subtle sense organs (of hearing, touch, sight, taste, and smell), which correspond to the five external sense organs.
- The five subtle motor organs (of speech, grasping, locomotion, excretion, and procreating) which correspond to the five external motor organs.

The *buddhi*, *ahaṅkāra*, and *manas* together are called the *citta* — the mind — in the *Yoga Sūtras*. Throughout this book, I will use "mind" as a synonym for *citta*. *Citta* is pronounced as "chitta."

The gross external body consists of the following components:

- The five external sense organs (ears, skin, eyes, tongue, and nose).
- The five external motor organs (tongue, hands, legs, genitals, and excretory organs)
- The brain, which coordinates them (traditionally grouped with the above two kinds of organs, but mentioned here separately for clarity).

The other organs, like the heart, lungs, stomach, and liver, are not mentioned because they are the supporting organs for the above external organs.

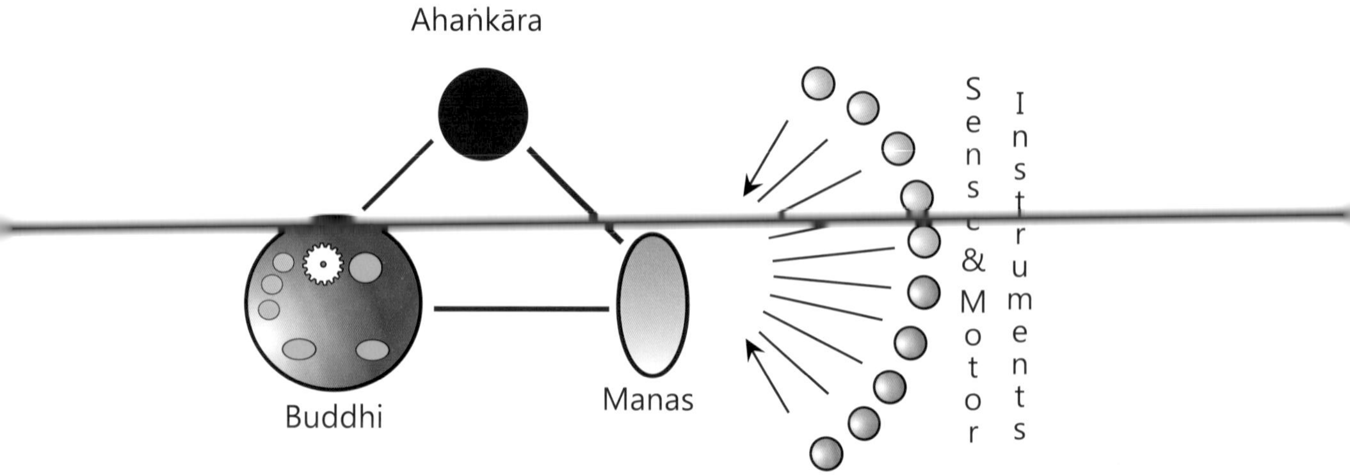

Representation of subtle body

Representation of the mind

The mind consisting of *buddhi*, *ahaṅkāra*, and *manas* will be represented by the diagram on the right. The white gear represents a mental activity. The blue and orange circles represent active and inactive impressions respectively.

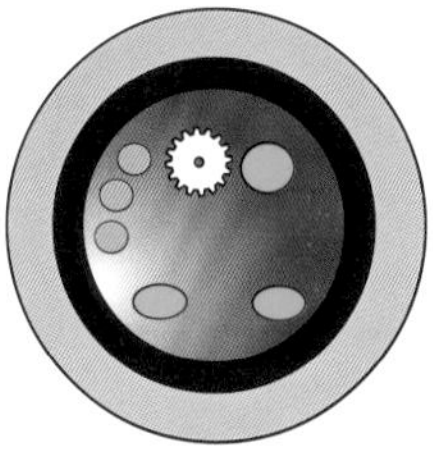

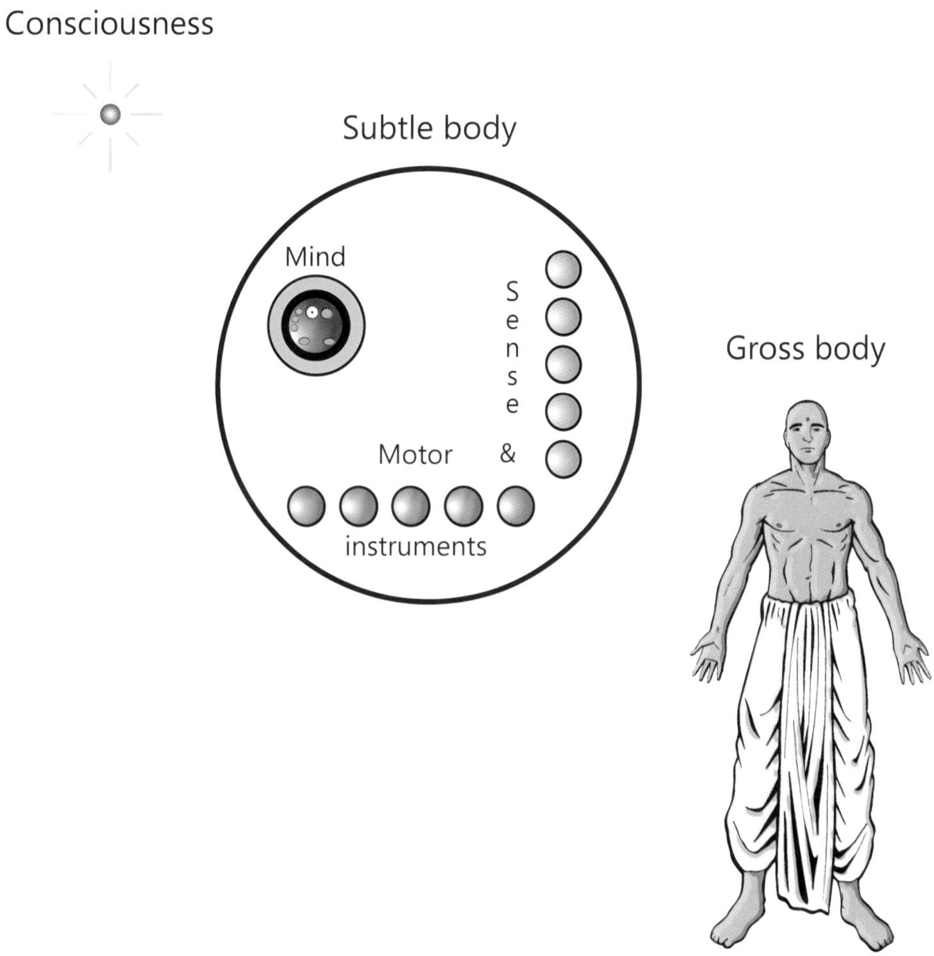

Representation of consciousness, subtle body, and the gross body

Subtle Body is Persistent Across Rebirth

The subtle body which contains the mind does not perish with the outer body. When a person's body dies, the soul along with the subtle body migrates to another body i.e., it takes birth in a new body. The subtle impressions stored in the mind are intact but, they may not be active. That is why we do not remember actions performed in our previous birth. The body we attain is based on the cumulative merit and demerit of our actions performed in the previous births. The subtle body persists across many births. It only dissolves into the primordial elements when the creation cycle ends or when a yogī attains liberation. At the beginning of a new creation cycle it is recreated. Consciousness is never created. It is unchanging and eternal.

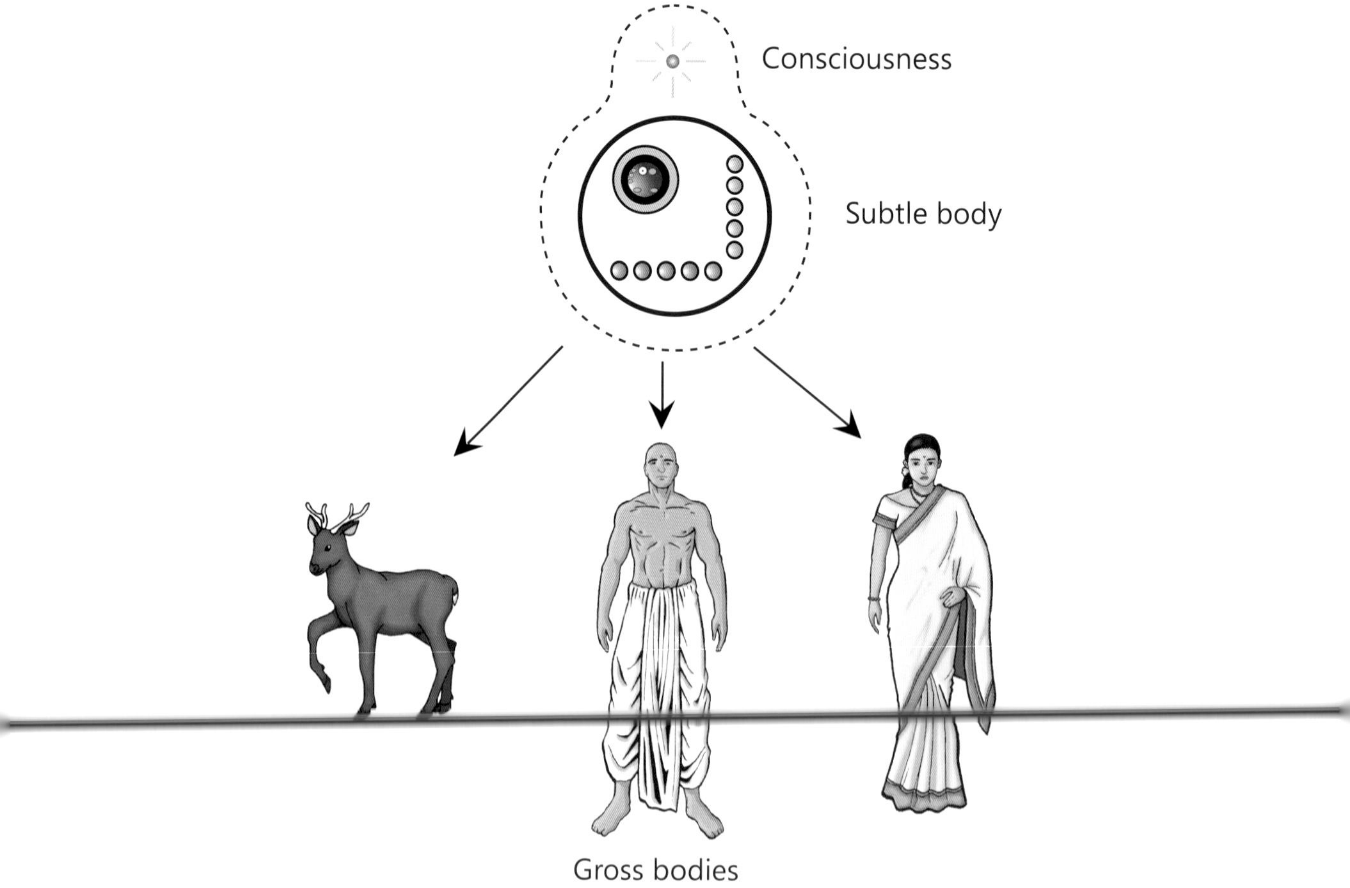

Subtle body persists across multiple births

Basis for Considering Soul as Different from and External to Mind

Both Sāṅkhya and Yoga offer observations and logic in support of the existence of the soul as distinct from the mind and body. One of these is the principle in Sāṅkhya that any combination of elements exists for a purpose other than the combination itself. That is, the purpose of an object with multiple components must be other than the simple existence of that object. For example, a chair has multiple components — the seat, back support, legs, and perhaps other smaller parts. A chair exists for someone to make use of it; a chair cannot sit on itself. This is true for any object or instrument in the universe. A thermometer does not measure the temperature for itself; it exists to indicate the temperature to someone other than itself. The same principle applies to our sense organs — the sense organs cannot sense themselves. It is instead the soul that experiences things through the sense organs. Further extending the principle, our mind — consisting of multiple impressions, thought processes, and emotions — cannot exist for its own sake. The mind cannot sense or know itself; it is experienced by the soul and it exists for the purpose of the soul. This is how Sāṅkhya and Yoga differ from some of the philosophies that do not accept the notion of a "soul" as an entity distinct from the mind. Further arguments in support of the existence of the soul are given in the fourth chapter of the *Yoga Sūtras*.

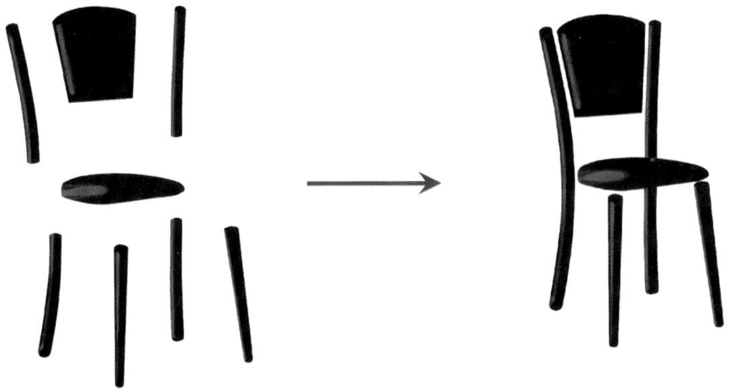

Residing Place of Soul in the Body

Since the soul or consciousness is different from the body and mind one might ask "where does the soul reside in the body?" Information on this is found in *Upaniṣads*, *Āyurveda* (*Carakasaṁhita* and *Śuśrutasaṁhita*), and the *Vedas*. There is no general agreement among scholars on this matter. In the rest of this sub-section I will present a few excerpts from the research done by Acharya Ananda Prakash and published in his work "Śarīr meṁ jīvātmā kā sthān. Aliabad: Arsha-Shodha-Samsthan, First Edition 2009."

Upaniṣads and *Āyurveda* use the word "*hṛd*" "the heart" to refer to the location of the soul. In Sanskrit "*hṛd*" can refer to both the brain-region (which is the seat of thoughts and emotions) and the cardiac region in the human body. Based on the descriptions of functions associated with this region in *Āyurveda*, it has been concluded by some scholars to mean the "brain."

स वा एष आत्मा हृदि
sa vā eṣa ātmā hṛdi – *Chāndogya 8.3.3*

"That soul is certainly in the hṛd (mind)."

योऽयं विज्ञानमयः प्राणेषु हृद्यन्तर्ज्योतिः पुरुषः
yo'yaṁ vijñānamayaḥ prāṇeṣu hṛdyantarjyotiḥ puruṣaḥ

– *Bṛhadāraṇyaka 4.3.7*

"This *puruṣa* (soul), endowed with knowledge, is luminous inside the hṛd (mind)."

चिन्तादिजुष्टं हृदयं प्रदूष्य बुद्धिं स्मृतिं चाप्युपहन्ति शीघ्रम्
cintādijuṣṭaṁ hṛdayaṁ pradūṣya buddhiṁ smṛtiṁ cāpyupahanti śīghram

– *Carakasaṁhita, "unmāda" chapter 9*

"Afflicted by worry (anxiety), the *hṛdaya* (mind), having corrupted the intellect, destroys the memory."

हृदयं चेतनास्थानमुक्तं सुश्रुत ।
तमोऽभिभूते तस्मिन्स्तु निद्रा विशति देहिनाम् ॥
hṛdayaṁ cetanāsthānamuktaṁ suśruta ।
tamo'bhibhūte tasminstu nidrā viśati dehinām ॥

– *suśrutasaṁhitā śarīrasthānam 4.34*

"O' Suśruta! *hṛdaya* is the place of consciousness of living beings. When *hṛdaya* is overtaken by *tamas*, [one] enters the state of sleep."

In *Vedas*, the words *devakośa*, *hiraṇyayakośa*, *svarga* and others are used to refer to the location of the soul. These too are taken to mean the "brain" by many.

Elements of Cosmos: Nature, Consciousness, and God

According to the traditional interpretation of the *Vedas*, the cosmos consists of three fundamental elements. They cannot be created or destroyed, but they interact with one another. This view is consistent with the model presented by Patañjali in the *Yoga Sūtras* and as explained by Vyāsa. It is also in agreement with the other *darśanas* (*Sāṅkhya, Nyāya, Vaiśeṣika, Pūrva Mīmāṁsā,* and classical *Vedānta*). The three elements are,

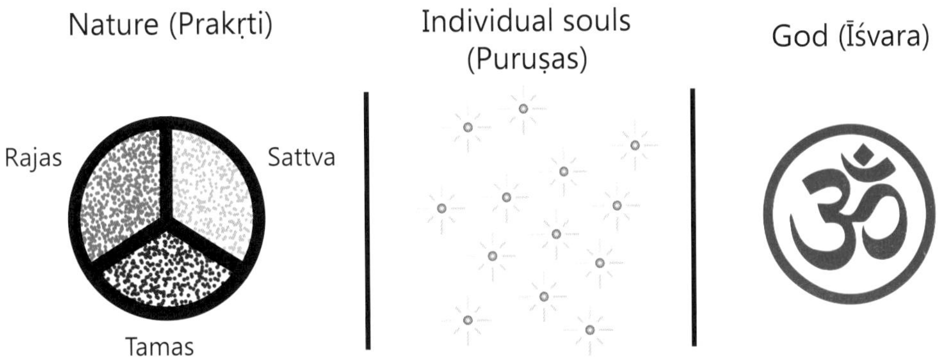

1. Nature (*prakṛti*) is matter, the fundamental elements that make up the physical universe. Everything that we perceive is made of matter, including our bodies and minds. Matter is eternal, but not conscious. *Prakṛti* consists of three classes of elements (*sattva*, *rajas*, and *tamas*), which will be discussed in detail while introducing the philosophy of Sāṅkhya

2. Individual consciousness is the soul (*puruṣa*), one for each living being. Individual souls are eternal and conscious. They are distinct from nature. Nature provides for the enjoyment and liberation of individual consciousness. Consciousness needs nature to gain knowledge. There are an infinite number of individual souls.

3. God (*Īśvara*) is the Supreme Soul (*Paramātmā*). God is eternal, conscious, and blissful. God is untouched by the things that limit individual consciousness. God is omniscient, omnipotent, and omnipresent. God does not need Nature to know anything; God knows everything by God's very nature.

Everything that we observe in this universe is an interaction of these three entities. This interaction is eternal — there is no beginning or end to it.

In order to bestow the knowledge and happiness that is inherent in himself (or herself, or itself, because God does not have a gender), God makes use of matter (*prakṛti*) to create the universe — which includes the planets, stars, our bodies and minds, through which individual souls can attain knowledge and bliss. Here, "creation" means the transformation of matter into the universe as we perceive; it does not mean that God creates things from "nothing." Similarly, destruction does not mean annihilation of objects into nothingness. Rather, it is the dissolution of objects into their individual elements. This happens in a cyclical fashion — there is no beginning or end to the cycle of creation and destruction.

It's important to note that a soul is an individual. It is not shared or collective, but it does inhabit a succession of bodies. It is not a being's thoughts, feelings, ego, or memories (collectively called *citta*, the mind). Rather, the soul is what gives the quality of consciousness to the mind. When the body dies, the soul, along with the subtle body, leaves the gross body and enters a newborn. This is the concept of reincarnation in *Vedas*.

What happens to my previous life's memories?

The literal memories may not be accessible by the brain of the new body, but they do exist, and a yogī in a deep state of meditation can examine the memories from his or her previous incarnations. Patañjali describes these powers of meditation in the third chapter of the *Yoga Sūtras*.

Why Are We Going Through All of This? What is the Purpose of Creation?

God is omniscient, omnipresent, and intrinsically blissful. God doesn't need anything to be happy, and perceives and knows everything directly without the need for any instrumentation. Souls (individuals), on the other hand, cannot perceive anything without the help of instrumentation. We cannot see without eyes, hear without ears, smell without a nose, and so on. The gross and subtle bodies are the instruments we use to attain knowledge and bliss. It is to this end that the soul makes use of the mind (and thus the body) during each successive life it takes on. This, broadly speaking, is the intent of creation — to bestow knowledge and bliss to individual souls. Creation's purpose will be discussed formally and in more detail in the *Yoga Sūtras*.

God as an agent of transformation

It is important to note that God is not considered the "creator" of matter or of our souls. Like God, we are a fundamental part of the cosmos, and so is matter. God is an agent of transformation that makes use of the already-existing matter for the already-existing souls (us). In that way God is the creator of the universe in the form we perceive. God is a special kind of consciousness, and — like our souls — does not have a gender, which is a characteristic only of material bodies. Consequently, in the *Vedas* God is referred to by all three genders (male, female, neuter).

Terminology

This book has introduced several terms from Sanskrit so far. This is a good time to revisit some of them, as we will be using them throughout the book.

- *Puruṣa* is the consciousness, or self. I also use "soul" and "spirit" to mean *Puruṣa*.
- *Citta* is the mind, consisting of the three internal instruments: intellect, ego, and *manas*.
- *Buddhi* is the Sanskrit word for intellect.
- *Ahaṅkāra* is the Sanskrit word for ego.
- *Manas* is the word used for the internal instrument that coordinates the ten organs. It is an instrument of desire and impulse.
- *Prakṛti* is the name for the fundamental elements that make up this universe. We use "nature" and "matter" as synonyms for *prakṛti*.
- *Īśvara* is the word used for God.

The Philosophy of Sāṅkhya

Kapila and Sāṅkhya-darśana

Sāṅkhya is actively studied as part of the six *darśanas* in traditional Indian schools (*gurukulas*) even today. The source of Sāṅkhya philosophy is Kapila's *Sāṅkhya-darśana*, which traditional Hindus believe to be more than twenty thousand years old based on writings that mention his place of birth as on the banks of the Sarasvatī river which dried up twenty thousand years ago. The exact date of Kapila's life is not known conclusively, however. He is mentioned in the story of the *Mahābhārata*, which took place five thousand years ago. Many modern scholars believe that the *Mahābhārata* went through considerable re-editing between 900 BCE and 400 BCE making it difficult to ascertain the time of Kapila. One can say that he lived much before the authoring of *Mahābhārata*.

Sāṅkhya-darśana is also known as *Sāṅkhya-pravacana-sūtra* or *Sāṅkhya-sūtras*. The actual text of *Sāṅkhya-darśana* may have undergone many changes over time, according to some scholars even reconstructed at a much later date. It is believed that well-redacted versions that are available today, demarcating the later additions to the text, preserve the core philosophy of Kapila. Many commentaries have been written on *Sāṅkhya-darśana* in several Indian languages. Another great work on Sāṅkhya called the *Sāṅkhya Kārikā* of Īśvarakṛṣṇa (400 CE), a seemingly abridged compilation of the principles found in the *Sāṅkhya-darśana*, is very popular. It is acknowledged by Īśvarakṛṣṇa himself that *Sāṅkhya Kārikā* is a short summary of Sāṅkhya philosophy expounded by the great sage Kapila. It omits a few topics such as God which some misconstrue as the denial of the existence of God. In order to get a more complete picture of Sāṅkhya one must also study the *Sāṅkhya-darśana* of Kapila.

The matter presented in this book is in accordance with the Sāṅkhya that is currently studied in the living Indian tradition. It is also in line with the kind of Sāṅkhya mentioned in the *Mahābhārata* and *Āyurveda*. Sāṅkhya has endured many misrepresentations over the past millennium, so I encourage readers to inquire about Sāṅkhya with an open mind. This chapter is dedicated to understanding the basic principles of Sāṅkhya, which will be useful in understanding the *Yoga Sūtras*.

Puruṣa — The Individual Consciousness

Sāṅkhya talks predominantly about the consciousness and its field of experience, matter. "Consciousness" here means an individual soul (the self), generally referred to in the original Sanskrit as a *puruṣa*. There are infinite *puruṣas*, and they are distinct from matter and its attributes. A *puruṣa*'s knowledge is limited, and its influence is also limited. Due to its proximity with matter, a *puruṣa* interacts with matter and experiences it. That experience is life. Matter serves a twofold purpose for a *puruṣa* — experience and liberation. Experience consists of the happiness and misery that result from different combinations of matter. Liberation consists of attaining true knowledge of both matter and one's own self, and subsequently detaching from matter.

There is another, special kind of *puruṣa* called *Īśvara*, or God, who is omnipresent, omnipotent, and omniscient. There is only one *Īśvara*. Sāṅkhya supports the presence and influence of God, as will be further explained in the subsection "Theism in Sāṅkhya."

Prakṛti — The Primordial Matter

The fundamental particles or forces that make up the universe are collectively called *prakṛti* (pronounced as "pra-kri-ti"). There is no exact English equivalent for the word *prakṛti* — it is often translated as "nature."

Prakṛti is composed of three *guṇas*. *Guṇa* means an ingredient, one of the primordial elements. We can think of the *guṇas* as fundamental particles or energies, but they are neither. They are much subtler than any particle or energy. These elements are not conceptual; they are real. The *guṇas* are the building blocks of all particles and all energies of the universe. Everything in the universe, including our bodies and minds, is made from a combination of these three *guṇas*. This is similar to how all the colors are created from the three basic colors (red, green, and blue).

In any given object or situation, one or two of these *guṇas* are dominant. The *guṇas* are not in equilibrium, and this combination of uneven amounts of *guṇas* is itself the process of creation. The objects formed or produced from the uneven combination of the *guṇas* are called "evolutes" of *prakṛti*. The Sanskrit term for any evolute is *vikṛti*. *Prakṛti* is the "producer" while *vikṛti* is the "produced." The reason these three *guṇas* are not in equilibrium is explained in the coming sections.

Guṇas

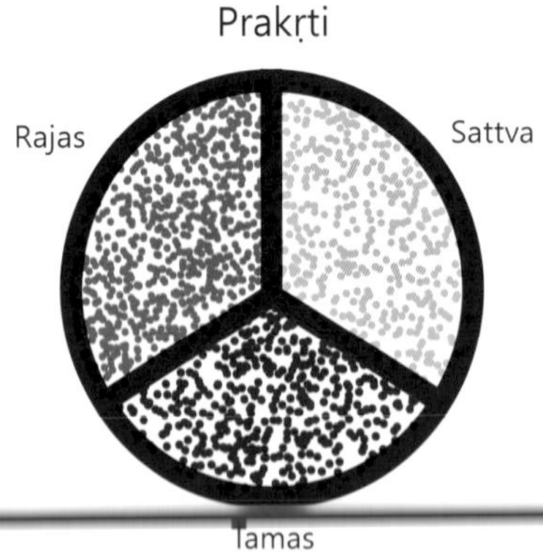

The three *guṇas* are *sattva*, *rajas*, and *tamas*.

Sattva is light (not heavy) and luminous. *Sattva* is conducive to knowledge, and is desirable on the path of self-realization. *Sattva* is like a mirror or telescope which one uses to see oneself or to see other things. In order to expand our understanding, we need to maximize the activity of *sattva* in our minds.

Rajas is the provoker, the motivator — that which is always moving. Movement is its essence, and it imparts movement to anything that comes into contact with it.

Tamas is heavy, and functions as a stabilizer. Its fundamental quality is to negate the movement of anything that comes into contact with it.

In short, *sattva* is responsible for illumination, *rajas* for movement, and *tamas* for stability. These three qualities are present in all objects in this universe. *Sattva* is dominant in the human mind; this is why the consciousness can understand things through the mind. In a table or chair, *tamas* is dominant, because it is static. *Rajas* is the cause of motion. In a burning fuel that propels automobiles, *rajas* dominates.

Sattva, *rajas*, and *tamas* are associated with the following qualities in ancient Indian spiritual and scientific literature:

- *Sattva*: illumination, understanding, appreciation, love, interest, lightness, knowledge, intelligence, happiness, honesty, delicacy, cleanliness, truthfulness, modesty, forgiveness, pleasantness.
- *Rajas*: movement, energy, productivity, longing, dislike, hot temper, fickleness, sadness, confusion, aggression, war, impulsiveness, desire, lust, anger.
- *Tamas*: stability, continuity, heaviness, attachment, dullness, depression, darkness, non-knowledge, laziness, fear, meekness, uninterest in work or activities, dreaming, sleep.

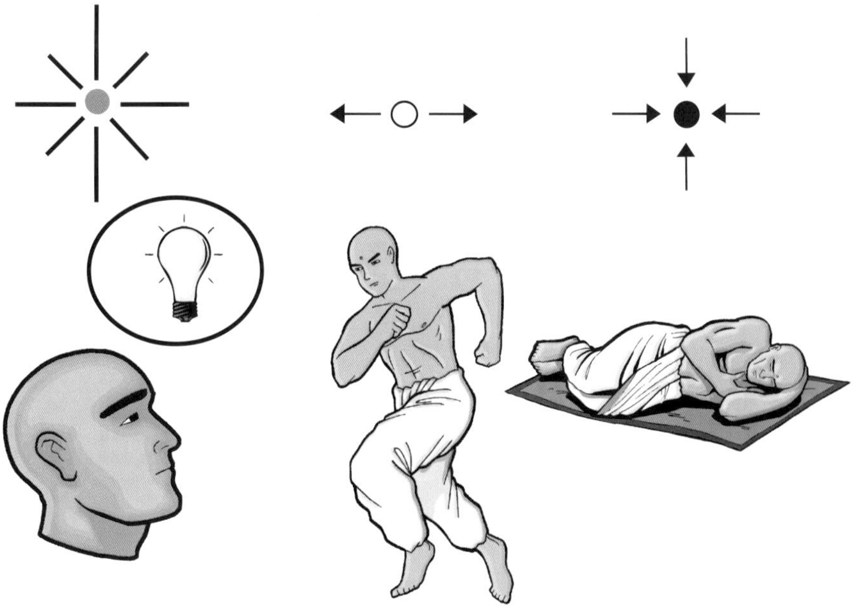

Characteristics of sattva, rajas, and tamas

Health and Happiness

When *sattva* is more active in the mind, we experience understanding, peace, inquisitiveness, and healthy attitudes. An active *tamas* can lead to an experience of stability, but also to a feeling of stagnation and dullness. When *rajas* is active it propels us toward change, either positive or negative. Maximizing *sattva* is desirable, but *rajas* and *tamas* cannot be eliminated completely. None of the three *guṇas* can function without the presence of the other two. Supported by *rajas* and *tamas*, a dominant *sattva* leads to knowledge, health and happiness. When *sattva* is not active due to the aggravation or over-activity of *rajas* and *tamas*, we experience disease and misery. Through the practice of Yoga, one can learn to cultivate sattva in the mind in order to gain discriminating wisdom and eliminate afflictions and ailments.

A good analogy is the act of writing on a board using a marker. The marker acts like *sattva* — without it, nothing can be written on the board, and we can't understand anything. The hand moving the marker acts like *rajas* — if the hand does not move the pen, nothing can be written and understood either. The board acts like *tamas* — without a stable surface, there is nothing to write on. In order to convey something through writing, all the three should exist and function properly. If there is a defect in the marker (say, lack of ink), the hand (excessive movement), or the board (an unstable or wobbly surface), we cannot achieve the purpose of writing.

Writing analogy of Sattva, Rajas and Tamas

Happiness is maximized by partaking sāttvic foods, developing healthy habits, and performing activities that are conducive to *sattva*. Such practice is also conducive to meditation and yoga. More information on the effects of food on the body and mind can be found in works related to *Āyurveda,* like the *Caraka-saṁhitā.*

More on Prakṛti

Prakṛti is a sort of proto-condition, or primordial state, in which the three *guṇas* exist uniformly and in equal proportions. *Prakṛti* in this state is called primordial (*pradhāna*), unevolved nature or root nature (*mūlaprakṛti*). In this state, *prakṛti* is called non-indicatory (*aliṅga*), because there is no differentiation between things and it cannot indicate anything. Due to its uniformity, the non-indicatory *prakṛti* is neither perceivable nor capable of being described; because it is undifferentiated, it is imperceptible. The word *liṅga* means a perceptible sign or characteristic, so something that is *aliṅga* has no perceptible characteristics. This concept is further elaborated in the next section.

Prakṛti is a collective name, not a single entity

सत्त्वरजस्तमसां साम्यावस्था प्रकृतिः

sattvarajastamasāṁ sāmyāvasthā prakṛtiḥ

– *Sāṇkhya-darśana* 1.61

"The equilibrium-state of sattva, rajas and tamas is *prakṛti*."

Prakṛti as defined by Kapila is the equilibrium-state of *sattva*, *rajas*, and *tamas*. It is a collective name for the multiple elements of *sattva*, *rajas*, and *tamas* combined together — just like the word "population," which is the collective term for multiple people together. Some misunderstand *prakṛti* as a single monolithic entity but it is not.

How We Perceive: Introducing Viveka

Variation is necessary in perceiving anything. This is why *prakṛti*, in its primordial, uniform state (with equal proportions of *sattva*, *rajas*, and *tamas*), does not indicate anything as there is nothing discernible about it. Consider walking into a well-lit room, where many things are visible in the presence of the light. At night, when everything is dark and the light is turned off, you can't see anything. Lack of light makes everything uniformly black. Because there is no differentiation in color, nothing can be seen.

On the other hand, if there is light but everything in the room reflects the same amount and the same kind of light — such as white — everything will look the same. It will be impossible to differentiate between any objects in the all-white room. Everything is apparently invisible due to the uniformity. This is how there can be imperceptibility even in the presence of light.

It doesn't matter what color you use for this example — if everything is uniformly red (blue, green, any color), nothing can be perceived then, either. One might say that at least the uniform color "red" is being perceived, but even that assumes that a color of "non-red" has been perceived before. Perception cannot occur if there is no presence of difference. This can be extended to other senses. If, for example, all sounds in the universe were in just one tone, pitch, and volume, then no auditory information could be perceived. It is uniformity of sensory data that makes something imperceptible; non-uniformity is the cause of all perception.

Such non-uniformity is essential to understanding in all fields of knowledge. For example, when I want to convey a message to a friend saying "I will be there at 7pm," I will not be much help if I write a note that utilizes only the letter "a" in the message. A sentence composed of just a string of the letter "a" ("aaaaaaaaaaaaa") doesn't convey my intended message. This is due to uniformity. The same is true in mathematics — one has to have multiple different equations in order to solve an equation with multiple variables. It is through superior discrimination — the ability to perceive distinctions and differences — that one attains expertise in any field.

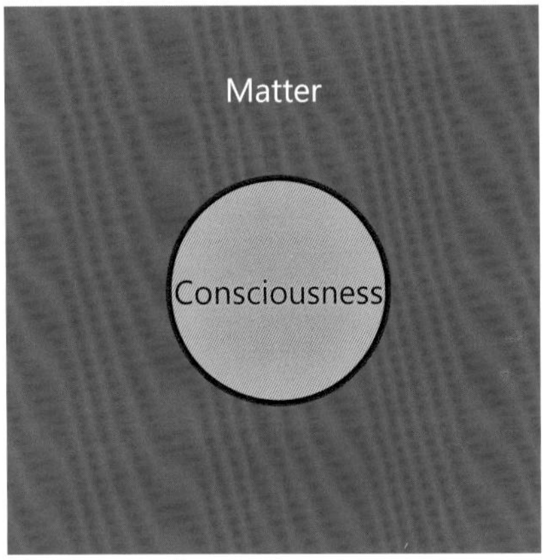

Nature (matter), in its primordial, uniform state does not indicate anything to the individual consciousness.

Black darkness | White darkness | Red darkness

$x - y = 2$	$x - y = 2$
$x - y = 2$	$x + y = 6$
$x = ?$	$x = 4$
$y = ?$	$y = 2$

Examples of uniformity not being conducive to understanding

Discrimination (Viveka)

Discrimination or discernment (*viveka*) is the ability to recognize differences between things. This is the sense of the word when we talk about someone having "discriminating tastes." *Viveka* is the underlying mechanism through which we understand everything. *Viveka* can be mildly or acutely developed. For example, most people can differentiate instantly between pictures of a cow and a tree, but when shown two similar patterns that differ only very subtly, they need time to perceive the difference.

Memory (*smṛti*) is a very important aspect of discernment. In order to compare two perceptions one needs to be able to load the impressions of perceptions into active memory. Improved memory leads to improved discernment. It is important to realize that the purpose of all the practices described in the *Yoga Sūtras* is to enhance the power of discernment. With this enhanced discernment, a yogī becomes capable of differentiating between the consciousness (*puruṣa*) — which is the true self — and the mind (*citta*). The power of discernment confers special knowledge of whatever the yogī wishes to understand. Many of the extraordinary abilities attained by a yogī are due to this heightened sensitivity to the differences between all forms of perceptions. This is very similar to how a mother can hear the sound of her newborn baby from the next room while talking to guests, even when the guests are unable to hear the baby.

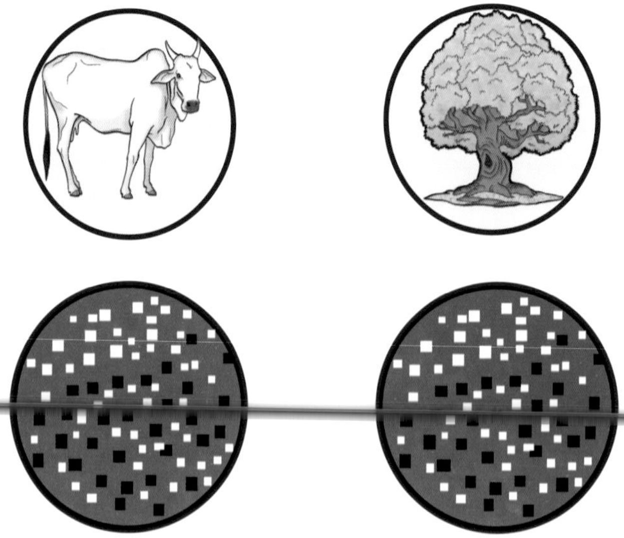

Other meanings of viveka

The word *viveka* is often used in the sense of knowing the difference between right and wrong. It can also refer to distinguishing between illusion and reality. English words to translate this idea include discernment and judgement.

Krama and Experience of Life

We experience our life every moment because of the constant change in the mind from one moment to another. This change results from the constant sensory input from our bodies, and also from the various thought processes. When the mind in the previous moment is exactly the same as in the next moment, then the subsequent moment cannot be perceived. There is also a limit to the subtlety of change that can be perceived by the consciousness. When a change in the mind is too small or subtle, then we (our souls) cannot perceive it. The term used for the minimum change that is perceptible by a soul between two consecutive moments is called *krama* (different from the word *karma*, which means action). The experience of life is possible because of this continuous perceptible change (*krama*) in our minds. However, a yogī in a deep state of meditation can stop the *krama* that happens in the mind (which is subtler than the brain). Then, after the yogī emerges from the meditative state, he or she can again experience the normal *krama* from our day to day activities. *Krama* will be revisited formally in the fourth chapter of the *Yoga Sūtras* (sūtra 4.33), where Patañjali defines it.

Evolution of Nature (Prakṛti)

So, then, non-uniformity is necessary for all perception. For the same reason, an uneven combination of the three *guṇas* leads to the formation of perceptible things. This is the process of creation. An object formed from the uneven combination of *guṇas* is called an "evolute" of nature. Sāṅkhya describes the sequence in which these evolutes are formed.

Intellect (Mahat), the First Evolute

The first product of the uneven combination of *sattva*, *rajas*, and *tamas* is called *mahat* — the intellect. Intellect is also called *buddhi* ("the thing through which you know"). Because of the new contrast resulting from an uneven combination of *guṇas* in intellect, nature attains a perceptible quality. In this state it is called *liṅgaprakṛti*, or "indicatory nature." It is also called *vyakta*, or manifested. Intellect is the building block for the rest of the universe.

Through intellect the soul perceives everything that is experienced in life. There is one intellect (*mahat* or *buddhi*) for each individual consciousness (*puruṣa*). After being allocated to each of the individual souls, the rest of the *mahat* undergoes further evolution.

An analogy — if the primordial nature is like grass, then when a cow eats the grass and produces milk, the milk becomes the first product, or evolute, of the grass. In this analogy, milk is like *mahat* from which all subsequent objects are produced.

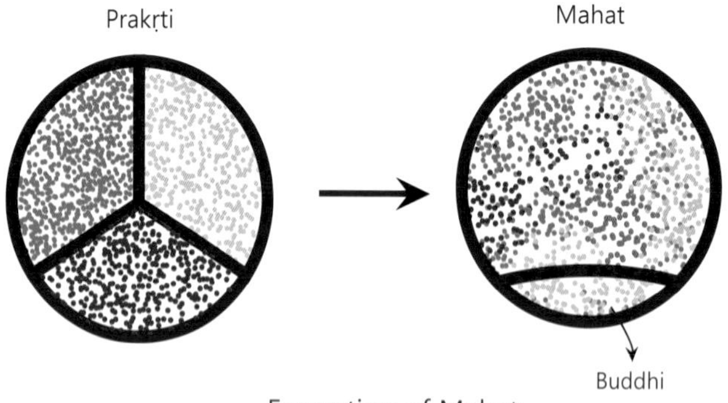

Formation of Mahat

Mahat and Buddhi

Mahat and *buddhi* are synonymous. However, the part of the *mahat* that is allocated to individual souls is called *buddhi*.

Ego (Ahaṅkāra), the Second Evolute

From *mahat*, with further combination with the three *guṇas*, ego (*ahaṅkāra*) is formed. Ego is the "material" that is responsible for the feeling of "I" and "my" in the mind. After being allocated to the individual souls, the rest of the ego undergoes further evolution. Ego forms the raw material for subsequent evolutes.

An analogy — as milk is like intellect (*mahat*), the yogurt from milk is like the ego (*ahaṅkāra*) formed from intellect. As ego is external to consciousness, the feeling of "I" is external to our pure consciousness.

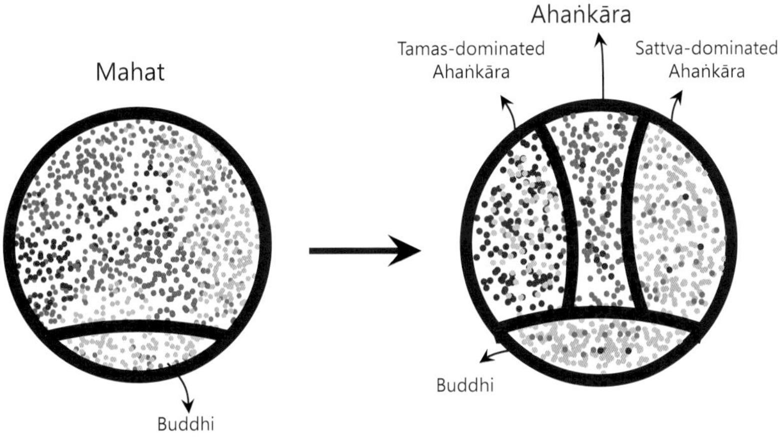

Formation of Ahaṅkāra

Sense Instruments and Tanmātras, Evolution Continued

Ego (*ahaṅkāra*) is divided into two parts: *sattva*-dominated ego ("active" ego), and *tamas*-dominated ego ("passive" ego).

Instruments of Knowledge and Action, and Manas

From the *sattva*-dominated ego, the following subtle instruments of perception are formed.

1. The five sense elements are called *jñānendriyas*, meaning "instruments of knowledge." The functions of the sense elements are hearing, touching, seeing, tasting, and smelling.
2. The five motor elements are called *karmendriyas*, meaning "instruments of action." The functions of the motor elements are speech, grasping, locomotion, excretion, and gratification.
3. *Manas* is the coordinator of these sense and motor elements. It is also the instrument responsible for desire and impulse.

The five sense and five motor elements mentioned above are not the external sense and motor organs that we can see with our eyes. They are the subtle elements that correspond to those external organs.

Tanmātras

From the *tamas*-dominated ego, the five subtle elements corresponding to sound, touch, sight, taste, and smell are formed. These subtle elements are called *tanmātras*. *Tanmātras* are the materials needed for the functioning of all senses.

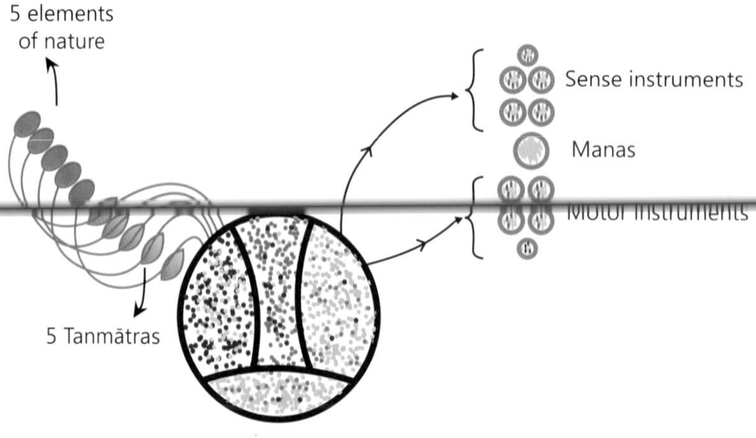

Formation of instruments, tanmātras, and elements of nature from Ahaṅkāra

Importance of Tanmātras

These *tanmātras* then form the supporting structure for the instruments of perception. They are the foundation on which the instruments rest. Without the *tanmātras* the instruments cannot function, as they need a foundation. *Tanmātras* act as the ground on which the trees of instruments are planted.

For example, take mercury, an element that is particularly sensitive to temperature. Though mercury expands in increasing heat and can therefore theoretically be used to measure temperature, it is not actually useful if it does not have the supporting structure of a thermometer — that is, a glass tube with a bulb to hold the mercury, and the markings to indicate temperature.

It is this role as a supporting structure that *tanmātras* play. All the sense elements of hearing, touch, sight, taste and smell rely on the *tanmātras* to function. Without them, the sense elements have no support. Just as a drawing cannot exist without the paper it is drawn on, so also the sense and motor instruments cannot function without the support provided by the *tanmātras*.

Evolution of the Gross Elements of Nature (bhūtas) — Space, Air, Fire, Water, and Earth

After being used as the supporting structure for the instruments, *tanmātras* undergo further evolution to form the five gross elements of our universe, which are space, air, fire, water and earth. These five elements of nature are called the *pañca-bhūtas*.

1. From the *tanmātra* of hearing, the element of space was formed.
2. From the *tanmātra* of touch, the element of air was formed.
3. From the *tanmātra* of vision, the element of fire was formed.
4. From the *tanmātra* of taste, the element of water was formed.
5. From the *tanmātra* of smell, the element earth was formed.

This is the final stage of the evolution of nature. No further evolution occurs after the five gross natural elements are formed. All gross objects — the bodies of all living beings, and of all other physical objects — are made of these five natural elements. The creative process ends with the formation of the 23 entities described above: *mahat*, *ahaṅkāra*, *manas*, ten *indriyas*, five *tanmātras*, and five gross elements of nature.

Formation of Objects

The evolution of nature (*prakṛti*) ends with the formation of the gross elements (space, air, fire, water and earth). Everything formed after that happens through a process of combination, in different proportions, of the five gross elements. This process of combining the fully-evolved gross elements to produce different objects is called transformation (*pariṇāma*) of the gross elements, as opposed to evolution of the subtle elements. Technically, the formation of both subtle and gross entities is called transformation, but it is important to distinguish between the two processes. The creative process ends after the formation of the 23 entities; objects formed after that result from the composition and decomposition of the (final) five gross elements — earth, water, fire, air, and space.

Elements of the Periodic Table

It is interesting to note from the above sequence of evolution described by Sāṅkhya that the gross element of space was formed after the formation of the mind, the internal sense and motor instruments, and the *tanmātras*. This implies that the elements of the modern periodic table must have formed after the *tanmātras*. Thus, the internal mind consisting of *buddhi* (intellect), *ahaṅkāra* (ego), *manas*, and the ten instruments are much subtler than atoms.

We can see that Sāṅkhya's list of elements consists of the five gross elements: space, air, fire, water and earth. This is a simplified list of elements to explain the process of evolution.

One other thing to note is that space is produced from the *tanmātra* of sound. Ancient Indians seem to have attributed "matter-like" qualities to space. In Sāṅkhya, space does not imply "nothing-ness" as most of us tend to think — it is also an entity produced from its elements.

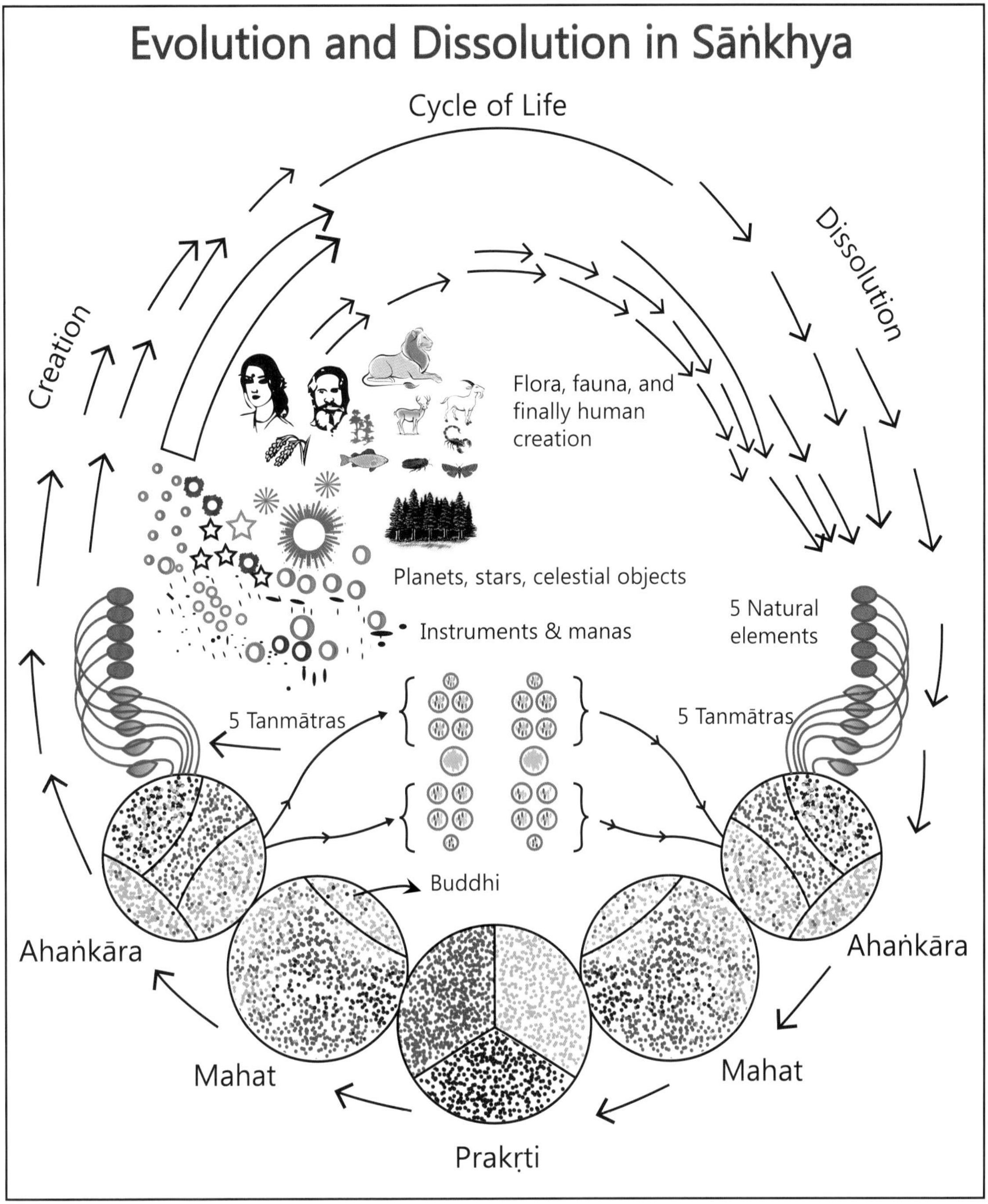

All illustrations of Sāṅkhya evolution have been provided by Acharya Ananda Prakash.

Overview of the Composition of Mind and Body

The mind (*citta*) consists of three evolutes of nature:

1. *buddhi* (intellect),
2. *ahaṅkāra* (ego), and
3. *manas* (coordinator of sense and motor elements, and also responsible for desire and impulse)

In Yoga, these three together are the *citta*, the mind. Whenever the *Yoga Sūtras* refers to the mind, it can be understood as the combination of these components. These three instruments are known as internal instruments — unlike the five sense and five motor elements, which are considered the external instruments of perception.

As described before, the subtle body consists of:

- *Citta*, the mind (*buddhi*, *ahaṅkāra*, *manas*).
- Five sense and five motor elements (ten total external instruments). The five sense and five motor elements convey perceptions to the *citta* through which the consciousness (*puruṣa*) perceives the world.

The *citta* is the container of 1) active impressions generated from the experiences of the external world, and 2) the mental activities generated by these active impressions. A second kind of impression that is not active, called a latent impression, also exists. Latent impressions are impressions gathered in this life or a past life, but that are not active. They are suppressed by dominant impressions, and so cannot sprout into mental activities. When the right circumstances arise, these latent impressions will turn into mental activities, and as a result have consequences.

This subtle body is fitted onto the gross body so that we can perceive the various objects in the universe. Our gross bodies are built from the five gross natural elements (space, air, fire, water and earth), and consist of ten organs (the five sense organs and five motor organs) and a brain.

Puruṣa Experiences Nature

The self (*puruṣa*) is the true consciousness, the real subject that experiences the perceptions conveyed by the mind. The instruments of consciousness — *buddhi*, *ahaṅkāra*, and *manas* — appear to be conscious, but it is really the consciousness that makes them active. The consciousness is external to the mind, not part of either the subtle or gross body.

When we perceive something external, the sensory input travels from our gross sense organs to the physical brain, and then to the subtle sense organs and to the mind. Once the mind is colored by the sensory input, our soul (*puruṣa*) is able to perceive it.

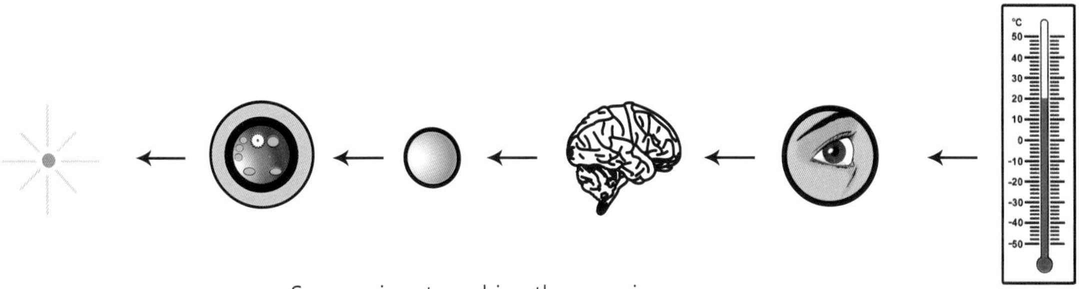

Sensory input reaching the consciousness

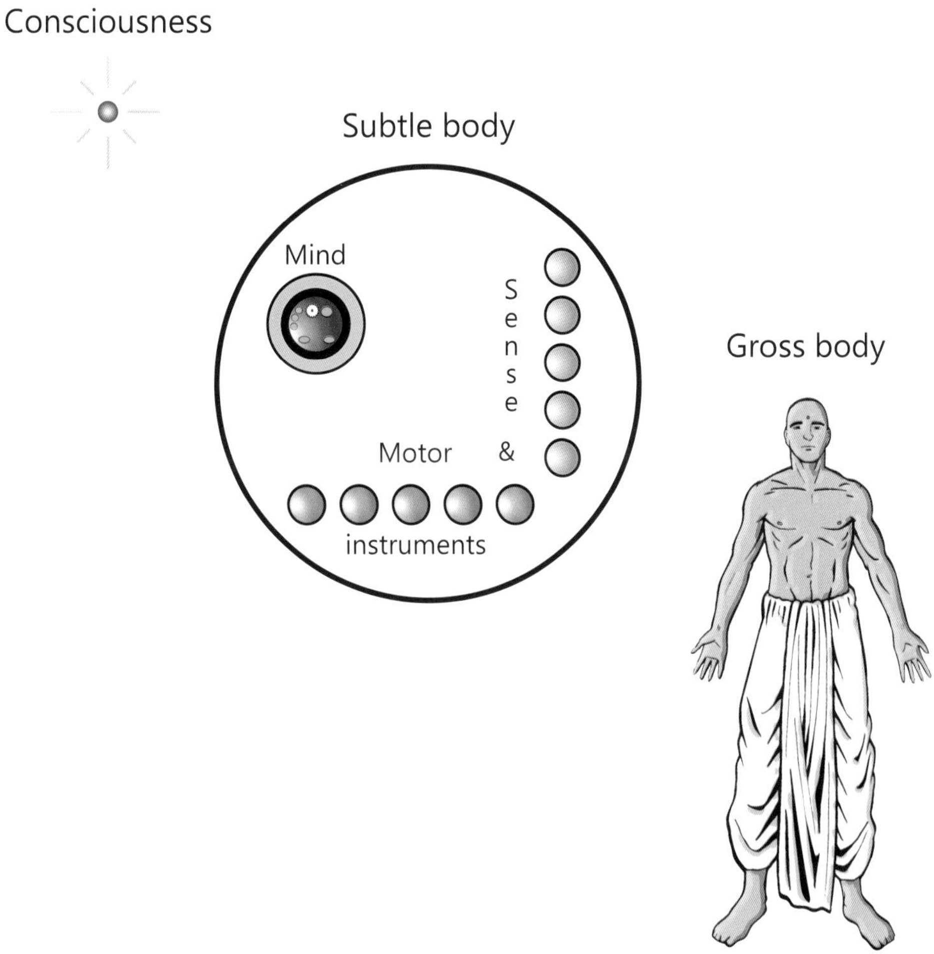

Cconsciousness, subtle body, and the gross body

Puruṣa is the Originator of Actions, Prakṛti is the Performer

Similarly, when we perform an action, that action originates from the soul. Then, the mind and the body carry out the action. However, they may not always carry out the action in the manner that we expect, as they (mind and body) act based on their current state and tendencies, and on the effects of previous actions. There is a misconception regarding Sāṅkhya that the soul does not perform any action. This is incorrect. According to Sāṅkhya, the soul performs action in the form of initiating the mind, but then the mind and body carry out the actions that we readily recognize. Since the details of carrying out an action are determined by the mind and the body, Sāṅkhya calls the mind the "actor" — to emphasize its role. *Bhagavadgītā* uses similar wording ("prakṛteḥ kriyamāṇāni" = "actions are performed by the nature" — verse 3.27). Many misunderstand that Sāṅkhya does not believe in the agency of the soul in performing actions. However, even though the mind is called the actor, Sāṅkhya still maintains that the true source of action is the soul.

The mind derives its power of agency from the soul. This can be clearly understood with the analogy of a car. While accelerating, the person driving the car only pushes the accelerator while the actual increase in speed is brought about by the car's machinery and fuel. Here the person acts as the soul and the car acts like the mind. In effect, all actions originate from the soul; the mind plays a big role in carrying out the actions. We can say that the soul performs the "internal action" while the body and the mind perform the visible "external action." The soul is more of a "director" than an actor.

Since the soul is the originator of action, it is also the receiver of any experience or consequence that results from that action. As the actions are varied, so is the resulting world. Patañjali also clarifies this agency of the soul in sūtra 4.3 of the *Yoga Sūtras*.

Status of Sāṅkhya in Indian Culture

Indians are greatly indebted to Kapila for his gift of knowledge to Indian culture. A number of concepts developed by Kapila now permeate Indian philosophy, science, and medicine. Kapila is celebrated in Indian culture as the best among the yogīs for propounding Sāṅkhya philosophy with his yogic insights. In *Bhagavadgītā*, Lord Krishna himself proclaims the greatness of Kapila by using Kapila's name to refer to the pinnacle of accomplishment:

सिद्धानां कपिलो मुनिः

siddhānāṁ kapilo muniḥ - *Bhagavadgītā* 10.26.

"I AM the sage Kapila among the perfected ones."

नास्ति साङ्ख्यसमं ज्ञानं नास्ति योगसमं बलम्

nāsti sāṅkhyasamaṁ jñānaṁ nāsti yogasamaṁ balam – *Mahābhārata* 12.304.2

"There is no knowledge like Sāṅkhya and no power like Yoga."

Theism in Sāṅkhya

Sāṅkhya is classified as one of the six orthodox systems of Indian philsophy. The term "orthodox" refers to their belief in God and the authority of the *Vedas* which are undisputably theistic. The *Mahābhārata* points to a theistic Sāṅkhya which considers Sāṅkhya and Yoga as one and the same (see the section "Unity and Coexistence of the Six Darśanas"). Again, Yoga is clearly theistic. There is evidence of theism in Kapila's *Sāṅkhya-darśana* itself.

स हि सर्ववित् सर्वकर्ता ॥

sa hi sarvavit sarvakartā ॥ *Sāṅkhya-darśana* 3.56 ॥

"He [God] is the knower and maker of all things."

ईदृशेश्वरसिद्धिः सिद्धा ॥

īdṛśeśvarasiddhiḥ siddhā ॥ *Sāṅkhya-darśana* 3.57 ॥

"The existence of a God like this is proven."

Based on the sūtras themselves, the claim that Sāṅkhya is atheistic is debatable. It seems that atheism may have been foisted on to Sāṅkhya at a period much later than the authoring of the *Mahābhārata* and *Yoga Sūtras*. The debate ultimately boils down to the interpretation of only a few sūtras in *Sāṅkhya-darśana* as God is not its primary topic of exposition. Also, at the end of each chapter in the commentary on the *Yoga Sūtras*, Vyāsa calls his exposition a "Sāṅkhya-exposition" (*Sāṅkhya-pravacana*) indicating theism in Sāṅkhya. The theistic views of Patañjali and Vyāsa are quite obvious.

Summary of Sāṅkhya

1. Consciousness is pure and unchanging. It is not made from any components — it is indivisible. It is different from nature and its elements.
2. Nature consists of three kinds of elements — *sattva*, *rajas* and *tamas*. Everything we experience is made of a combination of these three elements.
3. The process of evolution and transformation of nature results in the formation of minds, bodies, and other objects that we experience.
4. At any given time, the consciousness experiences the mind which is "colored" by the interaction of the sense and motor instruments with their objects (or due to thoughts in the mind).
5. Consciousness (the self) is not the same as the mind (nature). Confusing the mind with consciousness is ignorance, and the cause of all misery. (Our thoughts, emotions, and memories are all formed from *sattva*, *rajas*, and *tamas* - they are part of nature.)
6. Distinguishing consciousness (the self) from the mind (nature) is liberation.
7. When an individual consciousness attains liberation, the universe continues to exist for others who are not liberated.

In the context of the modern theory of evolution

Sāṅkhya does not deny the existence of either the consciousness or matter. It acknowledges the existence of both, and proceeds to study them with objectivity. It avoids extremism, and excels in describing both consciousness and nature with a healthy and well-balanced approach. As such, Sāṅkhya is not in opposition with the modern theory of evolution. Instead, it recognizes the evolution of our bodies and of all living creatures from the primordial elements. Sāṅkhya is one of the oldest systems of knowledge to describe, long before modern science, an evolutionary model that explains material reality. In Sāṅkhya, creation of the universe happens through the transformation of matter over billions of years — it is not an instant process. Sāṅkhya is a practical and organic body of knowledge that is rooted in reality, and it demonstrates that science and spirituality are not mutually exclusive.

The Science of Yoga

Misery and its Elimination

The four pillars of Yoga are the studies of the four aspects of misery — its nature, its cause, its elimination, and the methods to achieve that elimination. These are detailed below.

1. Misery (*heyam*): Misery is all of the frustration, sadness, and pain that we are yet to experience, and which we desire to avoid. This is a technical term in Yoga, and omits past and present misery because only the experience of future misery can be avoided or influenced.
2. Cause of Misery (*heya-hetuḥ*): Confusing consciousness (the soul) as the mind is the cause of misery. In other words, consciousness perceiving itself as the mind — which is the container of emotions, thoughts, ego and memory — is the cause of misery.
3. Elimination of Misery (*hānam*): The elimination of false knowledge (mistaking the mind for the self) and isolating pure consciousness in its own form leads to the elimination of misery.
4. Methods of eliminating misery (*hānopāyaḥ*): The eight limbs of yoga are the means to obtain discriminating wisdom which leads to elimination of misery.

Influencing our future experience

Much of the spiritual literature in India mentions knowledge, action, and meditation as the means to attain happiness and liberation. The eight limbs of yoga are Patañjali's elaboration of these three means with an emphasis on meditation.

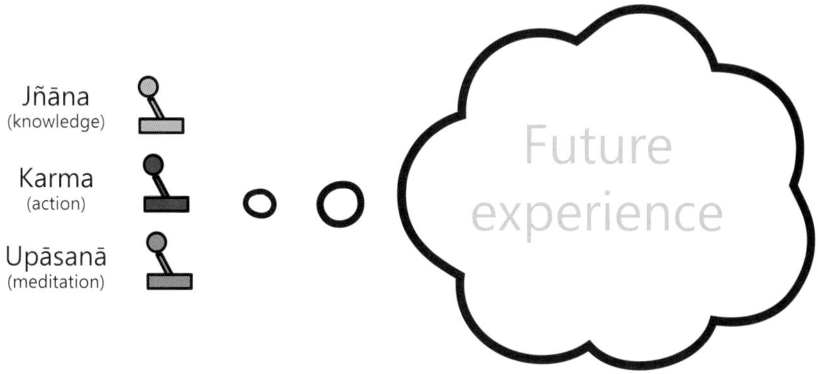

Citta, the Mind

In some philosophies, like some strains of Buddhism and Hinduism, the mind — and in fact all of reality — is thought to be merely an illusory and momentary state. In Yoga and Sāṅkhya, the mind is not an illusion; it is a real, durable entity that undergoes transformations by assuming the form of different objects. The concept of "taking or assuming the form" shouldn't be taken literally. It means that an "image" of the object being perceived is formed in the mind which is then experienced by the soul. When the mind is shifting from perceiving one thing to another, the state of such a mind is called *vyutthāna* — a diffused state. When it is concentrated on one thing, this results in a state called *samādhi* — a state of deep concentration.

Composition of Citta (the Mind)

As explained earlier, the mind is composed of intellect (*buddhi*), ego (*ahaṅkāra*), and the coordinator of sense and motor instruments (*manas*). They are the evolutes of nature.

States of the Mind

The human mind can exist in five states (also called *bhūmis*):

1. *Mūḍha* (stupefied): In this state, the mind is overcome by negativity. Addiction, violent behavior, and low self-esteem are some of the results of this state. *Tamas* is dominant.
2. *Kṣipta* (scattered, restless): In this state, the mind is unable to concentrate on anything. It constantly fluctuates, and inhibits accomplishments. *Rajas* is dominant.
3. *Vikṣipta* (distracted): In this state, the mind is able to focus only partially. An intermittent ability to concentrate is the characteristic of this state. Most people have some experience of this in everyday life. *Sattva* and *rajas* are dominant.
4. *Ekāgra* (focused, "one-pointed"): In this state, the mind can concentrate on one object of contemplation without wavering. The object in each subsequent moment is same as in the previous moment, which is why this contemplative state is called "one-pointed." This state is one of the goals of yoga. *Sattva* is dominant.
5. *Niruddha* (restrained): In this state, all mental activities are restrained. Impressions remain as impressions, without turning into mental activities. The consciousness is uninfluenced by mental fluctuations, and is established in its true form. This state is independent of the three *guṇas*. This is the ultimate goal of yoga.

State	Qualities	Results
Mūḍha : *Tamas* is dominant, with *rajas* and *sattva* partially effective. A person feels confused, frustrated, and lethargic.	Sleep, fatigue, attachment, fear, laziness, meekness, confusion	Ignorance, attachment, *adharma* (non-virtue, lack of *dharma*), non-prosperity
Kṣipta: *Rajas* is dominant, with *tamas* and *sattva* partially effective. The mind is drawn in different directions and cannot stay concentrated on one point.	Sadness, fickleness, worry, excessive interest in worldly pursuits	Ignorance and knowledge, attachment and detachment, *adharma* and *dharma*
Vikṣipta: *Sattva* and *rajas* are dominant, with *tamas* partially effective. The mind is drawn in different directions but can concentrate on one point for short periods of time.	Temporary happiness, pleasantness, forgiveness, dedication, fearlessness, consciousness, health interest/excitement, charity, valor, compassion	Knowledge mixed with ignorance, attachment, mostly *dharma* (virtue)
Ekāgra: *Sattva* is dominant, with just enough *rajas* and *tamas* to support *sattva*. The mind stays completely concentrated on one point without interruption.	Disinclination, in the sense of stoicism, non-involvement, non-attachment	Knowledge of things as they really are (true knowledge)
Niruddha: The effect of the *guṇas* is stopped. No further transformations (vṛttis) of mind occur, and only the impressions (*saṁskāras*) remain. All activities of the mind are eliminated, including concentration on any one point. Complete decoupling of the mind and soul occurs. Thus the soul, the self (*puruṣa*) remains in its own state.	*Puruṣa* remaining in its own state	Soul established in its own form (*svarūpa-pratiṣṭhā*)

Activities of the Mind Leading to Experience and Liberation

The activities of the mind (*citta*) are infinite, but they are classified into five categories of activities (*vṛttis*).

1. *pramāṇa* (correct knowledge)
2. *viparyaya* (incorrect knowledge, error)
3. *vikalpa* (imagination, conceptualization)
4. *nidrā* (sleep)
5. *smṛti* (memory)

These five activities lead either to afflictions — the bondage of body and mind — or to knowledge and self-realization — permanent bliss. Depending on whether the five activities cause afflictions or not, *citta* leads us in two paths: one toward *bhoga*, which is experience of the *prakṛti*, and the other toward *apavarga*, liberation resulting from true self-knowledge. This is depicted in the following picture

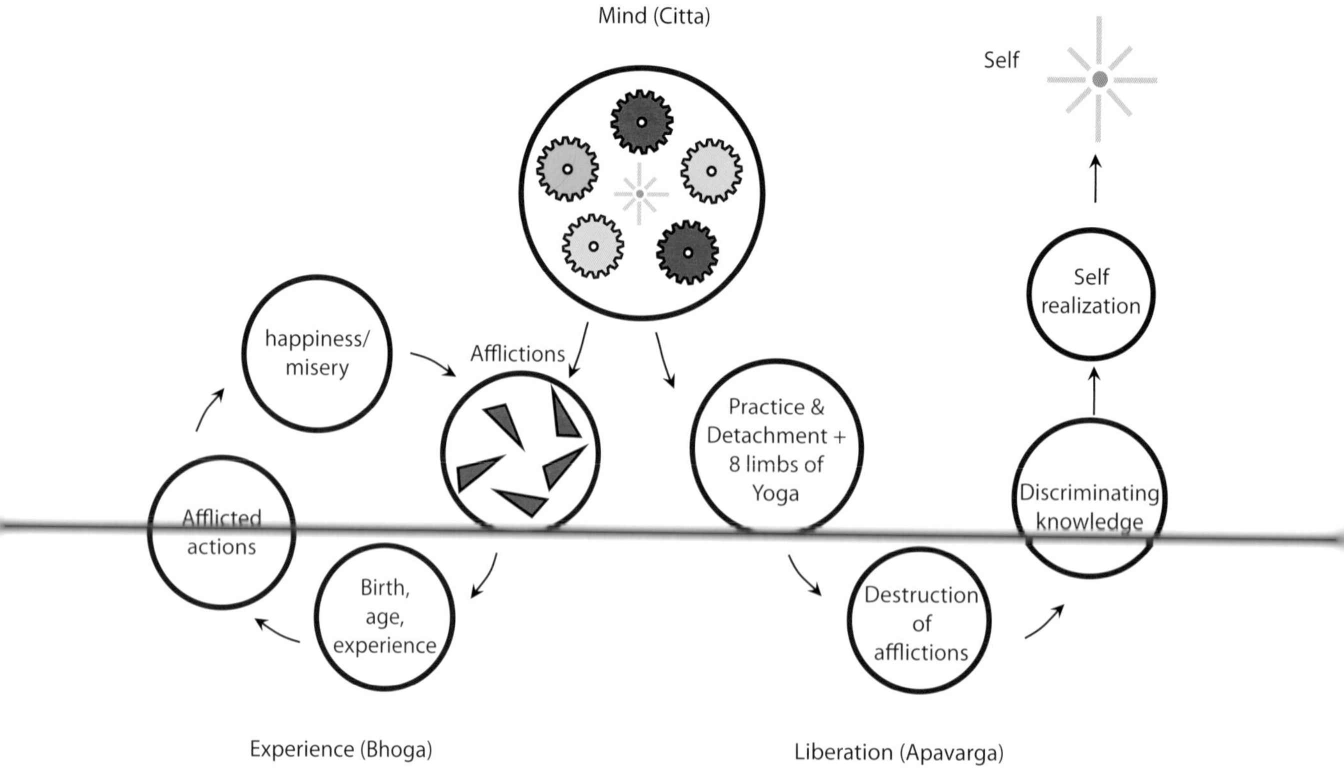

Two paths a consciousness can take: experience and liberation

Experience

The path of *bhoga* — the experience of the *prakṛti*, nature — leads to many things described below.

1. *Kleśas*, or afflictions: There are five afflictions, born from the activities of the mind. They are
    - incorrect knowledge
    - ego (this is different from *ahaṅkāra* which is the second evolute from *prakṛti*)
    - desire
    - hatred
    - clinging to physical life
2. These give rise to actions (*karma*) motivated by afflictions.
3. Such actions lead to birth, lifespan, and experience (pleasurable or miserable). In yoga these things are considered "bondage," in the sense that we are forced to experience what life presents to us, and while involved in such a bondage we are unable to experience our true selves. The goal of yoga is to attain complete independence, to be established in the true self.
4. Birth, lifespan, and experience can cause either happiness or misery, depending on whether the actions are virtuous or non-virtuous
5. This resulting happiness or misery reinforces the afflictions (we tend to desire things that are conducive to happiness, and to hate things that are not). Since afflictions lead to birth, lifespan and experience — this continues the cycle (or "bondage") of birth and death.

How do Impressions and Actions Work?

The mind which is present in the subtle body is a store-house of impressions. At the beginning of a creation cycle (of the universe) the mind is created with all the impressions and capabilities to operate all living bodies. But, only those impressions that are conducive to present the consequences of the actions we performed up until a previous life are activated. The other impressions remain latent — they may or may not become active depending on our future actions.

When we perform actions, they create new impressions of merit and demerit. The set of impressions of merit and demerit is called "the stock of karma." Depending on this stock of karma, some latent impressions might become active in the current or future lives to give us appropriate consequences. This process is never ending. Different consequences require us to take birth in different bodies of living organisms.

We only experience impressions currently "active" in our mind. If they are not active, we cannot experience them. This is the reason why most of us cannot recollect memories from a previous birth as those impressions are latent. The phenomenon is similar to the experience of

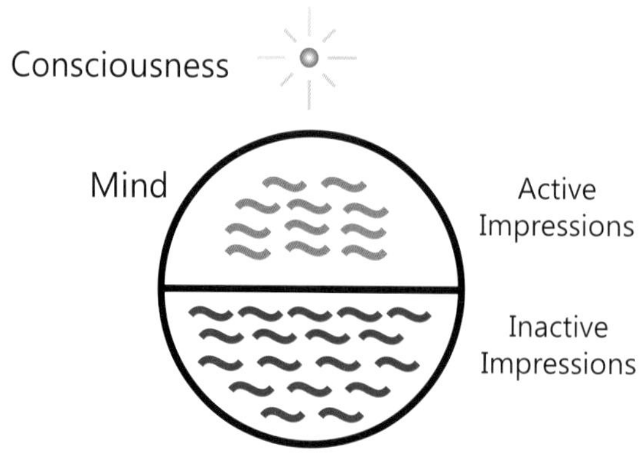

deep sleep. In deep sleep, even our current memories are temporarily clouded by *tamas* so much so that we are not even aware of our name, gender or the kind of body we are in. This shows that not all impressions are accessible to us at all times. As mentioned before, a yogī can see the dormant impressions in a deep state of meditation which will be discussed in the third chapter of the *Yoga Sūtras*.

Liberation

Conversely, the path of *apavarga* — the path of liberation — has different consequences.

1. Non-attachment, and the desire to perform practices that lead to self-realization.
2. Practice of the eight limbs of yoga, which destroys the *kleśas*.
3. This results in discriminating between the consciousness (*puruṣa*) and nature or matter (*prakṛti*) — discernment between the consciousness and the mind (and everything else external).
4. The consciousness is established in its true self, freed from the cycle of birth and death. This is the final state of liberation, of attaining oneness with the self (*kaivalya*).

Importance of Worldly Life (Bhoga)

The path to liberation is preceded by the experience of nature which we know as the worldly life. It is necessary for developing the wisdom and inclination for liberation. That is why *bhoga*, which is the experience of nature, is listed as one of the two main purposes of life in the *Yoga Sūtras* (sūtra 2.18). In order to achieve these two goals (of experience and liberation), Indian spiritual literature elaborates four pursuits of human life. They are called the four *puruṣārthas*.

1. Virtuous conduct and gaining spiritual knowledge (*dharma*)
2. Earning wealth (*artha*)
3. Fulfilling physical and mental desires (*kāma*)
4. Liberation from all misery (*mokṣa*), which is one of the main topics of *darśanas*.

All four are important for leading a fruitful life. Kaṇāda in his *Vaiśeṣika-darśana* states

यतोऽभ्युदय निःश्रेयससिद्धिः स धर्मः

yato'bhyudaya niḥśreyasasiddhiḥ sa dharmaḥ – *Vaiśeṣika-darśana* 1.2

That which leads to worldy prosperity and spiritual growth is dharma.

Virtuous conduct does not get in the way of worldly life. This synergetic coexistence of both wordly and spiritual pursuits is widely praised in Indian culture. It is seen both in spiritual and wordly literatures. The following hymn is from *Ṛgveda*.

पजापते न त्वदेतान्यन्यो विश्वा जातानि परि ता बभूव ।

यत्कामास्ते जुहुमस्तन्नो अस्तु वयं स्याम पतयो रयीणाम् ॥

pajāpate na tvadetānyanyo viśvā jātāni pari tā babhūva ।

yatkāmāste juhumastanno astu vayaṁ syāma patayo rayīṇām ॥ *Ṛgveda* 10.121.10 ॥

O' Lord of all people! There is no one other than you that governs all beings that are born. May we own the things desirous of which we pray to you and may we become the lords of wealth.

The great poet, Kalidasa, writes the following in praise of king Atithi of the Solar dynasty.

न धर्ममर्थकामाभ्यां बबाधे न च तेन तौ ।

नार्थं कामेन कामं वा सोऽर्थेन सदृशस्त्रिषु ॥

na dharmamarthakāmābhyāṁ babādhe na ca tena tau ।

nārthaṁ kāmena kāmaṁ vā so'rthena sadṛśastriṣu ॥ *Raghuvaṁśam* 17.57 ॥

Dharma was not impeded by *artha* and *kāma*. They both (*artha* and *kāma)* were not impeded by *dharma*. Neither *artha* was impeded by *kāma* nor *kāma* was impeded by *artha*. He (Atithi) was equally engaged in all the three.

Dharma lays the groundwork for the path towards liberation. After fulfilling the worldly pursuits, a person enters the renunciatory (*apavarga*) phase of life as described in the four stages of human life before.

About the Text of the Yoga Sūtras

With this knowledge, we now embark on exploring the *Yoga Sūtras* (aphorisms about yoga) composed by the great rishi Patañjali. The *Yoga Sūtras* consists of four chapters:

1. "Samādhipāda" explains what is meant by yoga and how the goal of yoga is attained. This chapter consists of 51 sūtras.
2. "Sādhanapāda" presents the practices that help in attaining the goal of yoga. It consists of 55 sūtras.
3. "Vibhūtipāda" talks about the various abilities that a practitioner gains on the path of yoga. It also touches on the Sāṅkhya philosophy. It consists of 55 sūtras.
4. "Kaivalyapāda" explains the Sāṅkhya principles on which yoga is based, and talks about the final stages in attaining the goal of yoga. It consists of 34 sūtras.

Patañjali describes the means of eliminating misery in just 195 lines. He is able to manage this remarkable feat by focusing on the root causes of all problems rather than individual problems. He describes the problem-creators (afflictions) in attaining self realization and the solution-creators (the eight limbs of Yoga) with amazing brevity and precision which is the hallmark of the "sūtra" style of writing.

The Yoga Sūtras

Samādhipādaḥ (Absorption)

Sūtras 1.1-1.11: Introduction to the Mind

अथ योगानुशासनम् ॥ १.१ ॥
atha yogānuśāsanam ॥ 1.1 ॥

atha = now
yoga = yoga
anuśāsanam = re-enunciation

Now begins the re-enunciation of the principles of yoga.

Most works authored by seers start with the word "*atha*," symbolizing an auspicious beginning. Yoga has been mentioned in earlier texts like the *Mahābhārata* and *Upaniṣads*, so it is clearly a practice that existed before Patañjali's time. It is codified and presented in a condensed form in the *Yoga Sūtras*, which is why the word "re-enunciation" is used in this sūtra.

The word yoga comes from the root word "*yuj*," a state of mental concentration more commonly called *samādhi*. This is a state of having only one mental activity remaining, or even none. When only one activity or thought remains this state is called *ekāgra*, and when no mental activity is active (all are restrained) it is called *niruddha*. This is the ultimate goal of yoga.

योगश्चित्तवृत्तिनिरोधः ॥ १.२ ॥
yogaścittavṛttinirodhaḥ ॥ 1.2 ॥

yogaḥ = the word yoga
citta = mind
vṛtti = activity, alternation, fluctuation
nirodhaḥ = regulating, restraining, stopping

Yoga means restraining the activities of the mind.

The consciousness (*puruṣa*) can perceive only what is shown to it by the mind (*citta*). Consciousness experiences the state of the mind at any given time. It identifies with the mind which gives rise to the feeling "I am the mind."

When one is involved in *sattva*-dominated activities like learning and understanding, feeling pleasant, and so on, consciousness experiences the states of *sattva*. This is the same for the active (*rajas*) and sedentary (*tamas*) experiences. As the activities of the mind are gradually restrained, the mind moves closer to the one-pointed state (*ekāgra*) wherein one can concentrate on one object without interruption.

At this stage, a yogī attains the distinction between the mind and the consciousness (*viveka-khyāti*). When the object of meditation in the one-pointed state, which is the last remaining mental activity, ceases — the yogī having restrained all mental activities — remains in his or her own true state, uninfluenced and uncontaminated by the thought patterns.

There are many questions that one might have about control of the mind. I will address a few of them below with some analogies. Kindly bear with the length of the commentary on this sūtra.

The Mind is Like a Forest

Normally, we identify with our thoughts and emotions — based on them, we assess our nature and self-worth. We think our thoughts and emotions are us. However, Yoga teaches that these things are in fact external to us. They happen in the mind, which is outside of our core self.

Imagine a man living in a forest. He encounters a wide variety of trees, shrubs, animals, birds, and insects, and watches them with amazement. Some things may frighten him, but after he learns to deal with them he can harness and benefit from them. He finds bushes that bear delicious and nourshing fruit, trees that have wood to make his shelter, herbs that can cure his ailments. He leads a symbiotic and peaceful life within nature. However, none of this is possible until he learns the survival skills necessary to live in the forest. Without such skills he can fall prey to wild animals, or starve to death.

Our mind is like a forest. We encounter thoughts and emotions in our mind, but quite often we don't know how to manage them and benefit from them. Instead, we identify with them and declare our own nature based upon them. Once we identify with these activities of the mind, we lose the ability to explore them further, and feel helpless when thoughts and emotions make us feel bad — leading to anxieties, insecurities, frustrations, and other unproductive behaviours.

Considering our core self as external to the mind results in a perspective that allows for better exploration and learning of our thoughts and emotions. We can manage them better, and make the best out of them.

Will I Lose My Character?

Since we believe that our "emotions" impart character to our "self," we might fear the prospect of not identifying with our mind. One might say, "If I can't identify with my mind or emotions, I lose my character — I lose my self." The truth is that emotions and thoughts impart character to our minds and bodies, not to our core self. We will not lose our character, because that character belongs to the "mind," which belongs to us. We are the owners or lords (*prabhu*) of our minds; they are always in our possession. So, the fear of losing our character is based on a misconception and an inaccurate assesment of our relationship with our minds.

Once we identify directly with our emotions, we have no room to enrich them. Instead, we accept them and become a slave to their nature — if the emotions happen to be good we feel good, and if they happen to be bad we feel bad. Instead of just accepting them as "us," we can step back and research our emotions with curiosity and enthusiasm. This gives us the opportunity to make emotions better and to change them if they are hurting us. This protects us from falling prey to frustrations.

On the other hand, when the emotions are exciting and pleasurable we can enjoy them by minimizing our feelings of anxiety. Usually, anxiety is the flip-side of excitement and success — excitement by its very nature has a destabilizing component. There is a sense of fear of loss in things that we achieve. Only when you are able to be peaceful and assured can you enjoy your success. This is rightly questioned in *Bhagavadgītā*:

अशान्तस्य कुतः सुखम्

aśāntasya kutaḥ sukham. - *Bhagavadgītā* 2.66

"Where is the happiness of a person who is not peaceful?"

Yoga gives us the knowledge and practices that help us manage our thoughts, emotions, and ego. Skillful management of your mind is true yoga. *Bhagavadgītā* makes a very relevant statement:

योगः कर्मसु कौशलम्

yogaḥ karmasu kauśalam. - *Bhagavadgītā* 2.50

"Yoga is skillfulness in actions."

In order to attain skillfulness in actions, one must attain skillfulness in managing one's own mind, as the mind is the key to performing all actions. With knowledge, peace, and self-assurance, one becomes skillful in all actions.

Emotions as Extracts, the Rasas

Emotions are constantly forming or brewing in our minds, and gradually pass through different states. We perceive emotions only after they become "gross" enough to be perceptible.

For example, you might have been reading a book for some time, and from seemingly nowhere comes an urge to eat ice cream. However, everything that we experience takes time and processing to take shape. With the observation and discernment (*viveka*) that comes from meditation, one can investigate any kind of feeling or sensation. Feelings or emotions are formed and triggered in many ways — by mental or bodily processes, actions, situations, interactions with objects, places, people, and so on. There are infinite kinds of feelings, and all of them are, according to Sāṅkhya and Yoga, formed from the three primordial elements of nature — these feelings all contain different amounts of illumination, activity, and stability.

Emotions are sometimes called *rasas*, the juices of fruits or extracts from plants, which we taste. One of the goals of Yoga as described in *Bhagavadgītā* is to learn to taste feelings without being afflicted by them. This is a difficult task, especially in the beginning of yoga practice when it is hard not to feel bad while experiencing things that are painful. But, with proper diet, meditation, learning and other memory-enhancing activities, one's observation becomes enhanced, resulting in a discerning vision (known by the word *āloka* as used in sūtra 3.25). Then, one can skillfully extract insights and a feeling of peace even from the most painful of emotions, and so overcome them. Just as one might fear a bee because of its painful sting but feels amazement looking at the same insect under a microscope and learning about its life cycle, one learns to be

amazed by all *rasas* with an observant mind, and to make the best of them — like a bee-keeper.

One needn't fear the prospect of meditation to restrain these thoughts. After all, we stop many of our mental activities all the time, unknowingly. In deep sleep, for example, there is only the one activity of sleep — all other mental activities are dormant. Sleep refreshes our body and mind, and meditation does considerably more than that. Meditation enhances memory, and acts as a seed of healthy enthusiasm and discernment (*viveka*) — which in turn leads to productive actions. Meditation charts a new course of understanding and enlightenment, and helps us attain enjoyment and liberation.

Restraining mental activities does not mean death to the brain

Since Yoga mentions restraint of the mind's processes, one might wonder, "Will I become brain-dead if I stop or restrain the activities of my mind?" This is not an issue. When a yogī enters a deep state of meditation, the body — including the brain — functions normally, just like in a deep sleep.

Some might further question if restraining the activities of the mind is the end of life. When the activities of the mind are restrained, we don't stop experiencing life, we actually experience the source of life which is our core consciousness. Practices of Yoga are meant to get us closer to the source of our life.

What is the Near-term Benefit of Practicing Yoga and Meditation?

Restraining the activities of the mind is a difficult feat. It can take years, decades or even several lifetimes to learn to completely restrain one's mind. Given such an effort, one might ask if there are any more immediate benefits to this practice.

We normally assume that pain or pleasure is caused by the external situations and objects that we interact with. As a result, we tend to think that manipulating these situations and objects is the natural way to eliminate misery, and when we don't have enough control over these external things we get frustrated. When we think that our selves and our minds are the same, we respond to situations in a "reflexive" fashion, with little control and not much certainty — which produces anxiety about the result. We end up facing the consequences without having much say in how those consequences make us feel.

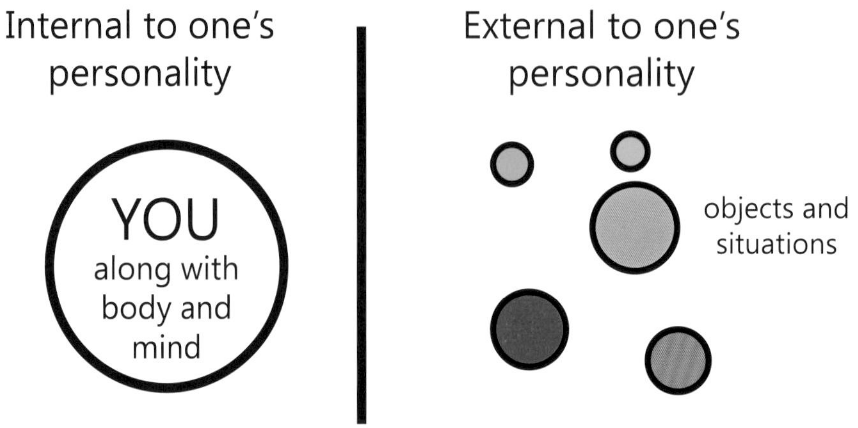

Perception without discernment

However, the inconvenience or misery resulting from such consequences can be avoided by practicing Yoga. By understanding the model of the mind, body, and soul presented by Sāṅkhya and Yoga, and by practicing meditation, we become more sensitive and can recognize the subtle differences between seemingly-similar sensations and perceptions. Practicing the eight limbs of yoga also improves memory (*smṛtipariśuddhi* — sūtra 1.43), which leads one to compare perceptions and sensations with more precision. This is how one's discernment is improved. With this superior sense of observation, a person notices and experiences that there are more parts of his or her personality, and that a lot of these parts are actually external to the core self. In addition, one may notice more parts to external situations.

This understanding is not an all-or nothing-process; it happens step by step. Slowly and gradually the core self of a person stops identifying with the body, the sense instruments, the mind, and all the thoughts and emotions in the mind. The more thoughts and feelings the self perceives to be external to it, the more avenues to eliminate misery open up, and the more situations one is able to manage with composure. The things that we used to view as the "self" are now revealed to be external to the self. This new-found discernment frees us from identifying with imperfections of the body, and the mind, and enables us to form healthy responses to the challenges and obstacles we face.

Knowing how internal and external things work and how to deal with them instills peace and confidence. As such, one can benefit from meditation even without having mastered it. Naturally, the more activities of the mind are restrained, the more one can benefit from the

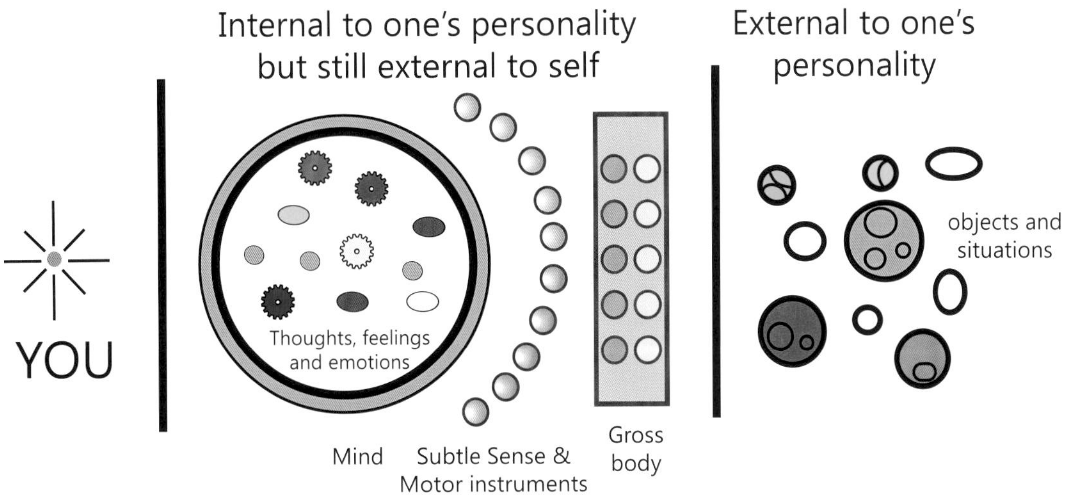

Perception with discernment

insights that come from the enhanced discernment. But, every step of practicing Yoga, even the early steps, leads to clarity of thought and equanimity.

> **Memory**
>
> Memory which aids in discernment includes both conscious and subconscious memories that our minds use to constantly evaluate objects, situations and people to decide whether our interactions with them are productive or not. This happens even when we are not aware of it.

The Feeling that Control of the Mind is Boring or Unnatural

Many skills that we gain over time at some point seem boring or unnatural, especially at the start. When learning to play a sport, in the beginning we might be frustrated, but we increasingly enjoy the activity after gaining some level of skill. We lose a lot if we give up without trying or examining new skills. Meditation is no different from the many other habits that take some practice to get good at. Kids take a while before getting accustomed to brushing teeth, taking showers, and maintaining personal hygiene on their own, but we certainly don't call it unnatural to stay clean. Being bored or frustrated when learning something new is a natural human feeling.

Some modern spiritual advisors take advantage of this inconvenient feeling to describe yogic practices in a negative light. This furthers their own personal doctrines or techniques of self realization, which they claim are "faster" or "easier." They seem to encourage the idea that faster or easier is somehow "natural." This is a very specious and misleading notion — I think everyone can agree that many worthwhile things take considerable effort to achieve.

As will be seen in the coming sūtras, Patañjali is very inclusive in his description of the various methods of self-realization — his aphorisms are mindful and accommodating of people's personal preferences. Like Sāṅkhya, Yoga too endures misrepresentations. I personally would be very wary of any advertised shortcuts to weight loss or spiritual growth. Gaining insight into one's own mind and spirit is no different from gaining insight into any other subject of interest — it requires some effort of studying and observation. There are no shortcuts in yoga. Yoga is an organic approach that cultivates habits and attitudes that have a lasting positive impact on us, and on those around us.

तदा द्रष्टुः स्वरूपेऽवस्थानम् ॥ १.३ ॥
tadā draṣṭuḥ svarūpe'vasthānam ॥ 1.3 ॥

tadā = then
draṣṭuḥ = observer, seer
svarūpe = own form (sva + rūpa)
avasthānam = established, abiding

Then, the seer is established in his own form.

When the activities of the mind are stopped, consciousness (the soul) remains in its own state. It is important to note that the functions of the physical body do not stop, just like in a deep sleep. Our breathing and involuntary functions continue — it is only the activities of the subtle mind that are restrained. In this state the consciousness stops identifying with the activities of the mind and the body, and attains complete independence and bliss.

वृत्तिसारूप्यमितरत्र ॥ १.४ ॥
vṛttisārūpyamitaratra ॥ 1.4 ॥

vṛtti = activity
sārūpyam = being of similar form
itaratra = elsewhere, in other times

At other times, it (the seer, consciousness) takes the same form as its [mind's] activities.

When activities are not restrained, the consciousness identifies with the activities of the mind — that is, it feels like a person with certain qualities. When our minds are undisciplined, we further identify with the things we think and do. For example, if you have a bad day at work, you may feel bad. If someone says something nice to you, you may feel happy. In fact, you were the same person all the time; however, your moods change depending on your circumstances. The core consciousness does not change. It is the mind that changes depending on the mental processes that happen at any given point of time.

Consciousness experiencing "a person perceiving the objects"

वृत्तयः पञ्चतय्यः क्लिष्टाक्लिष्टाः ॥ १.५ ॥
vṛttayaḥ pañcatayyaḥ kliṣṭākliṣṭāḥ ॥ 1.5 ॥

vṛttayaḥ = activities
pañcatayyaḥ = five fold
kliṣṭa = afflicting, troubling
akliṣṭāḥ = non-afflicting, not troubling

There are five kinds of activities, which are either afflicting or non-afflicting.

It is important to understand the different functions of the mind in order to control the mind. The activities of the mind are infinite in number, but are classified into five categories (which will be described in the following sūtra). Each category is further divided into either troubling (*kliṣṭa*) or not troubling (*akliṣṭa*). The word *kliṣṭa* literally means having an affliction (*kleśa*). An affliction is something that is detrimental or non-productive in achieving our goals. The afflictions are ignorance, ego, attachment, aversion, and clinging to physical life. These become the foundation for the consequences of karma — when your actions are motivated by afflictions they result in consequences, which can be pleasant or unpleasant.

The non-troubling mental activities are beneficial. They increase discriminating wisdom and give us the ability to control our actions.

The mind may exhibit troubled or serene states by turns alternating between those states. This alternation occurs continuously until the restrained state is obtained through the practice of yoga.

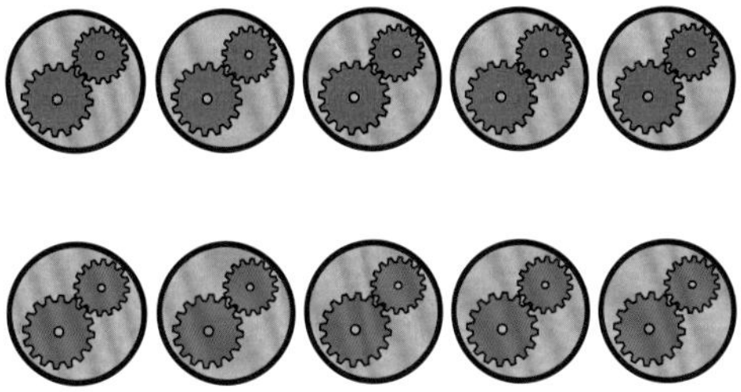

Afflicting and non-afflicting activities

प्रमाणविपर्ययविकल्पनिद्रास्मृतयः ॥ १.६ ॥
pramāṇaviparyayavikalpanidrāsmṛtayaḥ ॥ 1.6 ॥

pramāṇa = proof, evidence, means of correct knowledge
viparyaya = misconception
vikalpa = incorrect conceptualization based on words
nidrā = sleep
smṛtayaḥ = recollection (memory)

They [the mental activities] are proof, misconception, imagination, sleep, and memory.

Proof (*pramāṇa* = right measure, valid cognition) is the mental activity that deals with accurate understanding of facts. Misconception is understanding something in a way that is not true. Imagination creates mental images based solely on language. Sleep is more specifically dreamless sleep. Memory is the activity of accurately recollecting what has been experienced before. These five mental activities will be discussed further in the coming sūtras.

प्रत्यक्षानुमानागमाः प्रमाणानि ॥ १.७ ॥
pratyakṣānumānāgamāḥ pramāṇāni ॥ 1.7 ॥

pratyakṣa = direct perception
anumāna = inference
āgamāḥ = verbal testimony
pramāṇāni = methods of correct inference

Valid proofs are 1) direct perception through senses, 2) inference or deduction, and 3) reliable testimony.

1. Direct perception (*pratyakṣa*) involves perceiving something with your own sense organs. *Akṣa* means "eye" and *pratyakṣa* literally means simply "in front of your eyes."
2. Inference (*anumāna*) is the ability to deduce one thing from the existence of another. For example, fire produces smoke; so, if you see smoke, you can infer the presence of a fire even if you don't see the fire.
3. Testimony (*āgama*) is knowledge obtained from reliable sources. In spiritual matters we often rely on the testimony of people like yogīs and *rishis*, who tell what they have directly experienced. *Āgama* is "eye witness" testimony because it is a reliable report of someone else's experience.

Knowledge is of two types: general (*sāmānya*) and specific (*viśeṣa*).

- General or common knowledge is obtained when, for example, someone says that they saw a cow. The knowledge you have about that cow is general (you know what cows are generally like, but you have no specifics about that particular cow).
- Specific knowledge is obtained when you look at the cow yourself. This knowledge has the specifics about that particular cow.

Inference and testimony offer only general knowledge, which may contain some specifics but doesn't have the specificity of knowledge gained by direct perception. Only direct perception gives complete, specific knowledge.

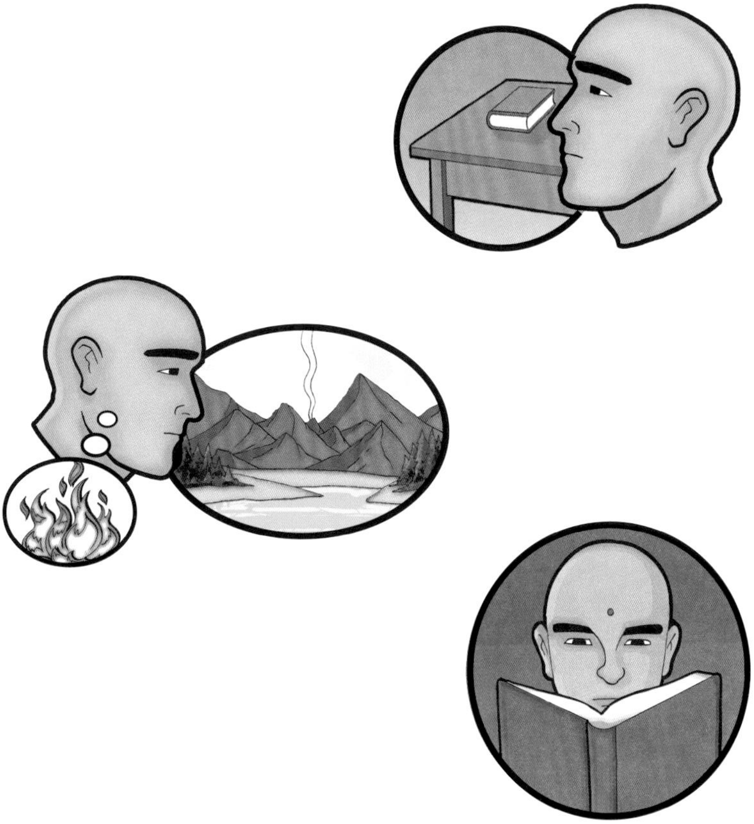

Direct perception, inference, and reliable testimony

विपर्ययो मिथ्याज्ञानमतद्रूपप्रतिष्ठम् ॥ १.८ ॥
viparyayo mithyājñānamatadrūpapratiṣṭham ॥ 1.8 ॥

viparyayaḥ = incorrect perception
mithyājñānam = wrong knowledge
atadrūpa = that which is not (literally "not that form")
pratiṣṭham = placed or established

Incorrect perception is perceiving a thing to be what it is not.

This sūtra is very clear and requires little explanation. Incorrect knowledge (*viparyaya*) can be eliminated by using proper methods of knowledge. When you see a rope from a distance or in faint light and think that it is a snake, you can resolve that misconception by closely examining the rope in a better light. This type of false knowledge is different from another kind, a lack of knowledge called ignorance (*avidyā*). *Avidyā* is the root of all our misunderstanding, and can be removed only by restraining the activities of the mind to attain discriminating knowledge.

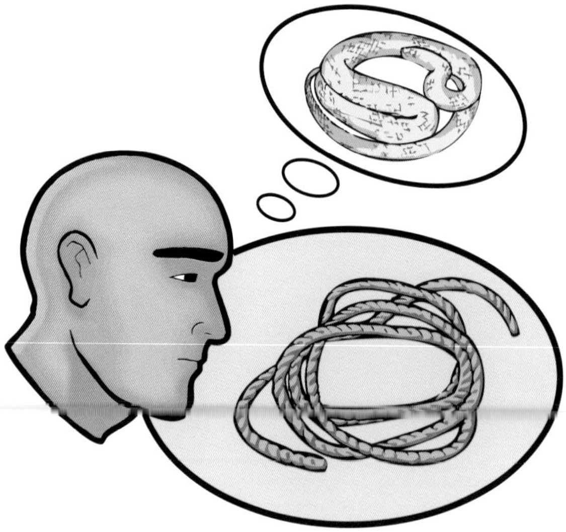

Incorrect perception

शब्दज्ञानानुपाती वस्तुशून्यो विकल्पः ॥ १.९ ॥
śabdajñānānupātī vastuśūnyo vikalpaḥ ॥ 1.9 ॥

śabdajñānānupātī = that which follows from verbal knowledge
vastuśūnyo = non-existence of the object
vikalpaḥ = imagination

Imagination follows from verbal knowledge devoid of a real object.

The mind can imagine things that don't exist in reality. For example, one can imagine a flying cow. With a knowledge of the concepts of "cow" and "flying," the mind can put them together to visualize a cow flying in the air. But, cows don't fly; therefore, there is no real basis for what was imagined. The image in the mind is without basis in fact (*vastuśūnya*). This ability of the mind to imagine things that don't exist is called *vikalpa*.

Imagination

अभावप्रत्ययालम्बना वृत्तिर्निद्रा ॥ १.१० ॥
abhāvapratyayālambanā vṛttirnidrā ॥ 1.10 ॥

abhāva = nothingness, absence
pratyaya = cognition, knowledge
ālambanā = basis, dependence on
vṛttiḥ = activity
nidrā = sleep

Sleep is a mental activity that depends on the absence of cognition.

Sleep (*nidrā*) is considered a mental activity, and here refers specifically to the state of deep, dreamless sleep. The lack of direct perception during sleep doesn't mean that nothing is happening — the fact that we are engrossed in it for hours means that our soul is "engaged" in that state. However, sleep is different from the other activities of the mind described earlier (valid proof, incorrect perception, and imagination). This is why we cannot articulate what happens in dreamless sleep. During sleep, the consciousness experiences a state that is not translatable into anything we experience when we are awake. Nonetheless, sleep has an effect on the mind and body — sometimes we feel that we have slept well and feel refreshed, and other times we feel lethargic after sleep. These effects are one of the main evidence cited by Vyāsa in considering sleep as a mental activity. *Tamas* is dominant in the mind during sleep.

Sleep

अनुभूतविषयासंप्रमोषः स्मृतिः ॥ १.११ ॥
anubhūtaviṣayāsampramoṣaḥ smṛtiḥ ॥ 1.11 ॥

anubhūta = experienced
viṣaya = object
asampramoṣaḥ = non-stealing, non-loss
smṛtiḥ = memory

Memory is the non-loss of [the impressions of] objects of experience.

When the sense organs come in contact with an object, impressions of that object are created in our minds. The mental processes responsible for retaining such impressions, and retrieving them later constitute memory.

All mental activities generate impressions, which result in memory. Like all mental activities, memory can also be troubling or non-troubling. A troubling memory distracts a person from what he or she wants to do or is doing, and such a memory can be a distraction in meditation. When the faculty of memory is refined (smṛtipariśuddhi — sūtra 1.43), it aids in maintaining continuous contemplation untainted by other impressions. This concept will re-appear in later discussion of the different kinds of perfections that can be attained through concentration.

This verse concludes Patañjali's introduction to the mechanisms of the mind. He has told us what the processes of the mind are in just eleven verses. Next, he will tell us how to control these processes.

> This is a good moment to pause and note that at any given point we are experiencing a mental activity that falls into one of the five categories described previously. Everything that we experience in life, whether while sleeping or being awake, is classified into these categories.

Memory

Sūtras 1.12-1.16: Methods of Restraining the Mind

Abhyāsa and Vairāgya

The next group of sūtras gives a general introduction to how to control the activities of the mind. The opening sūtras explained what the activities of the mind are; the next step is to achieve control over these activities.

अभ्यासवैराग्याभ्यां तन्निरोधः ॥ १.१२ ॥
abhyāsavairāgyābhyāṁ tannirodhaḥ ॥ 1.12 ॥

abhyāsa = practice
vairāgyābhyāṁ = by detachment (vairāgya)
tat = that (of their)
nirodhaḥ = restraint

Restraint of these [activities of mind] is achieved through practice and detachment.

The two most important tools for controlling the mind are

1. Consistent practice (*abhyāsa*)
2. Detachment (*vairāgya*)

These will be described in the coming sūtras.

तत्र स्थितौ यत्नोऽभ्यासः ॥ १.१३ ॥
tatra sthitau yatno'bhyāsaḥ ॥ 1.13 ॥

tatra = there (in restraint)
sthitau = stability, steadiness
yatnaḥ = effort
abhyāsaḥ = practice (abhyāsa)

Practice is the effort to remain steady.

The peaceful state when the activities of the mind are stopped is called *sthiti*. The effort, persistence, and enthusiasm to attain this peaceful state is called practice (*abhyāsa*).

स तु दीर्घकालनैरन्तर्यसत्कारासेवितो दृढभूमिः ॥ १.१४ ॥
sa tu dīrghakālanairantaryasatkārāsevito dṛḍhabhūmiḥ ॥ 1.14 ॥

sa = that (in this case, practice)
tu = indeed
dīrghakāla = for a long time
nairantarya = uninterrupted
satkārā = with attention, respect and regard.
āsevitaḥ = followed/served
dṛḍhabhūmiḥ = firmly established (literally "one with a firm ground")

This [practice] becomes firmly established when conducted for a long time with devotion and without interruption.

Vyāsa describes that practice is firmly established by

1. overcoming obstacles
2. restraint from sensual objects
3. studying works of knowledge and practicing introspection
4. devotion

Kinds of Detachment

दृष्टानुश्रविकविषयवितृष्णस्य वशीकारसंज्ञा वैराग्यम् ॥ १.१५ ॥
dṛṣṭānuśravikaviṣayavitṛṣṇasya vaśīkārasaṁjñā vairāgyam ॥ 1.15 ॥

dṛṣṭa = those that are experienced with the five senses
ānuśravika = those that are heard, or learned from reading
viṣaya = object
vitṛṣṇasya = of uninterest (of thirstless-ness)
vaśīkārasaṁjñā = called mastered (vaśīkāra)
vairāgyam = detachment

Completely mastered detachment is thirstless-ness towards objects experienced through senses or objects that are heard or learned from reading.

Objects of the senses are things experienced directly through the five senses, such as sexual pleasure, food, wealth, power, and so on. These objects are called *dṛṣṭa*. Other objects we desire are known by hearing or reading about them. These are called *ānuśravika*. In the present day, we can include in *ānuśravika* all other indirect forms of knowledge, like television and the Internet.

Practicing thirstless-ness (uninterest, lack of desire, lack of "thirst") in both kinds of desires is known by the term "mastered detachment," or *vaśīkāra-vairāgya*.

तत्परं पुरुषख्यातेर्गुणवैतृष्ण्यम् ॥ १.१६ ॥
tatparaṁ puruṣakhyāterguṇavaitṛṣṇyam ॥ 1.16 ॥

tatparaṁ = beyond that (detachment)
puruṣa = consciousness or self
khyāteḥ = from the vision, realization
guṇa = the three fundamental constituents of the universe (sattva, rajas, tamas)
vaitṛṣṇyam = thirstless-ness

Beyond that [detachment] is the thirstless-ness towards the three guṇas [sattva, rajas, and tamas], obtained through the realization of the self.

After continued practice of detachment, a yogī sees the defects of the two kinds of pleasure and seeks realization of the true self (*puruṣa*). The two kinds of experiences or pleasures explained in the previous verse are those perceived through senses and those that are heard or read about. They both do not provide complete satisfaction and do not last for ever. From this realization, a yogī becomes uninterested in the components of the universe (the *guṇas*) because everything that we experience is a combination of them. Detachment is therefore of two kinds, lesser (*apara*) and ultimate (*para*):

- Lesser detachment is the practice of detachment towards all worldly objects in the pursuit of the realization of consciousness.
- Ultimate detachment is the natural thirstless-ness towards the three *guṇas* and all of their manifestations — a thirstless-ness that comes with realizing the core consciousness. This detachment is not towards only worldly objects; it is also towards one's own mind, which is a combination of the three *guṇas*.

In a state of ultimate detachment, the yogī is completely satisfied and feels "I have attained what needs to be attained, the obstacles that need to be destroyed are destroyed, and the bondage to the cycle of birth and death is broken." The ultimate state of knowledge is complete non-attachment towards the *guṇas*. This is liberation (*kaivalya*).

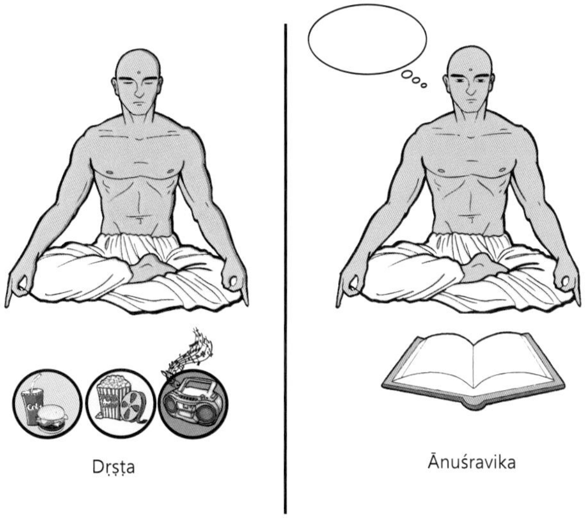

Para detachment

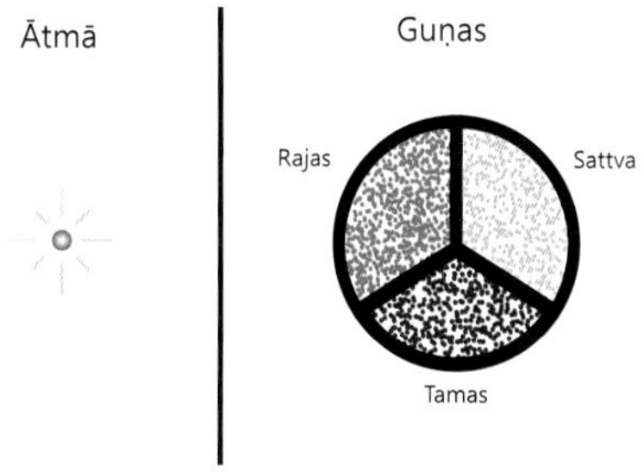

Apara detachment

Sūtras 1.17-1.22: Kinds of Samādhi

Samādhi with Awareness (samprajñāta)

Samādhi is a deep state of meditation in which mental activities are completely restrained. Only one thought remains constant in the previous, current, and subsequent moments, with no fluctuation; this is the object of meditation. In this state even awareness of the self is eliminated, leaving the object of meditation shining in isolation. This state is called "*samādhi with* awareness" (*samprajñāta*), as there is still an awareness of the object of meditation. This *samādhi* is different from the subsequent state of "*samādhi without* awareness," in which even the last remaining thought of the object of meditation is eliminated. Having completely restrained all mental activities, the consciousness is de-coupled from the mind and remains in its own state. This is the ultimate goal of yoga. Thus, *samādhi* is of two major types — with awareness (*saṁprajñāta*), and without awareness (*asaṁprajñāta*). There are also different kinds within each of these, which will be discussed in the subsequent sūtras.

वितर्कविचारानन्दास्मितारूपानुगमात्सम्प्रज्ञातः ॥ १.१७ ॥
vitarkavicārānandāsmitārūpānugamāt samprajñātaḥ ॥ 1.17 ॥

vitarka = gross thought
vicāra = subtle thought
ānanda = bliss
asmitā = the feeling of "I-ness," "self"
rūpa = form
anugamāt = accompanied with
samprajñātaḥ = with cognition, with awareness

[Samādhi] with awareness is accompanied by gross thought, subtle thought, bliss, and the feeling of "I."

There are four subtypes of *samprajñāta samādhi*, based on the thought or object on which the meditation is performed:

1. Gross thought (*vitarka*) is awareness of gross objects, perceived through the senses.
2. Subtle thought (*vichāra*) is reflection on the subtle elements (*tanmātras* and internal instruments).
3. Bliss (*ānanda*) is awareness with a sense of joy.
4. The sense of "I" (*asmitā*) is an awareness of the self. In this the meditation is performed on that part of the mind that is responsible for the feeling of "I."

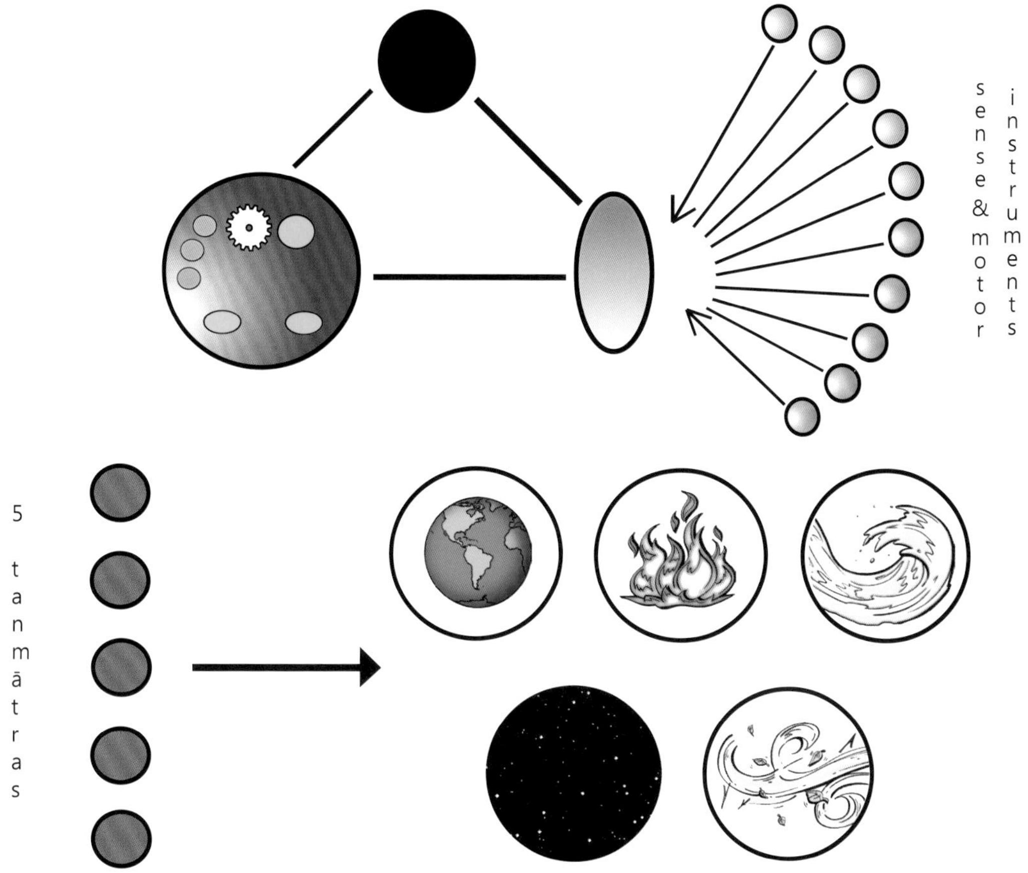

Objects of meditation in Samādhi with awareness (samprajñāta)

Samādhi without Awareness (Asamprajñāta)

विरामप्रत्ययाभ्यासपूर्वः संस्कारशेषोऽन्यः ॥ १.१८ ॥
virāmapratyayābhyāsapūrvaḥ saṁskāraśeṣo'nyaḥ ॥ 1.18 ॥

virāma = cessation, abatement
pratyaya = knowledge, idea
abhyāsa = practice
pūrvaḥ = preceding, previous
saṁskāra = impression
śeṣaḥ = remaining
anyaḥ = the other

The other [kind of samādhi] results from the cessation of activities of the mind and [leaves] impressions as a remainder.

The previous sūtra described *samādhi* with awareness; this sūtra talks about the other kind — *samādhi* without awareness, which does not have an object as its basis. If any object were the focus of meditation, then the mental activity related to that object would be still present in the mind. When even that last remaining thought activity is eliminated, the result is *samādhi* without awareness (called *asamprajñāta-samādhi*). The impressions of prior mental activities remain as impressions, but do not turn into mental activities.

Impression (*saṁskāra*) is a very important word in the *Yoga Sūtras*, and appears in eight sūtras. *Saṁskāra* refers to a mental impression that influences our behavior without us being aware of it. Every action is recorded in the mind as an impression, and the processing of these impressions consist of the following major aspects:

- The aspect that is responsible for the conscious and unconscious memory of the action. The conscious memory is what we remember of an action that we performed, while the unconscious memory is what is recorded by our mind in addition to the conscious memory.
- The aspect that records the merits or demerits of an action (righteous, unrighteous, or a mixture) that result in birth, longevity, and experience.
- The aspect that causes the mental impression to sprout into mental activity or to interact with other mental activities.

In *samādhi* without awareness, impressions do not sprout into mental activities.

भवप्रत्ययो विदेहप्रकृतिलयानाम् ॥ १.१९ ॥
bhavapratyayo videhaprakṛtilayānām ॥ 1.19 ॥

bhavapratyayaḥ = having birth or existence as the cause
videha = bodiless
prakṛtilayānām = of those that have dissolved into elements of nature

[The samādhi] obtained by the body-less and those who have dissolved into the elements of nature has birth as its cause.

There are two classes of bodiless beings, called *videhas* and *prakṛtilayas*, that this sūtra mentions. There are many meanings for the words *videha* and *prakṛtilaya*. Here is one of the interpretations:

- *Videha*: Through yogic practice some stay in a bodyless state after the material body dies. They stay in that state for a long time before eventually taking birth. In the body-less state, they are referred to as celestial beings. It can be inferred that they are still associated with the subtle body in that state. They have not reached the ultimate goal of yoga which is freedom from the mind and complete independence.
- *Prakṛtilaya*: By practicing concentration on subtle elements yogis stop identifying with the material body but still identify with subtle elements like *tanmātras*, sense instruments, ego, and intellect. They too like *videhas* remain in a bodyless state for a long time, absorbed in the subtle elements of nature, before taking birth.

The mental activities and impressions of both *videhas* and *prakṛtilayas* are not completely eliminated — these remain latent, or suppressed. As long as they are latent, yogīs experience a state similar to *asamprajñāta-samādhi*. After that, when the impressions turn into mental activities, yogīs come back to the cycle of life and death.

Only birth and some residual practice of yoga is all that is needed for them to attain *asamprajñāta-samādhi* in the subsequent life. They are inclined to yogic practice by birth. Since birth is a major factor in attaining *samādhi* the *asamprajñāta-samādhi* obtained by these beings is called *bhavapratyaya* ("dependent on birth" or "needing birth"). This interpretation takes *bhavapratyaya* as a kind of *asamprajñāta-samādhi*. There is also another interpretation where it is taken to mean a kind of *samprajñāta-samādhi* which leads to a future birth ("causing birth"). Both views seem appropriate.

श्रद्धावीर्यस्मृतिसमाधिप्रज्ञापूर्वक इतरेषाम् ॥ १.२० ॥
śraddhāvīryasmṛtisamādhiprajñāpūrvaka itareṣām ॥ 1.20 ॥

śraddhā = devotion
vīrya = the energy and courage (to persist)
smṛti = accurate recollection, memory
samādhi = perfected state of concentration, absorption
prajñā = wisdom, discriminating knowledge
pūrvakaḥ = preceding
itareṣām = of others

The prerequisites for others are devotion, courage, memory, perfected concentration, and wisdom.

As opposed to *bhavapratyaya* — which depends on birth — this type of *samādhi* is called *upāyapratyaya*, and depends on a "plan or method" (*upāya*). The previous sūtra described how body-less beings attain *samādhi* without awareness. This sūtra describes how regular people can attain *samādhi*. The prerequisites for us are devotion, courage, memory, perfected concentration, and wisdom. Of these five qualities, the preceding quality leads to the following one:

1. When a yogī has faith and devotion (*śraddhā*) towards his practice, it results in the energy (*vīrya*) to pursue the practice further.
2. Persistent practice with energy (*vīrya*) leads to accurate recollection (*smṛti*).
3. Accurate recollection (*smṛti*) leads to perfected concentration (*samādhi*).
4. Perfected concentration (*samādhi*) leads to discriminating knowledge (*prajñā*).
5. Through this knowledge (*prajñā*), one attains *samādhi* without awareness (*asamprajñāta*).

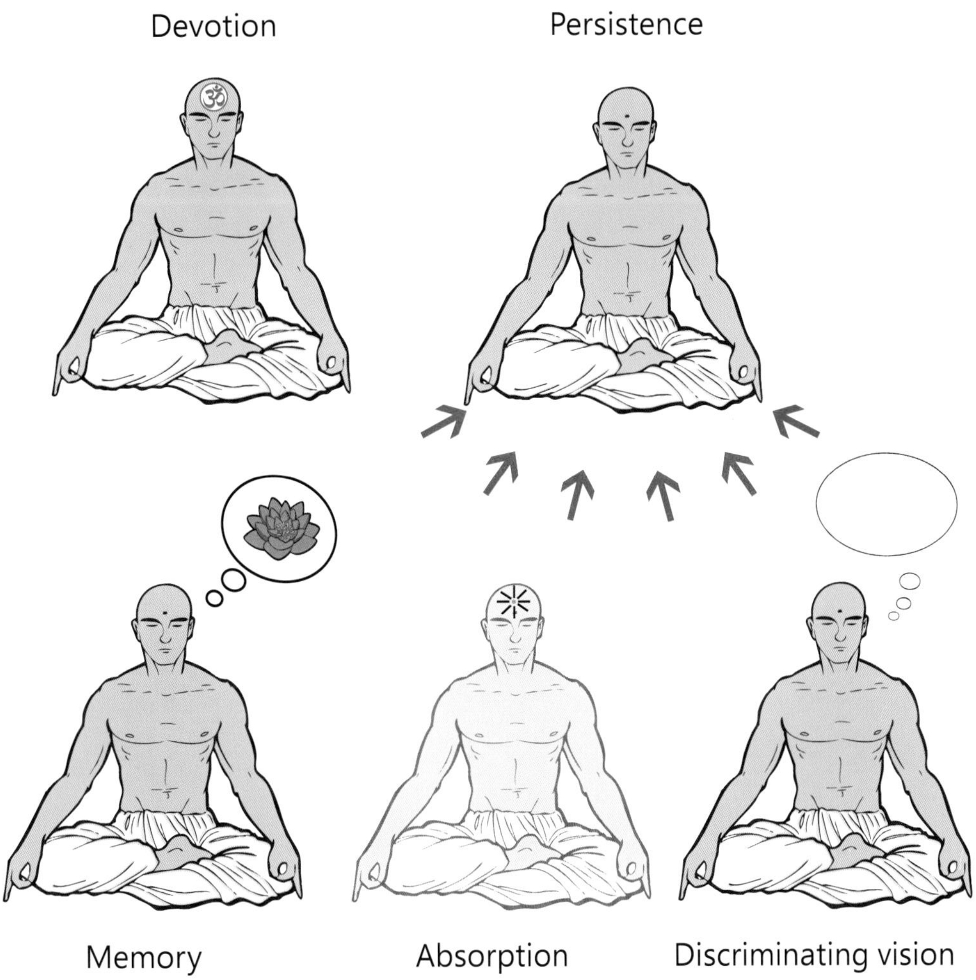
Devotion
Persistence
Memory
Absorption
Discriminating vision

तीव्रसंवेगानामासन्नः ॥ १.२१ ॥
tīvrasaṁvegānāmāsannaḥ ॥ 1.21 ॥

tīvra = intense
saṁvegānām = of those with vehemence
āsannaḥ = reached/attained

It [Samādhi] is obtained by those who practice with intense vigor and persistence.

Only those who work hard achieve yogic attainments. The word *vega* has a sense of energetic effort to it.

मृदुमध्याधिमात्रत्वात्ततोऽपि विशेषः ॥ १.२२ ॥
mṛdumadhyādhimātratvāttato'pi viśeṣaḥ ॥ 1.22 ॥

mṛdu = mild
madhya = moderate, medium
adhimātratvāt = excessive, extreme, intense
tataḥ = there
api = also
viśeṣaḥ = difference

Difference in result is due to mild, medium, and intense [practices].

Even among those practicing with intense vigor, there are differences between mild, medium, or extreme intensities. They attain *samādhi* without awareness (*asamprajñāta*) with varying speeds accordingly.

Sūtras 1.23-1.28: Devotion to God: Another Method

ईश्वरप्रणिधानाद्वा ॥ १.२३ ॥
īśvarapraṇidhānādvā ॥ 1.23 ॥

īśvara = master, lord (God)
praṇidhānāt = from fixing the mind, meditation, devotion
vā = or

Or, mental activities can also be restrained by meditating on or practicing devotion to God.

Meditating on God (*īśvara-praṇidhāna*) is another method for restraining the activities of the mind. Derived from the root *dhā* (to hold, to maintain, to bear), the word *praṇidhāna* means "well placed in the mind." The word *vā* in the sūtra which means "or," shows that this is an optional method.

क्लेशकर्मविपाकाशयैरपरामृष्टः पुरुषविशेष ईश्वरः ॥ १.२४ ॥
kleśakarmavipākāśayairaparāmṛṣṭaḥ puruṣaviśeṣa īśvaraḥ ॥ 1.24 ॥

kleśa = affliction
karma = action
vipāka = ripening, fruition, result, consequence
āśayaiḥ = by the resting place, repository
aparāmṛṣṭaḥ = untouched
puruṣa = consciousness
viśeṣaḥ = special
īśvaraḥ = master, lord (God)

God is a special kind of consciousness that is untouched by afflictions, actions, fruition, and the repository of impressions.

God (*Īśvara*) is free from afflictions, actions, the impressions of those actions, and the resultant fruition of actions. *Īśvara* is free from afflictions because He (She, It) does not operate with the help of a mind as we humans do. Afflictions reside in the mind, and God is therefore beyond the mind's limitations and afflictions. That *Īśvara* is free from actions does not entail that He (She, It) does not perform any actions; instead, it means that the actions — not being influenced by any afflictions — do not result in consequences (good, bad, or both). *Īśvara* is then also free from the set of impressions that result from those actions, because no such impressions accumulate when actions are performed without being influenced by afflictions. As a result, *Īśvara* is free from the fruition of actions, because actions free of afflictions and without impressions do not have consequences. This special consciousness (*Īśvara*, God) is not the same as the yogī who has attained the goal of yoga (*samādhi* without awareness).

तत्र निरतिशयं सर्वज्ञबीजम् ॥ १.२५ ॥
tatra niratiśayaṁ sarvajñabījam ॥ 1.25 ॥

tatra = there (in Īśvara)
niratiśayaṁ = unexcellable, limitless
sarvajña = omniscience
bījam = seed, origin, source

In Īśvara, the seed of omniscience is unexcellable.

God is the source (*bīja*) of the wisdom found in all beings. The source of all knowledge is called the seed of omniscience (*sarvajñabījam*), and God is unequalled and unsurpassable in such knowledge. All other beings have constraints on their ability to know things — we are constrained by time (awareness of past, present, and future) and by our senses. God does not have these restrictions, and so is omniscient.

पूर्वेषामपि गुरुः कालेनानवच्छेदात् ॥ १.२६ ॥
pūrveṣāmapi guruḥ kālenānavacchedāt ॥ 1.26 ॥

pūrveṣām = of the previous ones (teachers)
api = even, also
guruḥ = teacher, master
kālenā = by time
anavacchedāt = undivided, un-delimited

Īśvara is the teacher of former teachers as well, because He is not delimited by time.

Īśvara (God) is unlike ordinary beings, whose lifespan is limited and who must experience the cycle of birth and death. *Īśvara* is at the creation of the universe, and also at the creations of universes prior to this one. Because *Īśvara* is not limited by time, He (She, It) is the source of knowledge for all of the teachers who have come before us.

ॐ

तस्य वाचकः प्रणवः ॥ १.२७ ॥
tasya vācakaḥ praṇavaḥ ॥ 1.27 ॥

tasya = of Īśvara
vācakaḥ = signifier, name (verbal or auditory indicator)
praṇavaḥ = the sound "Oṁ."

Īśvara's signifier is "Oṁ."

The sound *Oṁ* is *praṇava*, which means "that by which *Īśvara* is well praised." *Īśvara* is known by this sacred name or sound. Usually, a word and the object (or concept) that it represents are related based on a specific language or cultural context. Within that language or culture, a word could mean different things at different times and places, depending on convention. However, rishis proclaim that — unlike other elements of language — the word *Oṁ* always denotes *Īśvara*, regardless of time or place. The syllable *Oṁ* is praised for its power to calm the mind.

The meaning of Oṁ

The meaning of *Oṁ* derived from the *Nirukta* — the Vedic etymology, which is the key to Vedic knowledge. It is presented here as compiled in Svami Dayananda Sarasvati's *Satyārthaprakāsh*. The sound *Oṁ* consists of the three sounds of the letters 'a', 'u', and 'm'. Each of these sounds has the following meanings.

a + u + m = aum

"A" stands for Virāṭ, Agni, Viśva.

- *Virāṭ*: The word *virāṭ* (illuminer) is derived from the root *raj* (to illumine, to shine). He who illumines and manifests the world in various forms is called *Virāṭ*.
- *Agni*: The word *agni* (worthy of worshipping) is derived from the root *añcu* (to move, to worship). He who is worth worshipping, knowing, and seeking is called *Agni*.
- *Viśva*: The word *viśva* (pervader) is derived from the root *viś* (to enter). He who pervades and exists in all worlds and beings is called *Viśva*.

"U" stands for Hiraṇyagarbha, Vāyu, Tejas

- *Hiraṇyagarbha*: The word *hiraṇyagarbha* (the womb of light) comes from *hiraṇya* (light) and "*garbha*" (source). God is called *hiraṇyagarbha*, because the sun and other heavenly luminous bodies are produced by and exist in him.
- *Vāyu*: The word *Vāyu* (mover) is derived from the root *va* (to move, to kill). God is called *Vāyu* because he moves, supports, and destroys all movable and immovable creatures, and is the most powerful of all.

- *Tejas*: The word *tejas* (illuminer) is derived from the root *tij* (to shine, to illumine). God is called *Tejas* because he is self-luminous, and illumines the sun and other luminous bodies.

"M" stands for Īśvara, Āditya, Prājña

- *Īśvara*: The word *Īśvara* (ruler, lord) comes from the root *iś* (to rule, to be wealthy). God is called *Īśvara* because He (or She, or It) is the master of all the bodies in the universe.
- *Āditya*: The word *Āditya* (immortal) is derived from the root *do* (to cut). He who is undivided by time is *Āditya*.
- *Prājña*: The word *Prājña* (knower) is derived from the root *jña* (to know). He who knows all movable and immovable bodies in the universe, and whose knowledge is clear and free from all doubt, is called *Prājña*.

One can contemplate on any of the above qualities of God while meditating on *Oṁ*.

तज्जपस्तदर्थभावनम् ॥ १.२८ ॥
tajjapastadarthabhāvanam ॥ 1.28 ॥

tat = that
japaḥ = repetition
tat = that
artha = meaning
bhāvanam = contemplation

The repetition of it [praṇava] and contemplation of its meaning [should be done].

Repetition of *praṇava* and reflection on its meaning is called *japa*. Through continued concentration on *Oṁ* one can eliminate the obstacles to the realization of inner consciousness.

प्रणवो धनुः शरो ह्यात्मा ब्रह्म तल्लक्ष्यमुच्यते।

अप्रमत्तेन वेद्धव्यं शरवत्तन्मयो भवेत्॥ २.२.४॥

praṇavo dhanuḥ śaro hyātmā brahma tallakṣyamucyate ।

apramattena veddhavyaṁ śaravattanmayo bhavet ॥ *Mundkopaniṣad 2.2.4* ॥

"Praṇva (*Oṁ*) is the bow, the arrow is the soul, and *Brahman* is its target; *Brahman* is pierced by the person who exhibits unwavering attention. That person then becomes one with *Brahman*, as the arrow becomes one with the target after piercing it."

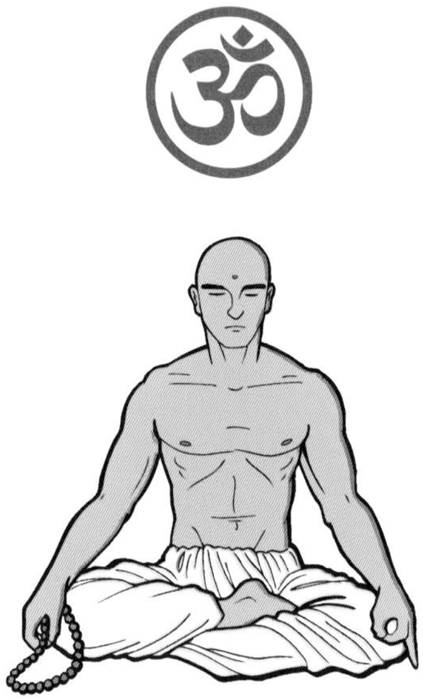

Japa

Sūtras 1.29-1.32: Obstacles and Their Elimination

ततः प्रत्यक्चेतनाधिगमोऽप्यन्तरायाभावश्च ॥ १.२९ ॥
tataḥ pratyakcetanādhigamo'pyantarāyābhāvaśca ॥ 1.29 ॥

tataḥ = then, from that (here, from īśvarapraṇidhāna, from devotion to God)
pratyak = inner
cetanā = consciousness
adhigamaḥ = attainment
api = and
antarāya = hindrance, obstacle
abhāvaḥ = absence, elimination
ca = and

From that, one attains the realization of inner consciousness and the cessation of obstacles.

"From that" here refers to devotion to God (*īśvarapraṇidhāna*). By this practice one attains insight into the real self, the "inner consciousness." As one becomes more aware that the consciousness (the self) is immutable and can remain uninfluenced by the mind, obstacles of all kinds subside.

Cessation of obstacles from devotion to God

What are Obstacles?

व्याधिस्त्यानसंशयप्रमादालस्याविरतिभ्रान्तिदर्शनालब्धभूमिकत्वानवस्थितत्वानि चित्तविक्षेपास्तेऽन्तरायाः ॥ १.३० ॥

vyādhistyānasaṁśayapramādālasyāviratibhrāntidarśanālabdhabhūmikatvānavasthitatvāni cittavikṣepāste'ntarāyāḥ ॥ 1.30 ॥

vyādhi = sickness, physical and mental illness.
styāna = lethargy, apathy
saṁśaya = doubt
pramāda = negligence
ālasya = sloth, laziness
avirati = interest in worldly experiences, lack of detachment
bhrāntidarśana = confusion, misunderstanding
alabdhabhūmikatva = failure to attain a stage
anavasthitatva = instability
cittavikṣepāḥ = distractors of the mind
te = they
antarāyāḥ = obstacles

The obstacles — the distractors of the mind — are sickness, lethargy, doubt, negligence, sloth, lack of detachment, confusion, failure to attain a stage, and instability.

There are nine obstacles mentioned in this sūtra -

1. sickness
2. lethargy
3. doubt
4. negligence
5. sloth
6. lack of detachment
7. confusion
8. failure to attain a stage in yogic practice
9. and instability

These nine obstacles distract the mind, and are caused by the activities of the mind (*cittavṛttis*). When such activities subside, the obstacles are also eliminated.

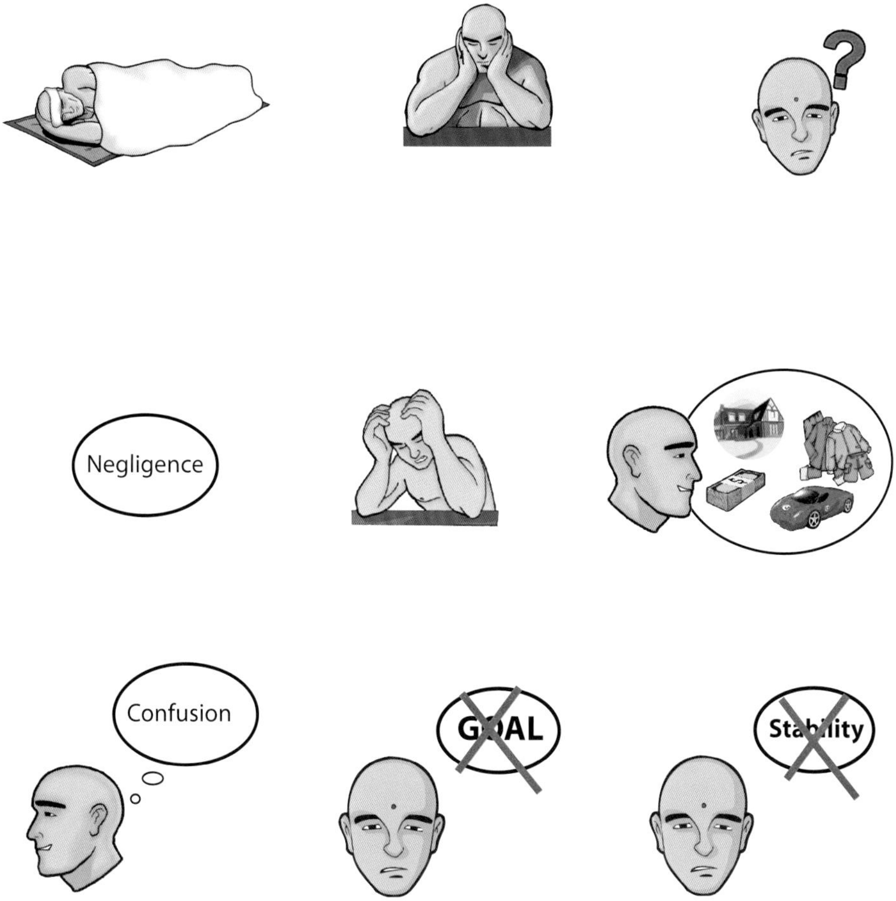

Sickness, lethargy, doubt, negligence, sloth, lack of detachment, confusion, inability to attain a goal, and instability.

Who is considered healthy and free from disease?

samadoṣāḥ samāgniśca samadhātumalakriyaḥ ।
prasannātmendriyamanāḥ svastha ityabhidhīyate ॥

– Suśruta Sūtrasthānam 15.41

A healthy person is one who has balanced bodily elements (*doṣa*), a balanced transforming fire (*agni*), balanced performance of bodily elements and waste materials (*dhātu-mala-kriya*), as well as tranquil soul, senses, and mind.

दुःखदौर्मनस्याङ्गमेजयत्वश्वासप्रश्वासा विक्षेपसहभुवः ॥ १.३१ ॥
duḥkhadaurmanasyāṅgamejayatvaśvāsapraśvāsā vikṣepasahabhuvaḥ ॥ 1.31 ॥

duḥkha = sorrow, misery
daurmanasya = dejection, depression
aṅgamejayatva = trembling, tremors of the limbs of the body
śvāsa = inhaling, panting, sighing
praśvāsāḥ = exhalation
vikṣepa = distractions
sahabhuvaḥ = accompaniment

Sorrow, dejection, trembling, inhalation, and exhalation accompany the distractions.

As discussed previously, misery (*duḥkha*) can be of three kinds — caused by one's own body and mind, caused by other beings, and caused by natural calamities. Dejection (*daurmanasya*) is the feeling when one's desires are unfulfilled or obstructed. Trembling of the body (*aṅgamejayatva*) is what it sounds like — the involuntary shaking of limbs. Inhalation and exhalation (*śvāsapraśvāsa*) refer here to uncontrolled breathing, basically to hyperventilation, which is not conducive to concentration. These distractions subside when the mind is stilled.

Sorrow, dejection, trembling, inhalation & exhalation

तत्प्रतिषेधार्थमेकतत्त्वाभ्यासः ॥ १.३२ ॥
tatpratiṣedhārthamekatattvābhyāsaḥ ॥ 1.32 ॥

tat = that (obstacles and their accompaniments)
pratiṣedārtham = to obstruct, counter
eka = one
tattva = that-ness, principle, factor
abhyāsaḥ = practice

To counter them [the obstacles and their accompaniments], practice on one principle.

Here, concentration on one principle or object is presented as the solution to all obstacles (both physical and mental) to concentration. Understanding the principles of Sāṅkhya and Yoga can motivate one to meditate but in order to completely eliminate the obstacles to meditation one should get started with meditation by concentrating on a single object. The means to obtaining clarity and stability of mind are described next.

Sūtras 1.33-1.39: Purity of thought

Behaviors That Aid in the Clarity and Stability of the Mind

मैत्रीकरुणामुदितोपेक्षाणां सुखदुःखपुण्यापुण्यविषयाणां भावनातश्चित्तप्रसादनम् ॥ १.३३ ॥
maitrīkaruṇāmuditopekṣāṇāṁ sukhaduḥkhapuṇyāpuṇyaviṣayāṇāṁ bhāvanātaścittaprasādanam ॥ 1.33 ॥

maitrī = friendliness
karuṇā = compassion
muditā = gladness
upekṣāṇāṁ = disinterest, disengagement
sukha = happiness
duḥkha = sorrow, misery
puṇya = virtue, merit
apuṇya = non-virtue, vice, de-merit
viṣayāṇāṁ = in regard to the things
bhāvanātaḥ = from directing one's thoughts
cittaprasādanam = clarity, purity of mind

Clarity of mind results from practicing friendliness toward those who are happy, compassion toward those in pain, joy toward the virtuous, and disinterest toward the non-virtuous.

Practicing proper attitudes towards various kinds of people will make the mind serene and pleasant regardless of the stimuli presented to it. This is clarity of mind. Clarity of mind enhances the ability to understand situations and imparts a better understanding of the self, which leads closer to perfection in concentration (*samādhi*).

Friendliness, compassion, and joy

Regulation of the Breath

प्रच्छर्दनविधारणाभ्यां वा प्राणस्य ॥ १.३४ ॥
pracchardanavidhāraṇābhyāṁ vā prāṇasya ॥ 1.34 ॥

pracchardana = exhaling
vidhāraṇābhyāṁ = restraining, retaining, holding
vā = or
prāṇasya = of the breath, of the vital airs

Or by exhaling and holding the breath [the mind can be stilled].

Regulating breathing can also help in stabilizing the mind. During the kind of breath regulation described in this sūtra, breath is slowly expelled, held outside for a time, then slowly inhaled. Many kinds of breath control are prevalent in yoga practice — one emphasizes holding the breath outside, another on holding it inside, and yet another on holding it without regard to inside or outside. All three practices stabilize the mind.

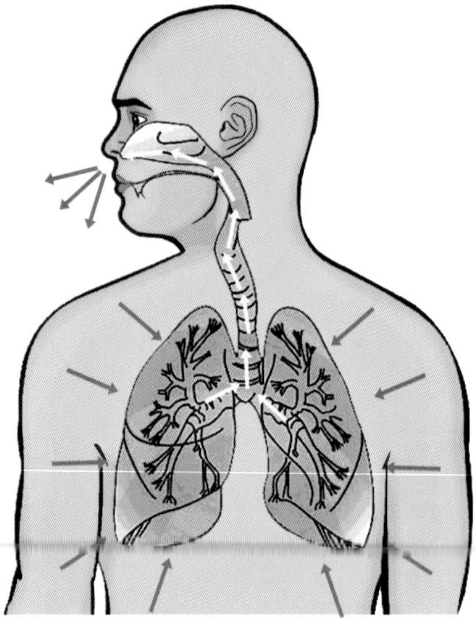

Holding the breath outside

Concentrating on a Unique Sensory Feeling

विषयवती वा प्रवृत्तिरुत्पन्ना मनसः स्थितिनिबन्धिनी ॥ १.३५ ॥
viṣayavatī vā pravṛttirutpannā manasaḥ sthitinibandhinī ॥ 1.35 ॥

viṣayavatī = having sense objects, experiences
vā = or, also
pravṛttiḥ = mental activity, perception, cognition
utpannā = that which arises, that which is born
manasaḥ = of the mind
sthitinibandhinī = one that binds the mind, causing steadiness

Or when a [extra] sensory perception arises, it can cause steadiness of the mind.

Vyāsa mentions that perfecting concentration on certain locations or objects results in an extraordinary feeling related to a particular sense. For example, when concentrating on the tip of the nose, one attains a supernatural sense of smell. Yogis perceive an extraordinary smell, divine and engrossing, that captivates the mind. Similarly, concentrating on the base of the tongue imparts a supernatural sense of taste. Concentrating on the palate imparts extraordinary visual power; on the center of the tongue, an extraordinary sense of touch; on the root of the tongue, an extraordinary sense of hearing. The arising of these extraordinary sensory feelings leads to unwavering faith and devotion in one's practice.

Knowledge from scriptures and inference can provide a common understanding about yogic powers, but the direct experience of these special powers affirms and solidifies a yogī's pursuit of discriminating knowledge.

Arising of special sensory perception

Concentrating on an Effulgent Feeling

विशोका वा ज्योतिष्मती ॥ १.३६ ॥
viśokā vā jyotiṣmatī ॥ 1.36 ॥

viśokā = a feeling free of grief, sorrow free, pleasant, cheerful
vā = or
jyotiṣmatī = resplendent, luminous

Or a sorrow free, luminous state of mind [can also cause steadiness of the mind].

A sorrow free, luminous state of mind promotes mental stability. Some examples for the "luminous feeling" (*jyotiṣmatī*) are,

- When the mind concentrates on the middle of the heart region, one acquires the knowledge of *buddhi* (specifically, that it is different from *puruṣa*). Persisting in that state, one sees a brilliant light resembling a sun, moon, planet, or jewel.
- When the mind concentrates on the pure feeling of "I-ness," a feeling arises that resembles a still ocean without waves.

These too will bring about the stability of the mind.

Grief-free luminous state

Concentrating on Inspiring Personalities

वीतरागविषयं वा चित्तम् ॥ १.३७ ॥
vītarāgaviṣayaṁ vā cittam ॥ 1.37 ॥

vītarāga = (one who is) free of desire
viṣayaṁ = object
vā = or
cittam = mind

Or contemplating on one who is free from desire [can also cause steadiness of the mind].

To attain stability of mind, one can also meditate on any person — in the present or the past — who is free from desire.

Meditating on greed-free personalities

Concentrating on an Object in the Dream

स्वप्ननिद्राज्ञानालम्बनं वा ॥ १.३८ ॥
svapnanidrājñānālambanaṁ vā ॥ 1.38 ॥

svapna = dream
nidrā = dreamless sleep
jñāna = knowledge
ālambanaṁ = support
vā = or

Or using knowledge obtained from a dream or sleep as the basis of meditation [can also cause steadiness of the mind].

Sometimes dreams present a vision that is very unlike the things we come across in the real world. Such a vision can be unique and entrancing, and can capture the attention for a long time. Or, the sensation or notion that results from dreamless sleep can become an object of meditation. Making use of these visions or sensations as an object of meditation can also stabilize the mind in concentration.

Concentrating on an Object of Your Liking

यथाभिमतध्यानाद्वा ॥ १ ३९ ॥
yathābhimatadhyānādvā ॥ 1.39 ॥

yathā = as
abhimata = desired, liked
dhyānād = from contemplating on
vā = or

Or concentrating on any object one likes [can also cause steadiness of the mind].

In fact, any object of one's interest can be used to gain stability of mind. As such, any person — irrespective of faith — can attain *samādhi*. This is the of last several sūtras that have given alternative methods for cultivating stability of the mind.

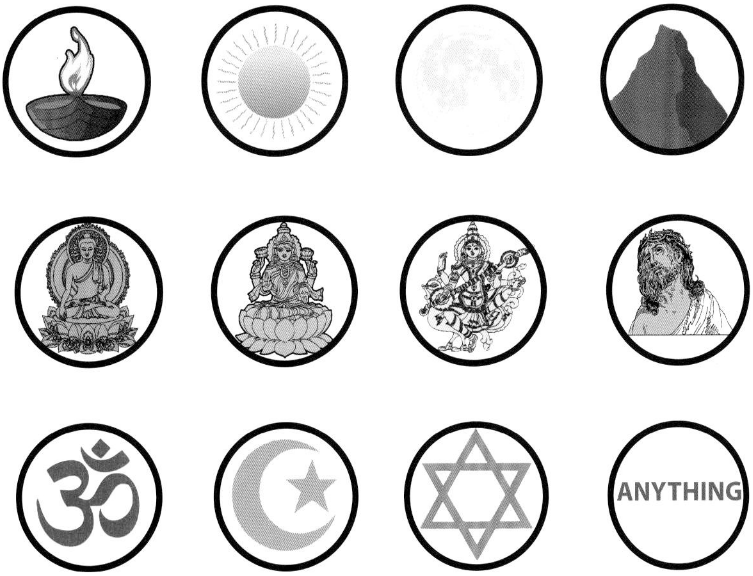

Sūtras 1.40-1.51: Stages in Attaining Samādhi

Concentrating on the Minutest and the Largest of Objects

परमाणुपरममहत्त्वान्तोऽस्य वशीकारः ॥ १.४० ॥
paramāṇuparamamahattvānto'sya vaśīkāraḥ ॥ 1.40 ॥

parama-aṇu = most minute element
parama-mahattva = greatest, largest
antaḥ = up to
asya = of this one (here, of a yogī)
vaśīkāraḥ = control, mastery

The yogī's mastery [extends from] the most minute objects to the largest.

When mental activities are restrained, a yogī's control encompasses the full range of human existence, from the most minute objects to the largest. This is the first verse in a series of sūtras discussing the state of mind of a person who has controlled his or her mental activities.

Perfected Concentration (Samāpatti), Analogy of a Crystal

क्षीणवृत्तेरभिजातस्येव मणेर्ग्रहीतृग्रहणग्राह्येषु तत्स्थतदञ्जनता समापत्तिः ॥ १.४१ ॥
kṣīṇavṛtterabhijātasyeva maṇergrahītṛgrahaṇagrāhyeṣu tatsthatadañjanatā samāpattiḥ ॥ 1.41 ॥

kṣīṇa = dwindled, attenuated
vṛtteḥ = of the mental activities
abhijātasya = of pure, high quality, transparent
iva = like
maṇeḥ = of a jewel, crystal
grahītṛ = the grasper (the knower)
grahaṇa = the grasping (the instruments of knowledge - sense instruments, and the mind)
grāhyeṣu = in the object that is grasped, experienced, known
tat-stha = situated in that (the object)
tad-añjanatā = the state of being colored by that object
samāpattiḥ = completion, perfection (of concentration)

Completion [samāpatti] is [the state] in which the activities of the mind are attenuated and [the mind] takes on the form of the grasper, grasping, and the grasped like a transparent jewel takes on color [from its surroundings].

When the activities of the mind are stilled, the mind takes the form of any object that it is focused on. Like a pure crystal that takes the color of an object placed behind it, a mind whose activities have subsided also takes the form of whatever object it concentrates on. Such a mind gains the ability to take the form of the knower (consciousness), the instruments of knowledge (all five senses, and intellect), and the object that is known. This completion or perfection is called *samāpatti*. Here, the word *samāpatti* is used as another name for "*samādhi* with awareness." *Samādhi* and *samāpatti* are very often used interchangeably.

Analogy of a crystal

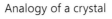

Samādhi with Word, Meaning, and Knowledge Intertwined (Savitarkā)

तत्र शब्दार्थज्ञानविकल्पैः संकीर्णा सवितर्का समापत्तिः ॥ १.४२ ॥
tatra śabdārthajñānavikalpaiḥ saṁkīrṇā savitarkā samāpattiḥ ॥ 1.42 ॥

tatra = there (in that state)
śabda = sound or word
artha = meaning, object denoted or signified
jñāna = knowledge
vikalpaiḥ = by the impressions, fancies, imaginations
saṁkīrṇā = mixed
savitarkā = accompanied conceptualization, deliberation, thinking
samāpattiḥ = completion, perfection of concentration, absorption (samādhi)

Samādhi with conceptualization has the concepts of word, meaning, and knowledge mixed together.

1. "Word" (*śabda*) is the word used to refer to an object — for example "cow."
2. "Meaning" (*artha*) is the object denoted by the word, or something connoted by the word.
3. "Knowledge" (*jñāna*) is the understanding or recognition of what you are looking at.

These three things are often mixed together in our mind. Mastering concentration with these three notions mixed together is called "*samādhi* with conceptualization" (*savitarkā*).

Samādhi with Singular Concentration (Nirvitarkā)

स्मृतिपरिशुद्धौ स्वरूपशून्येवार्थमात्रनिर्भासा निर्वितर्का ॥ १.४३ ॥
smṛtipariśuddhau svarūpaśūnyevārthamātranirbhāsā nirvitarkā ॥ 1.43 ॥

smṛti = memory
pariśuddhau = when purified
svarūpa = own form, self
śūnyā = void
iva = like
artha = object, meaning
mātra = merely
nirbhāsā = shining, manifesting
nirvitarkā = perfected concentration without conceptualization

Samādhi without conceptualization occurs when the memory is purified, [the meditation is] devoid of its own form, and the object alone manifests.

When the faculty of memory is refined it is able to recognize the boundaries between a word (*shabda*), the object it signifies (*artha*), and the knowledge of the object (*jñāna*). The mind will be able to concentrate on the object signified without superimposing the related word and knowledge (or mental mechanisms of cognition). In that state, one forgets about even one's own self (the "I am meditating" is also stopped). Only the gross object remains as the focus of meditation. This state is called "*samādhi* without conceptualization" (*nirvitarkā*).

Concentration on Subtle Entities

एतयैव सविचारा निर्विचारा च सूक्ष्मविषया व्याख्याता ॥ १.४४ ॥
etayaiva savicārā nirvicārā ca sūkṣmaviṣayā vyākhyātā ॥ 1.44 ॥

etayā = by this
eva= only
savicārā = concentration with subtle reflection
nirvicārā = concentration without subtle reflection
ca = and
sūkṣmaviṣayā = one with subtle object
vyākhyātā = is known or explained

In a similar manner [to savitarkā and nirvitarkā], the concentration with subtle reflection and the concentration without subtle reflection on subtle objects (savichārā and nirvichārā) are explained.

Just like *savitarkā* and *nirvitarkā* are meditations on gross objects, *savichārā* and *nirvichārā* are meditations on subtle objects.

What are subtle objects? The subtle objects are the earlier evolutes of nature, before the five gross natural elements — space, air, fire, water and earth — were formed. They are

1. the *tanmātrās* which are the building blocks of the gross natural elements.
2. the five subtle sense instruments and five subtle motor instruments (*indriyas*), the coordinator of instruments (*manas*), ego (*ahaṅkāra*), and the intellect (*buddhi*).

In a manner similar to concentration on gross objects, if the mind in meditation contains a mixture of the word, object, and knowledge of the subtle object meditated upon, this is called *samādhi* with subtle reflection (*savichārā*). When the mind is able to concentrate on only the subtle object without contemplating the word and the knowledge of it, this is called *samādhi* without subtle reflection (*nirvichārā*).

There is also an overlap with another set of awarenesses that occurs while meditating on subtle entities. There is a mixed awareness of *time*, *space*, and *cause*. Time, simply enough, refers to an awareness related to time and its passing. Space signifies the space occupied by the object (if applicable) and the grosser object of which it is a part. Cause refers to the factors responsible for the formation of the object. Enjoyment and liberation are the two most important causes. This mixture of temporal, spatial, and causal awareness is present in *samādhi* with subtle reflection. In *samādhi* without subtle reflection, even this mixture is eliminated, and only the direct perception of the entity remains.

सूक्ष्मविषयत्वं चालिङ्गपर्यवसानम् ॥ १.४५ ॥
sūkṣmaviṣayatvaṁ cāliṅgaparyavasānam ॥ 1.45 ॥

sūkṣma = subtle
viṣayatvaṁ = object-ness
ca = also
aliṅga = imperceptible, non-indicatory, undifferentiated
paryavasānam = extending up to, terminating at

This subtlety extends down to undifferentiated [nature].

The subtle objects of meditation that were mentioned before are still relatively concrete when compared to the undifferentiated primordial nature (*aliṅga-prakṛti*) from which all objects evolved. Nothing is subtler than *sattva*, *rajas*, and *tamas*, which are the fundamental elements or forces of nature. As explained earlier in the section on Sāṅkhya philosophy, nothing can be understood when these three elements are in equilibrium in their primordial state. Therefore, the subtlety of objects that can be meditated on extends up to the primordial elements (*prakṛti*).

Samādhi with Seed

ता एव सबीजः समाधिः ॥ १.४६ ॥
tā eva sabījaḥ samādhiḥ ॥ 1.46 ॥

tāḥ = they (previously mentioned savitarka, nirvitarka, savicāra, and nirvicāra samādhis)
eva = are indeed
sa-bījaḥ = with seed
samādhiḥ = perfected state of concentration, absorption

These [previously described four samādhis], indeed, are samādhis with seed [bīja].

The seed (*bīja*) is an object on which contemplation is practiced. The perfected concentration that depends on an object, subtle or gross, is called "*samādhi* with seed" (*sabīja*). Of the four *samādhis*, *savitarkā* and *nirvitarkā* depend on gross objects, while the *savicārā* and *nirvicārā* depend on subtle objects.

Savitarkā contains the awareness of the word, meaning, and knowledge of the gross object, while *savichārā* contains the same relating to the subtle object. In addition, *savicārā* also contains an awareness of time, space, and causal factors of the subtle object.

Nirvitarkā contains only the gross object as the object of meditation, free from an awareness of the word and the knowledge associated with the object. Similarly, *nirvicārā* contains only the subtle object as the object of meditation, free from the word and knowledge. In addition, *nirvicārā* is also free from the awareness of time, space, and causal factors of the subtle object.

निर्विचारवैशारद्येऽध्यात्मप्रसादः ॥ १.४७ ॥
nirvicāravaiśāradye'dhyātmaprasādaḥ ॥ 1.47 ॥

nirvicāra = concentration without subtle reflection
vaiśāradye = in the proficiency (when it is obtained)
adhyātma = inner self
prasādaḥ = purity, clarity

Clarity about self is gained when proficiency is attained in the samādhi without subtle reflection [nirvicāra].

When *samādhi* without subtle reflection (*nirvicāra*) is perfected, there is a steady flow of illuminating *sattva* in the mind without being overpowered by *rajas* and *tamas*. The mind becomes capable of taking the form of any object of meditation and revealing it as it is to the consciousness without any misconceptions. In this state the mind is said to be purified and reflects an image of the consciousness leading to an understanding of the core self.

Vyāsa quotes:

prajñāprāsādamāruhya
aśocyaḥ śocato janān ।
bhūmiṣṭhāniva śailasthaḥ
sarvānprājño anupaśyati ॥

Having climbed on top of the purified intellect, a yogī free from all sorrow and pain sees the rest of the people in sorrow, just as a man having climbed a hill sees all the other men on the ground beneath.

Truth-bearing Knowledge

ऋतम्भरा तत्र प्रज्ञा ॥ १.४८ ॥
ṛtambharā tatra prajñā ॥ 1.48 ॥

ṛtam = truth
bharā = bearing
tatra = in that state
prajñā = knowledge or wisdom

In that state [nirvicāra], the knowledge is truth bearing [knowledge reveals truth].

In the state when proficiency in *samādhi* without subtle reflection (*nirvicāra*) is attained, the mind can perceive the pure nature of any object.

Also, a yogī can attain true knowledge when he or she engages in the three learning practices:

- from scriptures,
- from inference, and
- from meditation

Special Knowledge from Samādhi

श्रुतानुमानप्रज्ञाभ्यामन्यविषया विशेषार्थत्वात् ॥ १.४९ ॥
śrutānumānaprajñābhyāmanyaviṣayā viśeṣārthatvāt ॥ 1.49 ॥

śruta = that which is heard or learned from scripture
anumāna = inferred
prajñābhyām = knowledge
anya = other
viṣayā = object
viśeṣa = special
ārthatvāt = due to knowledge

This [true knowledge] is different from the knowledge obtained from scriptures and inference due to its special nature.

True knowledge (*prajñā*), mentioned in the previous sūtra, is of a special kind: it is directly perceived. It is therefore different from the knowledge obtained from scriptures and inference.

As mentioned earlier, knowledge is of two types:

1. Specific knowledge
2. Common knowledge

When you know about something by hearing or reading about it, the knowledge that you get is called common knowledge. For example, someone who has never seen a cow can know about them by seeing a picture in a book. Such knowledge is common knowledge, containing generic information about cows. When you directly perceive an object with your own sense organs, that knowledge is called specific knowledge, or *viśeṣajñāna,* as it contains specifics of that particular object. When a person sees a cow in the field, that knowledge is called specific knowledge, as it contains details about that particular cow. Only direct perception with one's own sense organs (and mind) can give both common and specific knowledge. Scriptures and inference can give you only common knowledge.

This sūtra emphasizes that the knowledge you get from the *nirvicāra-samādhi* is special, going beyond common or general knowledge. Also, since the mind is made of *mahat* — the first evolute of nature — and all objects in the universe evolved from the same *mahat*, the mind can experience objects that are beyond the grasp of even our external sense organs.

Arresting Impressions

तज्जः संस्कारोऽन्यसंस्कारप्रतिबन्धी ॥ १.५० ॥
tajjaḥ saṁskāro'nyasaṁskārapratibandhī ॥ 1.50 ॥

tat-jaḥ = born from that (in this case, nirvicāra-samādhi)
saṁskāraḥ = impression
anya = other
saṁskāra = impressions
prati-bandhī = restrainer, obstructer

The impression born from that [nirvicāra-samādhi] becomes the restrainer of other impressions.

The impressions formed by *samādhi* without subtle reflection (*nirvicāra-samādhi*) prevent other impressions from turning into activities of the mind.

Samādhi Without Seed (Nirbīja)

तस्यापि निरोधे सर्वनिरोधान्निर्बीजः समाधिः ॥ १.५१ ॥
tasyāpi nirodhe sarvanirodhānnirbījaḥ samādhiḥ ॥ 1.51 ॥

tasya = of that
api = even
nirodhe = upon restriction
sarva = all
nirodhāt = from stopping
nir-bījaḥ = without seed
samādhiḥ = perfected state of concentration, absorption

When such impressions are restrained, having restrained everything [one attains] samādhi without seed.

Truth-bearing (*ṛtambharā*) impressions are generated by *samādhi* with seed, with the support of an external object. These impressions stop other impressions from turning into mental activities. Although truth-bearing impressions are also impressions, they do not lead to the afflictions that in turn lead to birth and death. When even these impressions are restrained (i.e., the thought of restraining other mental activities is restrained), the mind enters the *niruddha* state in which all mental activities are restrained.

The mind merges into its constituent elements of nature (*sattva*, *rajas*, and *tamas*) and the pure consciousness is free from identification with the mind. There is no mental activity for the consciousness to perceive. This state is the "*samādhi* without seed" (*nirbīja*), in which the consciousness remains in its own true essence, untainted by either the intellect or the mind. This is the ultimate goal of yoga.

Sādhanapādaḥ (Practice)

Sūtras 2.1-2.2: Kriyā-yoga

तपःस्वाध्यायेश्वरप्रणिधानानि क्रियायोगः ॥ २.१ ॥
tapaḥsvādhyāyeśvarapraṇidhānāni kriyāyogaḥ ॥ 2.1 ॥

tapaḥ = austerity, purificatory actions like enduring dualities, discipline
svādhyāya = self-study of scriptures, and introspection
īśvara-praṇidhānāni = devotion to God (offering all actions and results to God)
kriyā-yogaḥ = yoga of action

Austerity, study of scriptures, and devotion to God constitute yoga of action.

Austerity (*tapas*) is the behavior of bearing all hardships and dualities while performing one's duties in life. Dualities are pairs of extremes — such as heat and cold, or praise and insult. In addition, there is a saying: "cultivating good habits is tapas and abstaining from bad habits is tapas" (śamastapo damastapaḥ).

Svādhyāya is the studying of scriptures on one's own. It also means reciting or repeating hymns or prayers, and can also be interpreted as the study of one's own self — introspection. *Īśvarapraṇidhāna* is devotion to God and meditation on God.

Since the mind is imprinted with impressions from many lives, it takes dedicated practice in the form of *tapas*, *svādhyāya* and *īśvarapraṇidhāna* to tame it and bring it under control. Practicing these three things results in the dominance of *sattva*, which helps in gaining discriminating wisdom and increases enthusiasm to pursue yogic goals. *Sattva-guṇa* is conducive to leading a virtuous and fruitful life, since it is associated with knowledge and prosperity. The practice of *kriyā-yoga* is especially suited for a worldly person. It aids in countering afflictions and attaining higher states of yoga.

Kriyā-yoga: austerity, study of scriptures, and devotion to God

समाधिभावनार्थः क्लेशतनूकरणार्थश्च ॥ २.२ ॥
samādhibhāvanārthaḥ kleśatanūkaraṇārthaśca ॥ 2.2 ॥

samādhi = perfected state of concentration, absorption
bhāvanārthaḥ = for causing
kleśa = affliction, obstacle
tanū-karaṇa = making thin or attenuate
ārtha = purpose
ca = and

It [yoga of action] is for bringing about samādhi and the attenuation of afflictions.

The practice of *kriyā-yoga*, yoga of action, helps in attaining the deep state of meditation (*samādhi*) and attenuates obstacles to such a degree that they no longer hinder a yogī. Obstacles become burnt and are rendered powerless, like burnt seeds that cannot sprout. When obstacles are subdued like this, the yogī attains discriminating wisdom and understands the difference between the intellect and the consciousness.

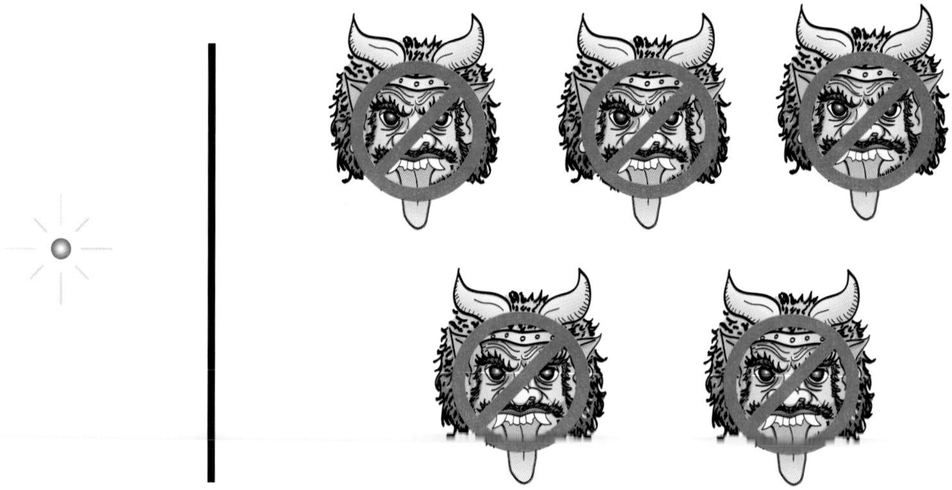

Subduing afflictions

Sūtras 2.3-2.14: Afflictions (kleśas)

अविद्यास्मितारागद्वेषाभिनिवेशाः क्लेशाः ॥ २.३ ॥
avidyāsmitārāgadveṣābhiniveśāḥ kleśāḥ ॥ 2.3 ॥

avidyā = incorrect knowledge (knowing a thing the way it is not)
asmitā = ego (confusion between the self and the mind - thinking "I am the mind")
rāga = attachment
dveṣa = aversion, hatred
abhiniveśāḥ = clinging to physical life, fear of death
kleśāḥ = obstacles, afflications

Incorrect knowledge, ego, attachment, aversion, and clinging to physical life are the five afflictions.

The afflictions of incorrect knowledge, ego, attachment, aversion, and fear of death are the five obstacles. Here, the word ego is used in a special sense to translate *asmitā*. This is different from *ahaṅkāra* which is the second evolute of nature which is also translated as "ego". *Asmitā* is the confusion between the self and the mind. Thinking "I am the mind" is *asmitā*. In order to develop detachment (*vairāgya*) and practice (*abyāsa*) one needs to have the senses and mind under control. Afflictions (*kleśas*) are mental activities that prevent us from commanding the mind and restraining it. These afflictions are the deep-rooted, pre-programmed tendencies that we display when dealing with situations in our daily life. When active, afflictions increase the influence of the forces of nature over consciousness. This sets into motion the cycle of cause and effect that brings about the consequences of actions. These consequences breed attachment to favorable experiences and aversion to unfavorable experiences. Such forces of attachment and aversion distract the mind by pulling it in different directions — a distracted mind cannot focus, and fails to see the true nature of objects. The yogī must overcome afflictions in order to be free from the consequences of actions, to restrain the mind, and to attain discriminating wisdom. Each of the five afflictions is described in the coming sūtras.

अविद्या क्षेत्रमुत्तरेषां प्रसुप्ततनुविच्छिन्नोदाराणाम् ॥ २.४ ॥
avidyā kṣetramuttareṣāṁ prasuptatanuvicchinnodārāṇām ॥ 2.4 ॥

avidyā = incorrect knowledge, ignorance
kṣetram = ground
uttareṣāṁ = of the latter (of the ones listed after avidyā)
prasupta = dormant
tanu = attenuated, diminished
vicchinna = interrupted, broken
udārāṇām = aroused, magnified, elevated, fully active

Incorrect knowledge is the ground for the rest [of the afflictions], which can be in dormant, attenuated, interrupted, or fully-active states.

Avidyā is the ground for the rest of the four afflictions (*kleśas*), which can be found in four states: 1) dormant, 2) attenuated, 3) interrupted, and 4) fully active.

- The dormant (*prasupta*) state is like a healthy seed — it still has the potential to sprout and be activated in the presence of an object. For an adept yogī who has realized the difference between the mind and the self, the afflictions can no longer sprout or activate.
- In the attenuated or diminished (*tanu*) state, the afflictions are weakened and partially subdued by the practice of their complements — that is, by practicing friendship towards happy, compassion towards distressed, joy towards virtuous, and forbearance towards non-virtuous people. Diminished state of afflictions is conducive to healthy and productive behaviour.
- In the interrupted state (*vicchinna*), an affliction is inactive because another affliction or mental activity is currently active. For example, in a moment of attachment, aversion is absent.
- In the fully-active state (*udāra*), the affliction is unchecked. Spontaneous anger, chronic addiction, and depression are some examples of this state.

In the following sūtras, the five afflictions will be further described.

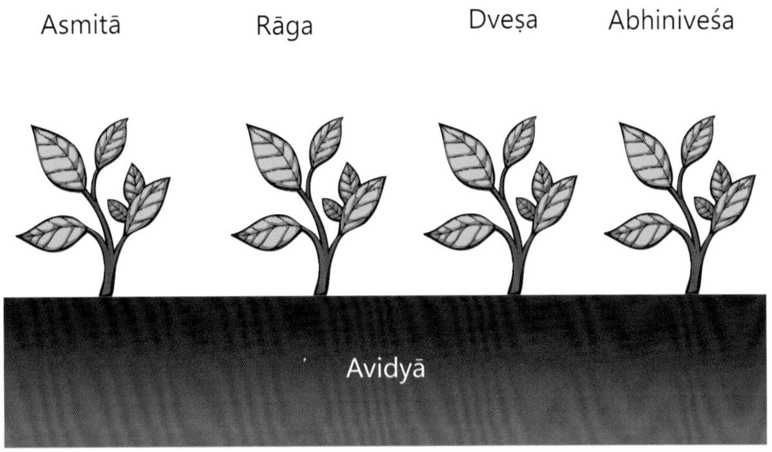
Asmitā
Rāga
Dveṣa
Abhiniveśa
Avidyā

Dormant
Attenuated
Interrupted
Fully active

Avidyā

अनित्याशुचिदुःखानात्मसु नित्यशुचिसुखात्मख्यातिरविद्या ॥ २.५ ॥
anityāśuciduḥkhānātmasu nityaśucisukhātmakhyātiravidyā ॥ 2.5 ॥

anityā = temporary, non-eternal, impermanent
aśuci = unclean
duḥkha = misery, pain, sorrow
anātmasu = non-self
nitya = eternal
śuci = clean
sukha = pleasure, joy
ātma = self
khyātiḥ = knowledge, perception, vision
avidyā = incorrect knowledge

Perceiving the temporary as eternal, the impure as pure, misery as joy, or the non-self as the self is called incorrect knowledge.

For example, to consider the world, sky, moon, and the stars as eternal is *avidyā*. To consider that our bodies are pure and clean is *avidyā*. To consider any temporary gratification that hurts us in the long term as pleasure is *avidyā*. Later, sūtra 2.15 elaborates that all things that we experience are fraught with pain. Our inability to recognize this is *avidyā*. To consider our body, mind or other non-self attributes as the self is *avidyā*.

Asmitā

दृग्दर्शनशक्त्योरेकात्मतेवास्मिता ॥ २.६ ॥
dṛgdarśanaśaktyorekātmatevāsmitā ॥ 2.6 ॥

dṛk = seer
darśana = seeing
śaktyoḥ = power, ability
eka-ātmatā = one-ness
iva = like
asmitā = the feeling of 'I'-ness (ego)

I-ness is to consider the power of the seer [consciousness] to be the power of seeing [the intellect, the mind].

To think "I am the mind" is to express the affliction called "ego" (*asmitā*). This is superimposing the pure consciousness onto the mind. According to yoga, all misery arises out of this false understanding. In reality, consciousness (*puruṣa*) is external to the mind (*citta*). When the true nature of consciousness and mind are known, the result is the liberation of the pure consciousness from its entanglement. Note that the word "ego" is used for both *asmitā* and *ahaṅkāra*. *Ahaṅkāra* is the second evolute of nature as described in Sāṅkhya philosophy, while *asmitā* is a mental process that leads to the superimposition of the true self onto the mind.

Superimposition of mind over consciousness

Rāga

सुखानुशयी रागः ॥ २.७ ॥
sukhānuśayī rāgaḥ ॥ 2.7 ॥

sukha = pleasure, happiness
anuśayī = that which follows
rāgaḥ = attachment

Attachment is that which follows pleasure.

When we experience things that are pleasant, we become attached to them. This attachment is called *rāga*. We become attached not just to things, but to their memories as well.

Rāga

Dveṣa

दुःखानुशयी द्वेषः ॥ २.८ ॥
duḥkhānuśayī dveṣaḥ ॥ 2.8 ॥

duḥkha = misery
anuśayī = that which follows
dveṣaḥ = aversion

Aversion is that which follows misery.

When we experience anything that is painful or miserable, we develop aversion (*dveṣa*). Our aversions are often due to things that happened in the past. It is the memories that are the true source of our aversions.

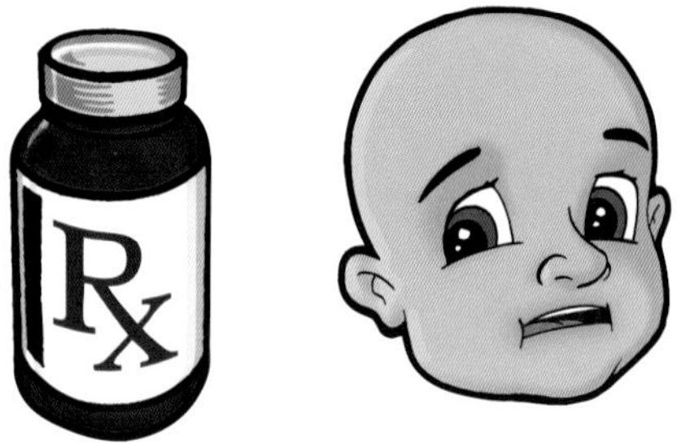

Dveṣa

Abhiniveśa

स्वरसवाही विदुषोऽपि तथारूढोऽभिनिवेशः ॥ २.९ ॥
svarasavāhī viduṣo'pi tathārūḍho'bhiniveśaḥ ॥ 2.9 ॥

sva-rasa = own essense
vāhī = carrying
viduṣaḥ = learned
api = also
tathā = like that
ārūḍhaḥ = mounted, arisen, established
abhiniveśaḥ = clinging to physical life, fear of death

The instinct to preserve oneself is established even in the learned.

The survival instinct or clinging to physical life (*abhiniveśa*) is established even in the learned. All living beings have the feeling, "May I not cease to exist; may I continue to live." From the illiterate to the learned, this feeling is common to all. This is seen even in insects and worms — they experience this impression due to previous experiences of death. The consciousness has no death, it is eternal.

Survival instinct in all beings

Elimination of Afflictions (Kleśas)

ते प्रतिप्रसवहेयाः सूक्ष्माः ॥ २.१० ॥
te pratiprasavaheyāḥ sūkṣmāḥ ॥ 2.10 ॥

te = they (afflictions, or kleśas)
prati-prasava = counter-flowing, dissolving into components
heyāḥ = abandoned, overcome, destroyed
sūkṣmāḥ = having made minute (attenuated)

These subtle afflictions are overcome by reverse-flow [of the mind toward its components].

Afflictions are made subtle and overcome when the mind (*citta*) is dissolved and merged back into its components (*sattva*, *rajas*, and *tamas*), which is the subtlest state. Through meditation, the afflictions become like burnt seeds and disappear when the mind dissolves back into nature having fulfilled its purpose. Here, the afflictions which become like burnt seeds are called subtle afflictions.

ध्यानहेयास्तद्वृत्तयः ॥ २.११ ॥
dhyānaheyāstadvṛttayaḥ ॥ 2.11 ॥

dhyāna = meditation, contemplation
heyāḥ = abandoned, overcome, destroyed
tad = those
vṛttayaḥ = mental activities (afflictions are also mental activities)

Those mental activities [afflictions] are overcome by the practice of meditation.

The five afflictions described in this chapter are born out of the five primary mental activities that were described at the beginning of the first chapter. The five afflictions are also mental activities which can be considered as the "detrimental child processes." They are weakened by the practice of *kriyāyoga* and then completely eliminated through meditation (*dhyāna*).

Overcoming afflictions

Effect of Afflictions on Actions

क्लेशमूलः कर्माशयो दृष्टादृष्टजन्मवेदनीयः ॥ २.१२ ॥
kleśamūlaḥ karmāśayo dṛṣṭādṛṣṭajanmavedanīyaḥ ॥ 2.12 ॥

kleśa-mūlaḥ = having afflictions (kleśas) as its root
karma-āśaya = the stock of merit and demerit of actions (called the "stock of karma")
dṛṣṭa = seen, present (current life)
adṛṣṭa = unseen, future (next life)
janma = birth, life
vedanīyaḥ = felt, experienced, known

The stock of karma having afflictions as the root is seen in the present life or the future.

All actions result in impressions on the mind (*citta*). The combination of merit and demerit associated with such impressions is called "the stock of karma" (*karmāśaya*). If actions are motivated by afflictions, the corresponding impressions formed are also "colored" with afflictions. Such impressions result in the consequences that we experience in our current and future lives.

Virtuous karma — consisting of helping others, practicing *japa* (repeating hymns or *Oṁ*), *tapas* (practicing austerity), attaining *samādhi*, and devotion to God — can have immediate results. This also holds true for the opposite kind of actions — harming those who are frightened, diseased, or meek, or the pious who come for refuge. This means that one can acquire impressions that have consequences in the current life. Some karma results in consequences that need a future life to be experienced or consumed.

Beings who are liberated, however — such as adept yogīs who have attained discriminating wisdom and reached the stage of *asamprajñāta-samādhi* — do not gather any new consequences of afflictions that can be experienced in the future life. The impressions formed do not result in consequences because their actions do not have merit or demerit.

Actions fraught with afflictions result in consequences (fruits)

सति मूले तद्विपाको जात्यायुर्भोगाः ॥ २.१३ ॥
sati mūle tadvipāko jātyāyurbhogāḥ ॥ 2.13 ॥

sati = in its existence or presence
mūle = while having the root
tad = that
vipākaḥ = maturation, fruition, consequence, result
jāti = birth, category, class
āyuḥ = span of life, longevity
bhogāḥ = experiences

In the presence of the root [of afflictions], the fruitions of karma result in birth, lifespan, and experience.

The set of impressions of karma that lead to consequences is called *karmāśaya*. This set of impressions is caused by afflictions. So, afflictions are the real root (*mūla*) of the problem. The storehouse of karma is the source for the consequences of actions, which influence the births of future lives. There is a discussion in the commentaries on how many actions can result in how many births. It is presented below.

Does One Action Result In One Birth?

One action cannot result in one birth, simply because many actions are performed in each life. If one had to experience a separate birth for the consequences of each action, then there would be an exponential increase in the number of births one experienced as a result of each lifetime.

Does One Action Result In Many Births?

Similarly, one action cannot result in multiple births, because this would result in an even-more-increased number of births than the paradoxical situation above.

Do Many Actions Result In Many Births?

Many actions cannot result in many births because a person can perform multiple actions in one lifetime, and each of those actions would have to result in multiple births.

Do Many Actions Result In One Birth?

This seems to be the most reasonable view. The sum of all impressions put together determines the next birth.

Impressions can be dominant (due to intensity of afflictions) or subordinate (due to mildness of afflictions). Dominant impressions play a major role in determining the next birth. The subordinate ones may remain as they are, become altered, or merge with impressions from actions in the next birth. Dominant *karmāśaya* is therefore called "well-determined" *karmāśaya*, while subordinate *karmāśaya* is called "uncertain" *karmāśaya*.

Some commentaries suggest that good *karmāśaya* can nullify bad *karmāśaya*, but this is not consistent with the model of the mind that Patañjali presents. Good *karmāśaya* can suppress negative consequences temporarily, but does not annihilate them completely. If such nullification were possible then one could eradicate previous karma impressions completely with new karma. This means there would be no future birth, even though that person had not achieved discriminating wisdom (distinctness of consciousness and mind). This contradicts the rest of the sūtras. That is why the consequences must be experienced, whether good or bad.

Purāṇas on karma

Here is an oft quoted verse which is found in multiple *Purāṇas.*

mābhuktaṁ kṣīyate karma
koṭikalpashatairapi ।
avaśyameva bhoktavyaṁ
kṛtaṁ karma shubhāshubham ॥

– *Brahmavaivarta-purāṇa 33.45*

All (consequences of) actions should be experienced, whether good or bad. The unexperienced karma will not subside even after hundreds of crores of *kalpas*. (one crore = 10 million, kalpa = 4,320 million years).

ते ह्लादपरितापफलाः पुण्यापुण्यहेतुत्वात् ॥ २.१४ ॥
te hlādaparitāpaphalāḥ puṇyāpuṇyahetutvāt ॥ 2.14 ॥

te = they, these (birth, lifespan, and experience)
hlāda= pleasure
paritāpa = misery, distress, pain
phalāḥ = fruits
puṇya = virtue
apuṇya = non-virtue, vice
hetutvāt = having the cause

Due to virtue and non-virtue, they [birth, lifespan, and experience] are either pleasurable or miserable.

Our birth, life, and experiences can be pleasurable or miserable depending on the virtue or non-virtue of our previous actions. Virtuous actions lead to favorable experiences, while non-virtuous actions lead to unfavorable experiences.

Non-harming, compassion, truth, honesty, self-control, and disregard for material possessions are referred to as restraints (*yamas*). Cleanliness, a pleasant attitude (even in the face of adversity), austerity, spiritual study, and devotion to God are called observances (*niyamas*). Both are virtuous actions that are beneficial for us. The opposing qualities — anger, greed, harm, untruth, and promiscuity — result in pain and misery. For yogīs, even pleasure is undesirable, as it still involves pain. How is this possible? That is explained in the next sūtra.

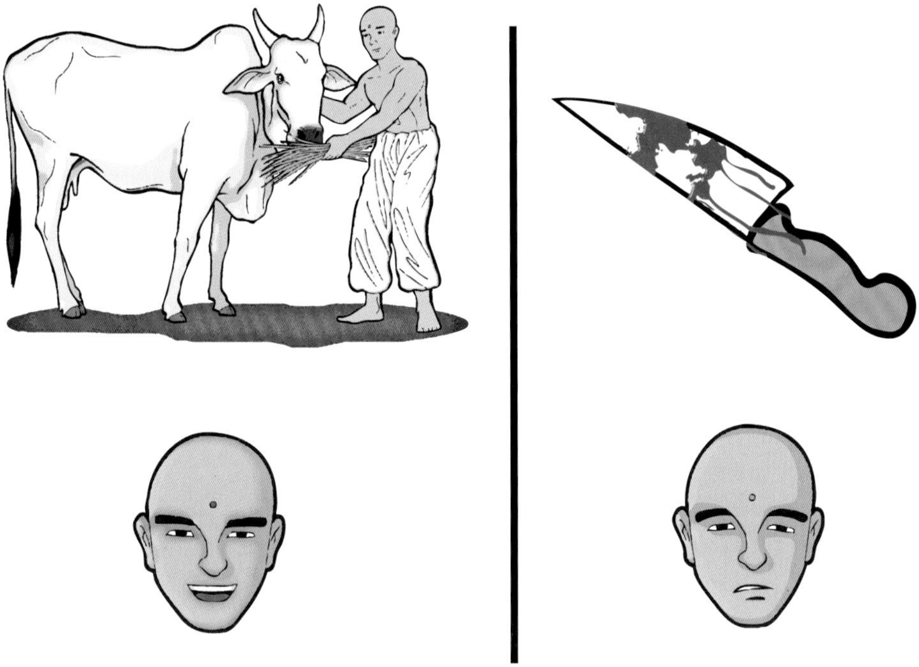

Virtuous actions (non-harming, etc)
leading to happiness

Non-virtuous actions (harming, etc)
leading to misery

Sūtras 2.15-2.26: Misery, The Cause of Misery, Its Elimination, and the Means of Elimination

Kinds of Misery

परिणामतापसंस्कारदुःखैर्गुणवृत्तिविरोधाच्च दुःखमेव सर्वं विवेकिनः ॥ २.१५ ॥
pariṇāmatāpasaṁskāraduḥkhairguṇavṛttivirodhācca duḥkhameva sarvaṁ vivekinaḥ ॥ 2.15 ॥

pariṇāma = change, transformation, consequence
tāpa = pain, hardship
saṁskāra = impression
duḥkhair = by the miseries
guṇa-vṛtti = functions of guṇas
virodhāt = due to conflict or opposing nature
ca = and
duḥkham = sorrow, misery
eva = only
sarvaṁ = everything
vivekinaḥ = of the discerning

Because of sorrows due to change, hardships, impressions, and the conflicting operations of the guṇas, all experiences are sorrowful to a discerning person.

This sūtra explains the four different ways we experience misery.

1. Misery due to change or consequence (*pariṇāma*) is called *pariṇāmaduḥkha*. Everything changes all the time. When these changes are undesirable to us we feel frustrated and miserable. For example, most people want to be healthy and young all the time. Aging is an unavoidable change that we must all experience. The prospect of this change causes distress.

2. Misery due to hardship and anxiety (*tāpa*) that one undergoes in order to achieve and maintain objects of pleasure is called *tāpaduḥkha*. For example, a person has to work hard to earn an income, which he uses to acquire possessions. The hardship and pain experienced in such a pursuit falls in this category.

3. Misery due to impressions of attachment and longing (*saṁskāra*) is called *saṁskāraduḥkha*. When we enjoy something, it produces an impression in the mind. The longing experienced for enjoying such a pleasure causes distress. For example, if a person enjoys a fabulous vacation, after coming back to work the memories of the vacation may create a longing to return to vacation.

4. Misery due to the conflicting operations of the *guṇas* is inherent in the nature of the universe. The three *guṇas* always occur in combination. *Sattva* — which results in pleasure, enthusiasm and knowledge — is never found by itself, but always in combination with *rajas* and *tamas* — which cause anxiety and dullness. The three qualities are combined in uneven proportions in all objects. Pleasure is always fraught with some amount of pain, though we fail to notice it. Just as a government includes both a ruling party and opposition parties, so is pleasure always mixed with pain.

Due to these four reasons, a discriminating yogī sees everything as fraught with misery, and pursues liberation from all kinds of misery through discriminating wisdom. There is an analogy to the eye that describes how an ordinary person sees pleasure as pleasure while a yogī sees pleasure as fraught with pain. The eye is more sensitive than the skin. While walking in the woods, if we unknowingly brush a cobweb with our hand, there is no pain. But, if we happen to walk into a cobweb such that it touches our eyeball, we experience pain. Even though the physical impact of the cobweb is the same in both cases, because the eye is very sensitive, we feel pain. Similarly, a yogī's sensitive perception can recognize the pain interspersed between pleasures. That is why he or she seeks to eliminate it.

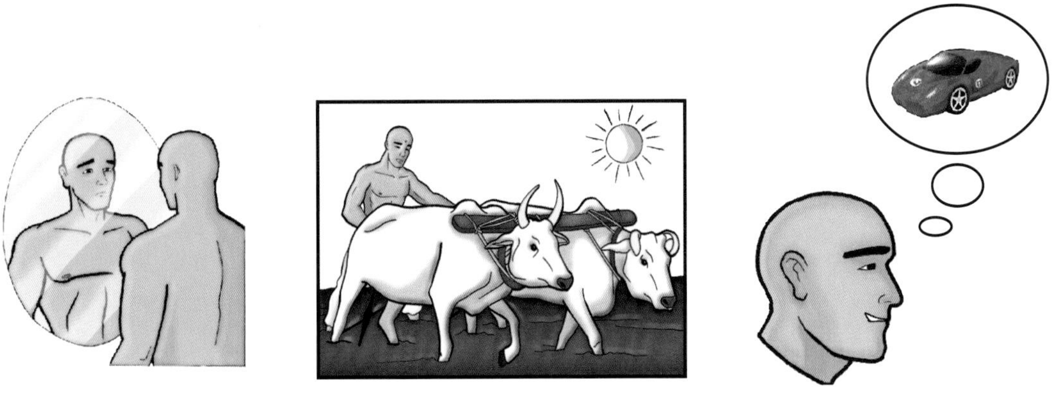

Misery due to change, hardships, and longing

Misery

हेयं दुःखमनागतम् ॥ २.१६ ॥
heyaṁ duḥkhamanāgatam ॥ 2.16 ॥

heyaṁ = that which should be avoided
duḥkham = misery, pain
anāgatam = that which is yet to come

Misery that has not yet come should be avoided.

Suffering in the past cannot be avoided in subsequent moments, as it has already been experienced. Suffering in the current moment also cannot be avoided. Only future sorrow can be avoided, as that is the only thing under our control.

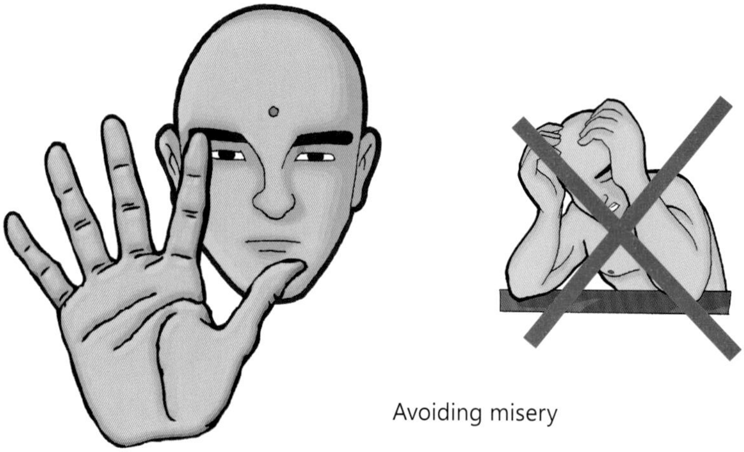

Avoiding misery

द्रष्टृदृश्ययोः संयोगो हेयहेतुः ॥ २.१७ ॥
draṣṭṛdṛśyayoḥ saṁyogo heyahetuḥ ॥ 2.17 ॥

draṣṭṛ = seer (consciousness)
dṛśyayoḥ = the seen, that which is seen (everything that is experienced)
saṁyogaḥ = joining, conjunction
heya = that which needs to be avoided, overcome (misery, pain)
hetuḥ = cause

The union of the seer and the seen is the cause of misery.

The union of the seer (consciousness) and the seen (mind, body, external objects) is the cause of pain, and pain is to be abandoned or avoided. The consciousness perceives only what is shown by the mind, and the mind takes the form of the objects that it comes into contact with. If the form that it takes is of pleasure due to the dominance of the *sattva-guṇa*, then the consciousness experiences pleasure. If the mind takes the form of pain due to the dominance of *rajas* and *tamas*, the consciousness experiences pain. In simpler words, the union is nothing but the consciousness identifying with the mind — experiencing those negative feelings as if it is the mind or body of a person, when it is not.

In yoga, the soul is called the "seer" (*draṣṭā*) because it sees or perceives nature. The objects of the senses and the sense organs themselves (including *citta*, the mind) — which compose the universe — are called the "seen" (*dṛśya*), because they are what is seen or perceived. According to Sāṅkhya and Yoga, the seer is unchanging and immutable, while the seen is constantly changing. By abiding only in the seer (the self) one is liberated from the mutations and miseries of the world. The coupling of the soul and the mind happens because of incorrect knowledge.

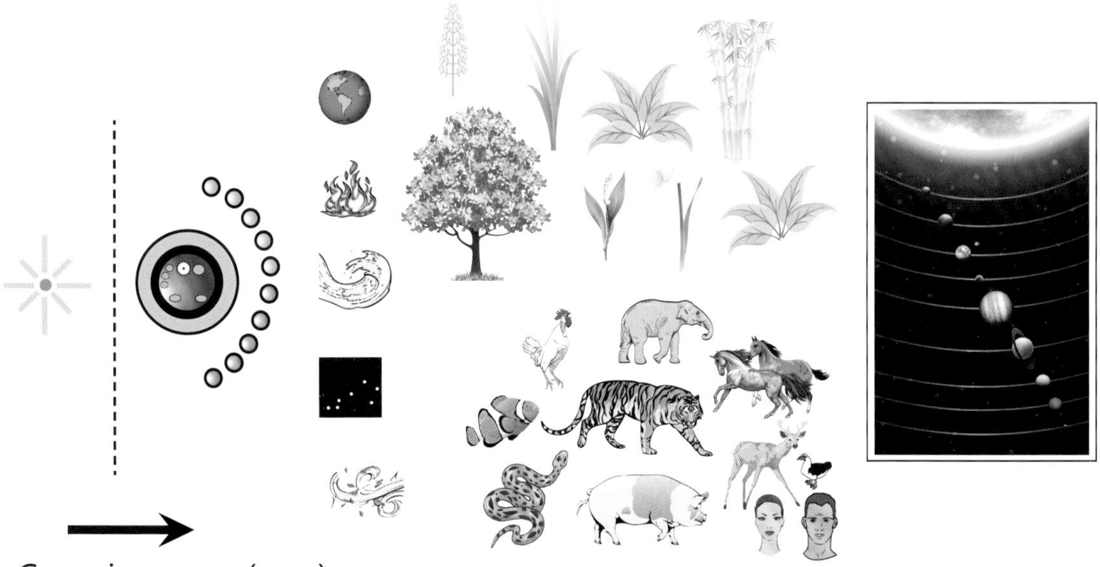

Consciousness (seer) coming into contact with objects (seen).

Description of the Seen (Nature, the Universe)

प्रकाशक्रियास्थितिशीलं भूतेन्द्रियात्मकं भोगापवर्गार्थं दृश्यम् ॥ २.१८ ॥
prakāśakriyāsthitiśīlaṁ bhūtendriyātmakaṁ bhogāpavargārthaṁ dṛśyam ॥ 2.18 ॥

prakāśa = illumination
kriyā = activity, movement
sthiti = stability
śīlaṁ = character, having a characteristic
bhūta = the elements of nature (earth, water, fire, wind, space)
indriya = instruments of cognition and action (which are thirteen in number)
ātmakaṁ = composed of, having the essence of
bhoga = enjoyment, experience
apavarga = emancipation, liberation
arthaṁ = for the purpose
dṛśyam = that which is seen (the universe, including our bodies and minds)

The nature of the "seen" is illumination, movement, and stability. It is composed of the instruments of perception and the objects made from the natural elements. Its purpose is enjoyment and liberation.

Here, everything that is not the seer (consciousness, the self) is called the seen. The seen includes everything from our minds and bodies to all objects in the universe. This sūtra explains the nature, content, and purpose of the universe.

Nature of the Universe

Three basic qualities are observed in all objects in the universe: illumination, movement, and stability. These correspond to the three fundamental particles or qualities: *sattva*, *rajas*, and *tamas*.

- *sattva* causes illumination and aids understanding
- *rajas* causes movement
- *tamas* causes stability or inertia

All objects contain an uneven mixture of these three *guṇas*. Our instruments of perception and action (the sense and motor organs), *manas*, ego, and intellect are all dominated by *sattva*. In the intellect, when *sattva* is undisturbed by *rajas* and *tamas*, we understand things and feel pleasant. When *rajas* and *tamas* are dominant we feel frustration, pain, depression, addiction, and so forth. These three qualities are present in both living and non-living objects.

Contents of the Universe

Patañjali classifies the components of the universe into two categories: instruments, and the objects that are sensed and acted on by those instruments.

1. Instruments here refer to the five sense organs, the five motor organs, intellect, *manas*, and ego — which together enable perception and action.
2. The things that are sensed include everything that we perceive with our sense organs. Everything is formed out of the five natural elements: earth, water, fire, air and space.

The Purpose of the Universe

The purpose of the universe is two-fold:

1. experience and enjoyment (*bhoga*)
2. detachment and renunciation (*apavarga*)

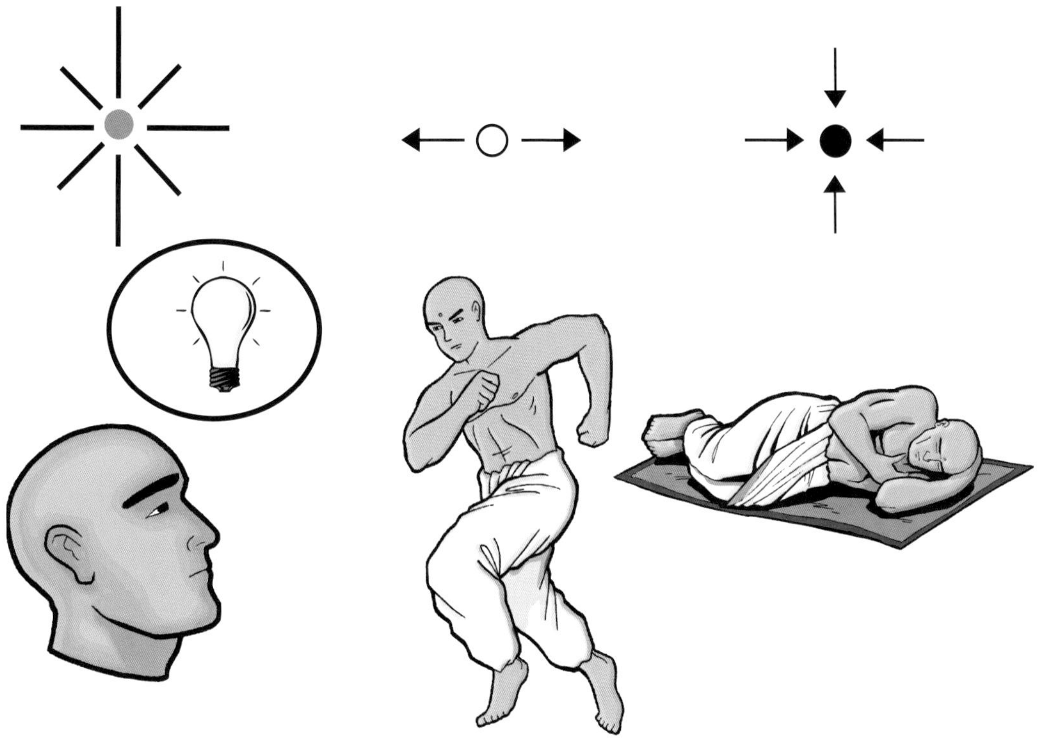

Illumination, acitivity, and stability - characteristics of all objects in nature

विशेषाविशेषलिङ्गमात्रालिङ्गानि गुणपर्वाणि ॥ २.१९ ॥
viśeṣāviśeṣaliṅgamātrāliṅgāni guṇaparvāṇi ॥ 2.19 ॥

viśeṣa = particularized
aviśeṣa = unparticularized
liṅga-mātra = purely indicatory
a-liṅgāni = non-indicatory
guṇa = fundamental elements or forces of nature
parvāṇi = states

The states of the guṇas are 1) particularized 2) unparticularized 3) indicatory, and 4) non-indicatory

Nature (*prakṛti*) has four different states (*parvāṇi*), each of which evolves from the one behind it. This is familiar from the discussion of evolution in the introduction.

1. Particularized (*viśeṣa*) refers to objects that are fully evolved and cannot evolve further. This is the name for the instruments of sense and action, *manas*, and the five natural elements (earth, water, fire, air, space).
2. Unparticularized (*aviśeṣa*) describes objects that are not fully evolved, and so can further evolve into other elements. These are the intermediate evolutes (the five subtle elements called *tanmātras*, and one *ahaṅkāra*).
3. Indicatory (*liṅga*) refers to the intellect (*buddhi* or *mahat*) that can be perceived (it has the capacity to indicate something), which is formed as the first evolute in an act of creation by introducing uneven combinations into the *guṇas*. Intellect can be dissolved into its components.
4. Non-indicatory (*aliṅga*), does not indicate anything. This is nature (*prakṛti*) in its primordial state of equilibrium of the three *guṇas*. The *guṇas* cannot be further dissolved into anything, as they are themselves the fundamental components.

Description of the Seer (Consciousness)

द्रष्टा दृशिमात्रः शुद्धोऽपि प्रत्ययानुपश्यः ॥ २.२० ॥
draṣṭā dṛśimātraḥ śuddho'pi pratyayānupaśyaḥ ॥ 2.20 ॥

draṣṭā = seer
dṛśi-mātraḥ = seeing-only, limited to the power of seeing or knowing
śuddhaḥ = pure
api = although, in spite of, also
pratyaya = knowledge, content of the mind, concept
anu-paśyaḥ = seeing, experiencing accordingly

The seer, is only [the power of] seeing. Although pure, it experiences the content of the mind.

Consciousness itself is simply the power to perceive; it, itself, is pure. Because the consciousness is in contact with the mind, it experiences things happening in the mind.

Consciousness is the pure seer or knower, which sees or knows through the intellect. When objects such as a cow or a pot color the intellect, they are known by the consciousness. All experience occurs through intellect. Even though consciousness is unchanging, its experience changes because of changes in the state of the intellect.

The Purpose of Nature and the Universe

तदर्थ एव दृश्यस्यात्मा ॥ २. २१ ॥
tadartha eva dṛśyasyātmā ॥ 2.21 ॥

tat = that
arthaḥ = purpose
eva = only, indeed
dṛśyasya = of the seen
ātmā = nature, essense

The essence of the seen is only for that purpose [of consciousness].

As explained in the previous verse, all that is experienced in the universe — including the body and the mind — is for the sake of consciousness, to provide experience and liberation to consciousness. Consciousness is the Lord; Nature is its servant.

Durability of Nature (Prakṛti)

कृतार्थं प्रति नष्टमप्यनष्टं तदन्यसाधारणत्वात् ॥ २.२२ ॥
kṛtārthaṁ prati naṣṭamapyanaṣṭaṁ tadanyasādhāraṇatvāt ॥ 2.22 ॥

kṛta-arthaṁ = one who has achieved what needs to be achieved
prati = towards, with regard to
naṣṭam = lost, ceased, dissolved
api = even though, never the less
anaṣṭaṁ = not lost, not ceased, not dissolved
tad = that (object)
anya = other
sādhāraṇatvāt = due to its common-ness

Although the object ceases to exist for the one whose purpose has been accomplished, it nevertheless remains in existence because of its commonality.

Everything that is perceived in this creation is for the experience and liberation of consciousness. However, things do not cease to exist after one soul attains liberation, even though the function of these things has been met. Instead, these objects remain for the benefit of other individual souls that are still in the process of accomplishing experience and liberation.

The Cause of the Union Between Consciousness and Nature

स्वस्वामिशक्त्योः स्वरूपोपलब्धिहेतुः संयोगः ॥ २.२३ ॥
svasvāmiśaktyoḥ svarūpopalabdhihetuḥ saṁyogaḥ ॥ 2.23 ॥

sva-svāmi = the owned and the owner
śaktyoḥ = of the power
svarūpa = own nature, form
upalabdhi = obtainment, apprehension
hetuḥ = cause
saṁyogaḥ = union, contact, correlation

The union of the ability of the owner (the power to see) and the ability of the owned (the power to be seen) is for the purpose of obtaining an understanding of true nature.

Everything that is seen is for the purpose of consciousness, so all objects are described as the property of consciousness, the "owned" (*sva*). Consciousness is the "owner" (*svāmi*). The uniting of consciousness with mind and objects causes cognition. This is experience (*bhoga*). Knowing the true nature of consciousness is liberation (*apavarga*). The union of consciousness and objects lasts until the ability to discriminate between the two is obtained.

तस्य हेतुरविद्या ॥ २.२४ ॥
tasya heturavidyā ॥ 2.24 ॥

tasya = of that (union)
hetuḥ = cause
avidyā = non-knowledge, ignorance

The cause of this [union] is ignorance.

This ignorance is when the consciousness identifies itself with the objects of its perception (the mind). Ignorance is when consciousness cannot differentiate between itself and the states of the mind. This is an example of self-identifying with a non-self — anything that is not the self. Ignorance is the cause of the union of the seer and the seen.

Elimination of Misery

तदभावात्संयोगाभावो हानं तद्दृशेः कैवल्यम् ॥ २.२५ ॥
tadabhāvātsaṁyogābhāvo hānaṁ taddṛśeḥ kaivalyam ॥ 2.25 ॥

tad = that
abhāvāt = from absence, elimination
saṁyoga = union
abhāvaḥ = absence
hānaṁ = cessation, abandoning
tad = that
dṛśeḥ = of the seer, consciousness
kaivalyam = alone-ness, isolation, independence, autonomy

The absence of the union [of seer and seen] results from the absence of that [ignorance]. That [cessation is] the isolation of the seer.

When ignorance is eliminated, the result is the isolation of the consciousness — consciousness is established in itself. Consciousness no longer identifies with the things of the world (including the mind). This is true independence or liberation (*kaivalya*).

Means of Elimination of Misery

विवेकख्यातिरविप्लवा हानोपायः ॥ २.२६ ॥
vivekakhyātiraviplavā hānopāyaḥ ॥ 2.26 ॥

viveka-khyātiḥ = discriminating knowledge, discerning vision
aviplavā = unchanging, unwavering, permanent
hāna = cessation
upāyaḥ = means

Unwavering discerning vision is the means of cessation.

The ability to discriminate between the consciousness and nature is *vivekahyāti*. When wrong knowledge becomes like a burnt seed, it ceases to sprout and results in pure *buddhi* that is devoid of impurities. At this stage, the yogī attains a superior quality of *vairāgya* (renunciation or aversion towards *prakṛti*) that is called *vaśīkāra-vairāgya*. This results in clear discriminating (*viveka*) knowledge, which in turn leads to liberation.

The Nature of Perfect Knowledge

तस्य सप्तधा प्रान्तभूमिः प्रज्ञा ॥ २.२७ ॥
tasya saptadhā prāntabhūmiḥ prajñā ॥ 2.27 ॥

tasya = of him (the one who attained discriminating knowledge)
saptadhā = seven kinds
prānta-bhūmiḥ = final level
prajñā = complete knowledge

[One who has obtained clear, discriminating knowledge] his knowledge is of seven kinds.

Commentators have listed seven qualities of true knowledge:

1. All that is to be abandoned (every kind of misery) has been abandoned.
2. All the causes of misery are attenuated and removed.
3. The overcoming of misery is attained through a restrained state of mind (*nirodha-samādhi*).
4. The means of overcoming, which is discriminating wisdom, have been attained.
5. Intellect (*buddhi*) has fulfilled its purpose.
6. The *guṇas* are dissolved into their components, and have no further purpose.
7. Consciousness (*puruṣa*) is free from the influence of the *guṇas* and, situated in its own true state, attains absolute independence. This is called *kaivalya*.

The consciousness (*puruṣa*) that attains all seven states is adept or skillful.

Sūtras 2.28-2.55: The Eight Limbs of Yoga

Patañjali describes the eight limbs of yoga (aśṭāṅga) to eliminate afflictions, restrain the activities of the mind, and attain liberation.

योगाङ्गानुष्ठानादशुद्धिक्षये ज्ञानदीप्तिराविवेकख्यातेः ॥ २.२८ ॥
yogāṅgānuṣṭhānādaśuddhikṣaye jñānadīptirāvivekakhyāteḥ ॥ 2.28 ॥

yoga-aṅga = limbs of yoga
anuṣṭhānād = by practicing
aśuddhi-kṣaye = when the impurities subside
jñāna-dīptiḥ = the kindling of knowledge, enlightenment
ā-viveka-khyāteḥ = extending to the point of discriminating knowledge

By practicing the limbs of yoga, knowledge is kindled extending to the point of discriminating vision while impurities subside.

Here Patañjali introduces the eight limbs of yoga. Discussion of this system continues through the second half of this book. These eight aspects, the eight "limbs" (*aśṭa-aṅga*), describe practical methods for achieving the goal of establishing consciousness in its own form.

Impurities are removed by practicing the limbs of yoga. This kindles the light of knowledge, which leads to discriminating wisdom (*vivekakhyāti*). As an axe cuts wood, the practice of the limbs of yoga removes the impurities of the mind. Just as virtue is the means of attaining happiness, so is the practice of the eight limbs of yoga the means of attaining discriminating wisdom.

यमनियमासनप्राणायामप्रत्याहारधारणाध्यानसमाधयोऽष्टावङ्गानि ॥ २.२९ ॥
yamaniyamāsanaprāṇāyāmapratyāhāradhāraṇādhyānasamādhayo'ṣṭāv aṅgāni ॥ 2.29 ॥

yama = restraint
niyama = observance
āsana = posture
prāṇāyāma = regulating, expanding vital airs
pratyāhāra = withdrawal of senses
dhāraṇā = placing attention, focusing on something
dhyāna = maintaining continued focus on something, meditating
samādhayaḥ = absorption
aṣṭau = eight
aṅgāni = limbs

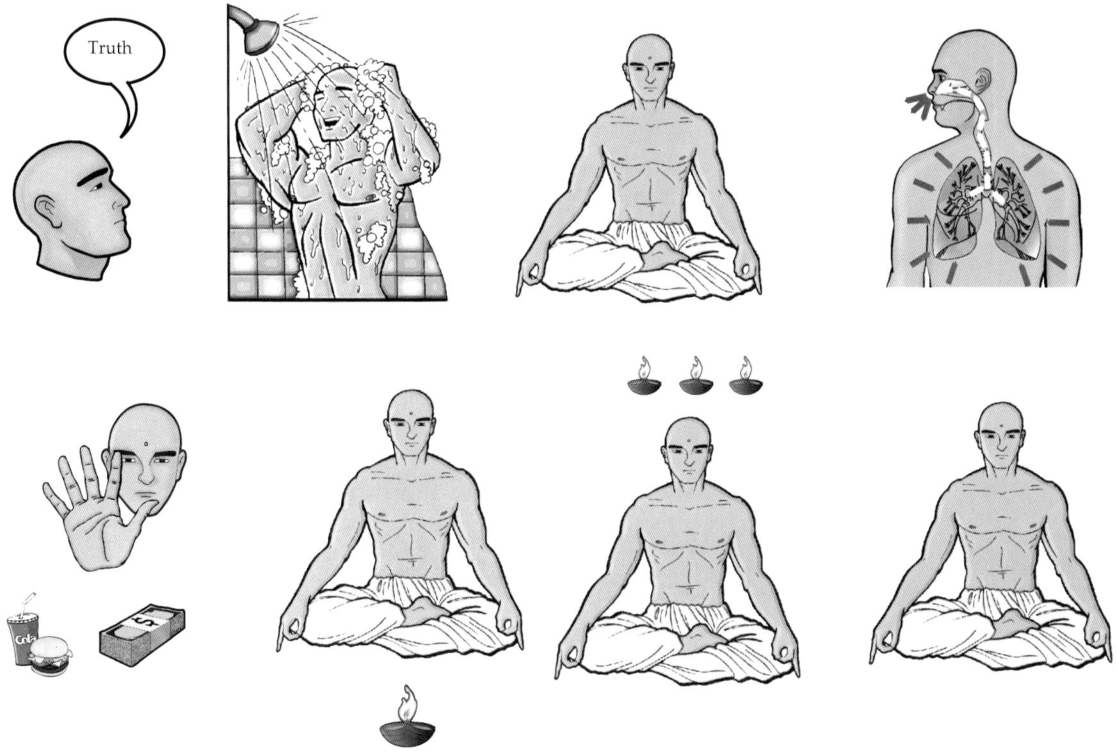

The eight limbs of yoga are,

1. yama (restraint)
2. niyama (observance)
3. āsana (posture)
4. prāṇāyāma (regulation, expansion of breath)
5. pratyāhāra (withdrawal of the senses)
6. dhāraṇā (placing attention, focusing on something)
7. dhyāna (maintaining continued focus on something, meditation)
8. samādhi (absorption)

The eight limbs are

1. restraining yourself from doing harmful things (*yama*).
2. encouraging yourself to do beneficial things (*niyama*).
3. stable and comfortable posture (*āsana*).
4. regulating the breath in order to stabilize the mind (*prāṇāyāma*).
5. detachment from the objects of the senses (*pratyāhāra*).
6. focusing the mind on something specific (*dhāraṇā*).
7. continuous contemplative focus on something specific (*dhyāna*).
8. complete absorption with the object of contemplation (*samādhi*).

Yama, the First Limb

अहिंसासत्यास्तेयब्रह्मचर्यापरिग्रहा यमाः ॥ २.३० ॥
ahiṁsāsatyāsteyabrahmacaryāparigrahā yamāḥ ॥ 2.30 ॥

ahiṁsā = non-harming, non-violence
satya = truth
asteya = non-stealing
brahmacarya = celibacy
aparigraha = non-grasping, abstinence from accumulating (objects of senses)
yamāḥ = restraints

Non-harming, truthfulness, non-stealing, celibacy, and non-accumulation of objects of senses are the restraints.

- *Ahiṁsā* is non-harming.
- *Satya* is the practice of truthfulness. Communication with others should not be deceitful, misleading, or fruitless. Rather, it should be kind and for the benefit of the listener.
- *Asteya* means not taking things from others without permission.
- *Brahmacarya* is practicing restraint in sexual matters.
- *Aparigraha* is the practice of not accumulating objects of senses, the things we don't need for surviving. This is the practice of not being greedy.

Yamas: Non-harming, truth, non-stealing, celibacy, and non-accumulation

जातिदेशकालसमयानवच्छिन्नाः सार्वभौमा महाव्रतम् ॥ २.३१ ॥
jātideśakālasamayānavacchinnāḥ sārvabhaumā mahāvratam ॥ 2.31 ॥

jāti = birth, species, class
deśa = place
kāla = time
samaya = situation, circumstance
anavacchinnāḥ = unbroken, not limited, un-separated
sārva-bhaumāḥ = in all places, universal
mahā-vratam = great vow

[Practicing these restraints] in all spheres — regardless of species, place, time, and circumstance — is the Great Vow.

Practicing the five *yamas* universally — regardless of the species, place, time, and circumstance — is called the "Great Vow." Most people can practice restraint most of the time in some of their actions. However, it is difficult to practice every restraint all the time. That is the Great Vow. There are no exceptions.

Some traditional examples of exceptions that people include,

1. A fisherman might practice non-injury towards all animals except fish.
2. A soldier might kill on the battlefield. If someone refuses to kill even in such situations, it would be an example of the universal commitment to non-harming that is part of the Great Vow.

More modern and familiar examples might include behaviors such as the following:

1. A person might not steal directly from another person, but might be comfortable cheating on taxes.
2. One might believe in truth, but tell a "white lie" to spare the feelings of another.
3. A person who has few possessions might nonetheless accumulate an unnecessary amount of clothing in the name of fashion.

Great vow is practiced regardless of species, location, time, and circumstance

Niyama, the Second Limb

शौचसंतोषतपःस्वाध्यायेश्वरप्रणिधानानि नियमाः ॥ २.३२ ॥
śaucasaṁtoṣatapaḥsvādhyāyeśvarapraṇidhānāni niyamāḥ ॥ 2.32 ॥

śauca = cleanliness, purity
saṁtoṣa = contentment (being satisfied with whatever one gets)
tapaḥ = austerities (enduring hardships in performing one's duties)
svādhyāya = self-study, study on one's own, introspection
īśvara-praṇidhānāni = devotion to God, meditating on God
niyamāḥ = observances, "niyamas"

Cleanliness, contentment, austerity, study of scriptures, and devotion to God are the observances.

- *Śauca* is both external and internal cleanliness. External cleanliness is keeping one's body and surroundings clean. Internal cleanliness means not being deceitful in mind, speech, and action.
- *Saṁtoṣa* means contentment, being satisfied with what one has.
- *Tapaḥ* is asceticism, austerity of life. This is avoidance of short-term self-gratification. It also means tolerating dualities like hunger and thirst, heat and cold, in performing one's duties.
- *Svādhyāya* is the study of scriptures, self-analysis, and meditating on *Oṁ*.
- *Īśvarapraṇidhāna* is devotion to God and surrendering all the fruits of one's actions to God.

वितर्कबाधने प्रतिपक्षभावनम् ॥ २.३३ ॥
vitarkabādhane pratipakṣabhāvanam ॥ 2.33 ॥

vi-tarka = transgressing, unwholesome thoughts
bādhane = when bothered, impeded, (also, to repel)
pratipakṣa = opposing
bhāvanam = thinking

When one is bothered by transgressing thoughts, oppositional thinking should be practiced.

When a practitioner of yoga gets transgressing thoughts that distract from the practice of *yamas* and *niyamas* — violence, hatred, envy, and so on — he or she should practice "oppositional thinking" (*pratipakṣabhāvanam*). This action is described in the following sūtra.

Niyamas: Cleanliness, contentment, austerity, study of scriptures, and devotion to God

वितर्का हिंसादयः कृतकारितानुमोदिता लोभक्रोधमोहपूर्वका मृदुमध्याधिमात्रा दुःखाज्ञानानन्तफला इति प्रतिपक्षभावनम् ॥ २.३४ ॥
vitarkā hiṁsādayaḥ kṛtakāritānumoditā lobhakrodhamohapūrvakā mṛdumadhyādhimātrā duḥkhājñānānantaphalā iti pratipakṣabhāvanam ॥ 2.34 ॥

vi-tarkā = transgressing, unwholesome thoughts
hiṁsa = harming
ādayaḥ = and the rest (ādi)
kṛta = done (by oneself)
kārita = caused to be done (by others)
anumoditā = approving, supporting (when done by others)
lobha-krodha-moha-pūrvakā = filled with greed, anger, and delusion
mṛdu-madhya-adhimātrā = of mild, medium, and high intensity
duḥkha-ajñāna-ananta-phalā = having unending fruits of misery and ignorance
iti = like this
pratipakṣa = contrary, opposite, opposing side
bhāvanam = thinking, cultivating, bringing about

Oppositional thinking is cultivating [the attitude] that transgressing thoughts, such as harming and the rest — done, caused to be done, or approved; arising from greed, anger, or delusion; minor, moderate, or excessive — result in unending fruits of misery and ignorance.

Oppositional thinking, *pratipakṣabhāvanam*, is explained in this sūtra. We need to keep in mind that negative thinking leads to misery for us. Cultivating this attitude helps us stop misleading thoughts or actions, because we think of the negative consequences. One way to stop negative thoughts is to think of their opposites. For example, if you are angry and thinking about hurting someone, stop for a moment and think about how you can instead help them.

Transgressing thoughts are the opposites of non-harming, truthfulness, non-stealing, celibacy, and non-grasping. Transgressing thoughts and actions multiply quickly. They can be performed by oneself, caused to be done by others, or supported by you when someone else does them. They can be caused by greed, anger, or delusion stemming from attachment. Moreover, they can be mild, moderate, or extreme in intensity. The combinations of those characteristics results in twenty-seven types of thoughts (3 x 3 x 3 = 27).

Each level of intensity can be further divided into three levels — slightly mild, somewhat mild, and very mild. In this way, there are actually eighty-one types of transgressing thoughts (27 x 3 = 81). Also, each of these types can be done in mind, speech, and action leading to innumerable negative thoughts, which can result in countless detrimental impressions of karma, leading to infinite fruits of misery and ignorance. This way of thinking about transgressing thoughts is called *pratipakṣabhāvanam* or oppositional thinking.

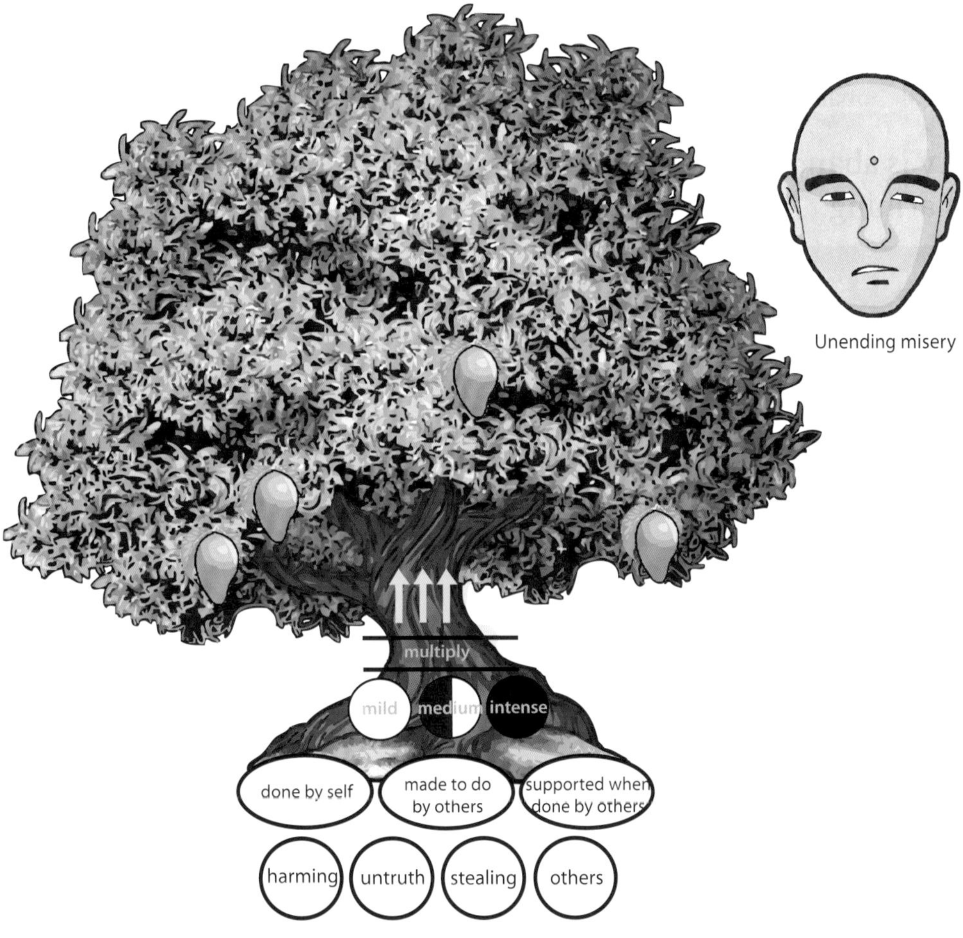

Various combinations of actions resulting in unending misery

Benefits of Yamas

अहिंसाप्रतिष्ठायां तत्सन्निधौ वैरत्यागः ॥ २.३५ ॥
ahiṁsāpratiṣṭhāyāṁ tatsannidhau vairatyāgaḥ ॥ 2.35 ॥

ahiṁsā = non-harming
pratiṣṭhyāyāṁ = when established
tat-sannidhau = in that presence
vaira = enmity
tyāgaḥ = abandonment

Enmity is abandoned in the presence of a well-established practice of non-harming.

Non-harming is praised as the core of all virtues and conduct (*dharma*). It should be practiced in mind, speech, and action. Vyāsa mentions that, when the practice of non-harming is established, all living beings will lose their enmity in the presence of such a yogī. Commentators add that even predatory animals will not attack their prey in the presence of such a person.

सत्यप्रतिष्ठायां क्रियाफलाश्रयत्वम् ॥ २.३६ ॥
satyapratiṣṭhāyāṁ kriyāphalāśrayatvam ॥ 2.36 ॥

satya = truthfulness
pratiṣṭhāyāṁ = when established
kriyā-phala = fruit of action
āśrayatvam = the nature of being a support

When truthfulness is established, [the yogī] becomes the basis for the fruitfulness of actions.

When the practice of speaking truth becomes well-established, a yogī can see the truth even when things are yet to manifest. Such a yogī's words become infallible. When he or she blesses someone to be virtuous, that person will become virtuous over time. "Basis for fruitfulness" means support or inspiration that a yogī becomes for other's actions.

अस्तेयप्रतिष्ठायां सर्वरत्नोपस्थानम् ॥ २.३७ ॥
asteyapratiṣṭhāyāṁ sarvaratnopasthānam ॥ 2.37 ॥

asteya = non-stealing
pratiṣṭhāyāṁ = when it is established
sarva = all
ratna = the best of a kind, jewel
upasthānam = being near

When non-stealing is established, the best of any kind of object (ratna) will become available.

To a yogī who has cultivated the practice of non-stealing, the best of all kinds of objects present themselves. The ordinary meaning of the word *ratna* is jewel; it can also mean wealth. Just as we say in English "that's a gem of a computer," meaning that it is a very good computer, the word *ratna* often refers simply to something excellent.

ब्रह्मचर्यप्रतिष्ठायां वीर्यलाभः ॥ २.३८ ॥
brahmacaryapratiṣṭhāyāṁ vīryalābhaḥ ॥ 2.38 ॥

brahmacarya = celibacy
pratiṣṭhāyāṁ = when it is established
vīrya = power, valor, strength
lābhaḥ = obtained

When celibacy is established, one gains power.

Celibacy (*brahmacarya*) results in strength and perseverance, both in mind and body. A yogī attains the different siddhis — the powers of yoga — with celibacy. Such a yogī becomes capable of imparting knowledge to others.

अपरिग्रहस्थैर्ये जन्मकथन्तासम्बोधः ॥ २.३९ ॥
aparigrahasthairye janmakathantāsambodhaḥ ॥ 2.39 ॥

aparigraha = non-grasping, non-accumulation (of objects)
sthairye = when stable
janma = birth
kathantā = "how-ness," knowledge of how things happen
sambodhaḥ = knowledge

When non-grasping is established, the knowledge of births past, present, and future arises.

Non-grasping (*aparigraha*) is not clinging to or accumulating material possessions that are not essential to survival. When such a practice is perfected, a yogī gains knowledge of the formation of one's own body in past, present, and future lifetimes. Questions about what leads to the present lifetime, and past, and future births, are answered.

Benefits of Niyama

शौचात्स्वाङ्गजुगुप्सा परैरसंसर्गः ॥ २.४० ॥
śaucātsvāṅgajugupsā parairasaṁsargaḥ ॥ 2.40 ॥

śaucāt = from cleanliness, purity
sva-aṅga = one's own limbs (body)
jugupsā = dislike, disgust, aversion
paraiḥ = with others
a-saṁsargaḥ = non-association, not coming into contact

From practicing cleanliness, one gains dislike for one's own body and refrains from coming into contact with others.

In our society, people are obsessed with their bodies. But, even the best gym-toned body will eventually die and turn into dust, and our bodies contain defects ranging from toothaches to cancer. A yogī practicing awareness of cleanliness loses attachment to his own body by seeing its imperfections. He develops a dislike for his own body, and also refrains from coming into contact with the bodies of others, as he sees that they are impure as well. One has to be mindful that these aphorisms were writtern in a time and culture where the phrase "dislike for one's own body" might not have the same negative connotation that it has acquired today.

सत्त्वशुद्धिसौमनस्यैकाग्र्येन्द्रियजयात्मदर्शनयोग्यत्वानि च ॥ २.४१ ॥
sattvaśuddhisaumanasyaikāgryendriyajayātmadarśanayogyatvāni ca ॥ 2.41 ॥

sattva-śuddhi = clarity of mind
saumanasya = pleasantness, peacefulness
eka-agrya = one-pointedness (focus)
indriya-jaya = control over sense
ātma-darśana = self- knowledge, self-awareness
yogyatvāni = capability, worthiness
ca = and, also

[From cleanliness], one also achieves clarity of mind, pleasantness, one-pointed concentration, control over the senses, and the capability to attain knowledge of the self.

Practicing the mental aspect of cleanliness (*śauca*), one gains clarity of mind, which leads to mental stillness, which leads to one-pointedness, which leads to control over the senses. When the senses are controlled, intellect develops the ability to reflect the true form of consciousness.

सन्तोषादनुत्तमसुखलाभः ॥ २.४२ ॥
santoṣādanuttamasukhalābhaḥ ॥ 2.42 ॥

santoṣāt = from contentment
anuttama = unexcelled
sukha = happiness
lābhaḥ = gain

From contentment, one attains unexcelled happiness.

Many commentators say that the happiness gained from the cessation of desire is many times greater than the pleasure received from enjoying sensory objects. This is because there is some level of anxiety (fear of losing that which is attained) associated with all experiences of pleasure.

कायेन्द्रियसिद्धिरशुद्धिक्षयात्तपसः ॥ २.४३ ॥
kāyendriyasiddhiraśuddhikṣayāttapasaḥ ॥ 2.43 ॥

kāya = body
indriya = senses
siddhir = perfection
aśuddhi = impurities
kṣayāt = from wearing away, dwindling, attenuated
tapasaḥ = from austerity, purificatory actions like enduring dualities, discipline

From the practice of austerities, impurities are attenuated. This results in the perfection of the body and the senses.

Asceticism (*tapas*) means tolerating extremes — hunger and thirst, heat and cold, praise and insult — as well as the absence of expression and speech while practicing meditation. Practice of tapas eliminates the impurities of the mind and helps in concentration. This concentration leads to powers. "Perfection of the body and senses" is the attainment of supernatural powers or siddhis related to the body, including clairvoyance, clairaudience, the ability to miniaturize or magnify one's body, and so on.

स्वाध्यायादिष्टदेवतासम्प्रयोगः ॥ २.४४ ॥
svādhyāyādiṣṭadevatāsamprayogaḥ ॥ 2.44 ॥

svādhyāyād = from study of scriptures , meditating upon them, and introspection
iṣṭa = desired
devatā = deity, luminous personalities, yogīs, ṛṣis
samprayogaḥ = contact (by the way of revelation)

From practicing the study of scriptures and introspection one receives the revelation of the desired luminous personalities (iṣṭadevatā).

Svādhyāya is the study of scriptures and meditation upon them. From this practice, one is able to perceive luminous personalities like rishis (sages) and *siddhayogīs* (yogīs who have attained the supernatural powers) as if they are there in person. The word *deva* — normally translated as God — is from the Sanskrit word "*div*," which means to shine. A *deva* is literally a shining being and refers to any luminous personality.

समाधिसिद्धिरीश्वरप्रणिधानात् ॥ २.४५ ॥
samādhisiddhirīśvarapraṇidhānāt ॥ 2.45 ॥

samādhi = perfected concentration, absorption
siddhiḥ = perfection, attainment
īśvara-praṇidhānāt = from devotion to God

From devotion to God, one attains perfected concentration.

Devotion to God consists of meditating on God in any form you prefer (*iṣṭa*) and surrendering all fruits of actions to Him (Her, It). This aids in achieving *samādhi*. Through *samādhi*, true knowledge of anything desired is revealed, even if the object belongs to another place and time.

Āsana, the Third Limb

स्थिरसुखमासनम् ॥ २.४६ ॥
sthirasukhamāsanam ॥ 2.46 ॥

sthira = stable
sukham = comfortable
āsanam = posture (āsana)

Posture is a stable and comfortable position.

A comfortable and stable posture (*āsana*) is essential to meditation. A sitting posture with straight back, head and neck aligned, is recommended in most yogic texts. As far as the *Yoga Sūtras* is concerned, a comfortable sitting posture that aids in meditation is the sole purpose of *āsana*. The use of postures has been expanded by Haṭha-yoga to help keep the body fit and healthy in addition to aiding in meditation.

The following are some of the yogic *āsanas* listed in the original commentary by Vyāsa.

1. *Padmāsana*: This is a well-known posture. Placing the right foot on the left thigh, and the left foot on the right thigh, one has to sit keeping the spine perfectly straight.
2. *Vīrāsana*: This is half of *Padmāsana*. One foot has to be kept on the opposite thigh, and the other foot below the opposite thigh.
3. *Bhadrāsana*: Placing the soles of feet on the ground before the perineum, and close to each other, the soles have to be covered by the two palms.
4. *Svastikāsana*: In this posture, one has to sit up straight with the soles of feet being stuck between the opposite thigh and knee.
5. *Daṇḍāsana*: The two legs have to be stretched out while being seated, closely fixing together the two heels and toes.
6. *Sopāśrayāsana*: In this posture, one squats tying the back and the two legs with a piece of cloth called "*Yoga-paṭṭaka*."
7. *Paryaṅkāsana*: In this, one has to lie down stretching the thighs and hands; it is also called *Śavāsana*, the posture of the dead.
8. *Krauñcaniṣadanāsana*: This has to be done by observing the resting posture of a heron.
9. *Hastiniṣadanāsana*: This has to be done by observing the resting posture of an elephant.
10. *Uṣṭraniṣadanāsana*: This has to be done by observing the resting posture of a camel.
11. *Samasaṁsthānāsana*: In this, the two feet (heels and toes) are pressed against each other while squatting.

Padmāsana

Vīrāsana

Bhadrāsana

Svastikāsana

Daṇḍāsana

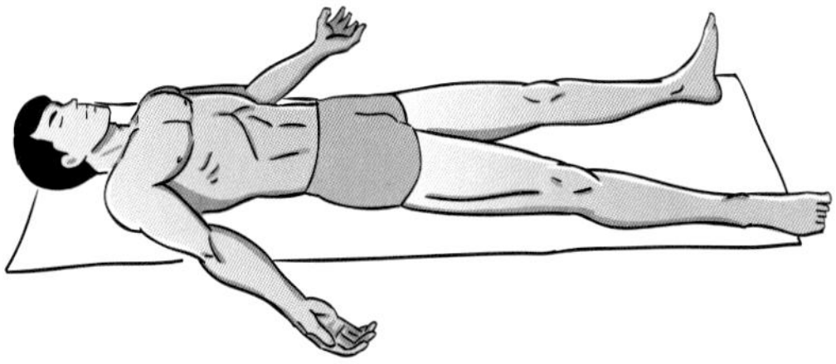

Paryaṅkāsana

The *Haṭhapradīpika*, which dates to the period between 1350-1550 CE, deals in detail with various postures and other physical practices that are helpful to yogic development. Only six postures have been illustrated. The postures numbered 6, 8, 9, 10, and 11 are subject to interpretation.

प्रयत्नशैथिल्यानन्तसमापत्तिभ्याम् ॥ २.४७ ॥
prayatnaśaithilyānantasamāpattibhyām ॥ 2.47 ॥

prayatna = effort
śaithilya = cessation, relaxation
ananta = infinite
samāpattibhyām = from perfected concentration, complete absorption

[Perfection in āsana] is obtained from relaxation of effort and meditation on the infinite.

Posture should not be stiff; all limbs should be relaxed. This brings about steadiness. Contemplation of the infinite can also result in steadiness. Some interpret "infinite" as the infinite God, while others think it refers to the cosmic serpent, *Ananta*, a figure in the *Puraṇas*.

Result of Āsana

ततो द्वन्द्वानभिघातः ॥ २.४८ ॥
tato dvandvānabhighātaḥ ॥ 2.48 ॥

tataḥ = from that (the perfection of āsana)
dvandvān = "two-two's," pairs of opposites
anabhighātaḥ = not attacked, un-assailed

From that [stable posture], one is not assailed by opposing pairs of dualities.

With the perfection of posture, one overcomes pairs of opposites, like heat and cold, or praise and insult.

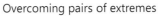

Overcoming pairs of extremes

Prāṇāyāma, the Fourth Limb

तस्मिन्सति श्वासप्रश्वासयोर्गतिविच्छेदः प्राणायामः ॥ २.४९ ॥
tasminsati śvāsapraśvāsayorgativicchedaḥ prāṇāyāmaḥ ॥ 2.49 ॥

tasmin = in that (posture)
sati = being present
śvāsa = inhalation
praśvāsa-yor = of exhalation
gati = movement (speed of the movement)
vicchedaḥ = interruption, cutting
prāṇa-āyāmaḥ = expanding vital airs, or restraining vital airs

In that [stable posture], interrupting the movement of inhalation and exhalation is called praṇāyāma, or breath control.

The breathing practices used in yoga are called *prāṇāyāma*. This is the regulation of the movement of air drawn in and expelled from the lungs.

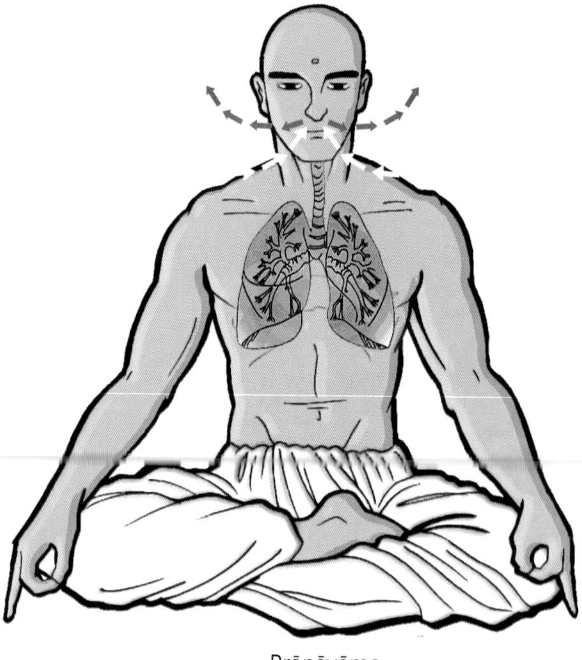

Prāṇāyāma

बाह्याभ्यन्तरस्तम्भवृत्तिर्देशकालसंख्याभिः परिदृष्टो दीर्घसूक्ष्मः ॥ २.५० ॥
bāhyābhyantarastambhavṛttirdeśakālasaṁkhyābhiḥ paridṛṣṭo dīrghasūkṣmaḥ ॥ 2.50 ॥

bāhya = external
ābhyantara = internal
stambha-vṛttir = arrested movement
deśa = place
kāla = time
saṁkhyābhiḥ = by number
paridṛṣṭaḥ = known
dīrgha = long
sūkṣmaḥ = subtle

Prāṇāyāma has external, internal, and arrested activities of breath. When observed through place, time, and number, these are long and subtle.

There are three kinds of *prāṇāyāma* described in this sūtra:

1. External operation: Stopping the breath after exhaling.
2. Internal operation: Stopping the breath after inhaling.
3. Arrested operation: Stopping the breath at any point of time.

Further, there are three aspects that distinguish the intensities of *prāṇāyāma* into the categories of mild, medium, and intense:

a. Place: In external operation, this is the space in front of the nose. Intensity is determined by the distance at which the exhaling air can move a cotton ball place in front. In internal operation, it is a space within the body extending from the sole of the foot to the tip of the head. When inhaling and stopping breath inside, one experiences the feeling of "crawling ants." The intensity is measured by how far this feeling is felt through the body. In arrested operation, the aspect of place is absent.

b. Time: This is the measure of how long the breath is stopped, either outside or inside. The longer it can be stopped, the greater the intensity of the *prāṇāyāma*.

c. Number: This is the number of repetitions of breath for each type of *prāṇāyāma* (external, internal or arrested). The higher the number, the greater the intensity.

With prolonged practice of *prāṇāyāma*, the time the breath can be stopped becomes longer, and the movement of the breath is slowed significantly, becoming subtle and imperceptible.

बाह्याभ्यन्तरविषयाक्षेपी चतुर्थः ॥ २.५१ ॥
bāhyābhyantaraviṣayākṣepī caturthaḥ ॥ 2.51 ॥

bāhya = external
ābhyantara = internal
viṣaya = realm (object)
ā-kṣepī = one that transcends
caturthaḥ = the fourth

The fourth kind of prāṇāyāma transcends external and internal operations.

The natural state attained after mastery of the previously-mentioned three *praṇāyāmās* is the fourth kind. The difference between the third kind (arrested operation, *stambhavṛtti*) and the fourth (*bāhyābhyantara-viṣayākṣepī*) is that in the third kind the breath is consciously stopped, restrained in that condition, and made long and subtle based on place, time, and number; however, the fourth kind is not a forceful practice, but one that naturally and spontaneously results from mastery of the first three *prāṇāyāma* practices and focusing the mind on a single object.

Benefits of Prāṇāyāma

ततः क्षियते प्रकाशावरणम् ॥ २.५२ ॥
tataḥ kṣīyate prakāśāvaraṇam ॥ 2.52 ॥

tataḥ = from that (practice of praṇāyāmā)
kṣīyate = becomes thin, attenuated
prakāśa = light, illumination
āvaraṇam = covering, veil

From that practice [praṇayama], the veil over illumination is thinned.

The "illumination" here refers to the light of discriminating knowledge (*viveka-jñāna*). This illuminating knowledge is obscured by a thick veil of karma that covers and muddles the intellect. This veil is responsible for the incorrect knowledge that propels us towards impure deeds. Our preconceptions developed from past actions and experiences prevent us from seeing things objectively. The practice of *prāṇāyāma* enables true knowledge to shine.

धारणासु च योग्यता मनसः ॥ २.५३ ॥
dhāraṇāsu ca yogyatā manasaḥ ॥ 2.53 ॥

dhāraṇāsu = in the matters of focusing the mind, in practicing dhāraṇā-s
ca = and, also
yogyatā = capability, fitness, worthiness
manasaḥ = of the mind

And also [from praṇāyāma] comes the ability to focus the mind, dhāraṇā.

Regulating the breath steadies the mind and aids in focusing on one object. Focusing the mind on one thing is called *dhāraṇā* which is the sixth limb of yoga.

Dhāraṇā

Pratyāhāra, the Fifth Limb

स्वविषयासम्प्रयोगे चित्तस्य स्वरूपानुकार इवेन्द्रियाणां प्रत्याहारः ॥ २.५४ ॥
svaviṣayāsamprayoge cittasya svarūpānukāra ivendriyāṇāṁ pratyāhāraḥ ॥ 2.54 ॥

sva = own
viṣaya = object
a-sam-prayoge = in non-conjunction, disconnection
cittasya = of the mind
sva-rūpa = own form, own nature
anu-kāraḥ = following, imitating
iva = like
indriyāṇāṁ = of the sense instruments (senses)
pratyāhāraḥ = withdrawal, turning back

Withdrawal of the senses [pratyāhāra] is, as it were, an imitation by the senses of the mind in disconnecting from objects.

When the mind does not contemplate the objects of the senses, the sense organs imitate the mind by ceasing to perceive those objects. Just as bees follow the queen bee when she leads them to a new colony (the phenomenon called "swarming") and settle wherever she does, when the mind is stilled, the senses cease their activity also. This is called *pratyāhāra*, or withdrawal of the senses. *Prati* means "backward" — the senses point inward instead of outward.

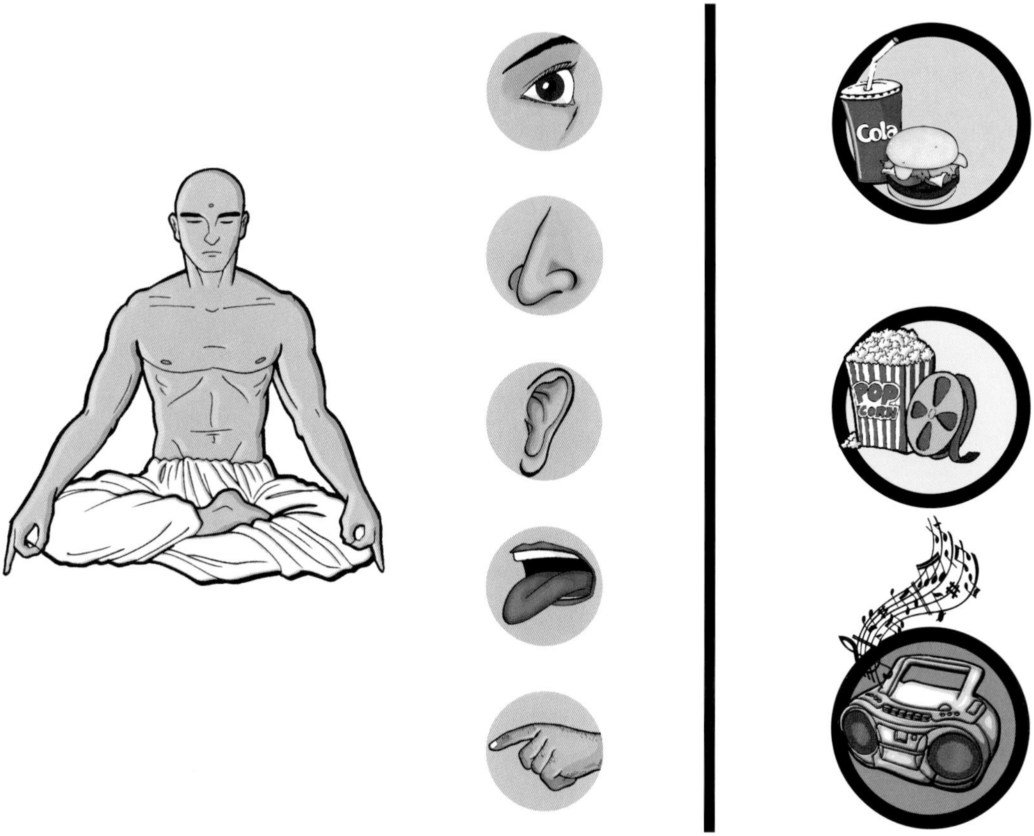

Pratyāhāra

Supreme Control of the Senses

ततः परमा वश्यतेन्द्रियाणाम् ॥ २.५५ ॥
tataḥ paramā vaśyatendriyāṇām ॥ 2.55 ॥

tataḥ = then, from that (withdrawal of senses)
paramā = highest, unexcellable, supreme
vaśyatā = control, mastery
indriyāṇām = of the sense instruments (senses)

From this comes supreme mastery over the senses.

When the mind attains one-pointed concentration, the senses naturally lose attachment to the objects of their perception. This is the highest control achieved through the practices of *yama*, *niyama*, *āsana*, *praṇāyāma*, and *pratyāhāra*, as described earlier.

There is a discussion of the mind and senses in *Kaṭhopaniṣad* that describes consciousness (the soul) as the passenger in a chariot, *buddhi* as the charioteer, *manas* as the reins, and the senses as the horses. Just as the charioteer must be skilled in order to reach the destination efficiently, a well-controlled mind is necessary to attain self-knowledge, the goal of yoga.

आत्मानं रथिनं विद्धि शरीरं रथमेव च।
बुद्धिं तु सारथिं विद्धि मनः प्रग्रहमेव च॥
इन्द्रियाणि हयानाहुर्विषयांस्तेषु गोचरान्।
आत्मेन्द्रियमनोयुक्तं भोक्तेत्याहुर्मनीषिणः॥

ātmānaṁ rathinaṁ viddhi śarīraṁ rathameva ca ।
buddhiṁ tu sārathiṁ viddhi manaḥ pragrahameva ca ॥ *Kaṭhopaniṣad 1.3.3* ॥
indriyāṇi hayānāhurviṣayāṁsteṣu gocarān ।
ātmendriyamanoyuktaṁ bhoktetyāhurmanīṣiṇaḥ ॥ *Kaṭhopaniṣad 1.3.4* ॥

"Know that the soul is the owner (passenger) of the chariot and that chariot is the body. Know that the charioteer (driver) is the intellect, and *manas* forms the reins. Senses are the horses and the sense objects are what is seen by the horses. Thus endowed with senses and manas, the soul is said to be the enjoyer (of the nature)."

Image of buddhi as a charioteer in Kaṭhopaniṣad

Vibhūtipādaḥ (Powers)

We now begin the third chapter of the *Yoga Sūtras*. The word *vibhūti* is generally taken to mean the extraordinary powers that are said to come to a yogī as a result of practice. These powers do not come without effort, however — the beginning of this chapter describes the practices that lead to one-pointed concentration. That ability to concentrate is key to the more advanced states of meditation. This chapter starts with *dhāraṇā* (concentration), the sixth of the eight limbs of yoga.

Sūtras 3.1-3.8: The Eight Limbs, Continued

Dhāraṇā, the Sixth Limb

देशबन्धश्चित्तस्य धारणा ॥ ३.१ ॥
deśabandhaścittasya dhāraṇā ॥ 3.1 ॥

deśa = point, location, place
bandhaḥ = fixing, binding
cittasya = of the mind
dhāraṇā = concentration, focusing, placing

Fixing the mind on a point is called concentration, dhāraṇā.

Choosing something specific and fixing the mind on it is called *dhāraṇā*. The mind can be fixed on something physical — such as a location or object — or a concept or idea. Patañjali suggests several specific themes for meditation. Common traditional points of focus include the following:

1. the navel or center of the body
2. the lotus of the heart
3. the center of the forehead (between the eyebrows)
4. the tip of the nose
5. the tip of the tongue
6. external objects — celestial objects like the sun, moon, or stars, or any mundane object, such as a statue.

Dhāraṇā

Dhyāna, the Seventh Limb:

तत्र प्रत्ययैकतानता ध्यानम् ॥ ३.२ ॥
tatra pratyayaikatānatā dhyānam ॥ 3.2 ॥

tatra = there (in that location where dhāraṇā is fixed)
pratyaya = conception, thought
eka-tānatā = extension of oneness, continuity in oneness
dhyānam = contemplation, meditation

Maintaining the continuity of a single thought is called contemplation, dhyāna.

In *dhyāna*, meditation is focused on a single object without any intervening thoughts. The same thought is maintained throughout previous, current, and successive moments. The literature gives an analogy to dripping oil — at the beginning oil drops come one after another, but when the flow of oil becomes steady the drops merge and form a continuous stream. This is the difference between concentration (*dhāraṇā*) and contemplation (*dhyāna*). At the beginning, one may find it hard to keep the mind focused on one thing. But, as we improve our ability to concentrate, we are increasingly able to keep attention on the same thing without interruption. This more continuous form of attention is called contemplation (*dhyāna*).

Dhyāna

Samādhi, the Eighth Limb

तदेवार्थमात्रनिर्भासं स्वरूपशून्यमिव समाधिः ॥ ३.३ ॥
tadevārthamātranirbhāsaṁ svarūpaśūnyamiva samādhiḥ ॥ 3.3 ॥

tad = that
eva = only, indeed
artha-mātra = consisting of only the object, object-only
nirbhāsaṁ = shining
sva-rūpa = own form, own nature
śūnyam = devoid of, empty
iva = like, as it were
samādhiḥ = perfected concentration, absorption

Absorption [samādhi] is that [contemplation] in which only the object shines forth as if it [the meditator] has lost its own form.

When *dhyāna* becomes deeper, the meditator loses awareness the word and the meaning associated with the object. Only the object of meditation remains in the mind. When meditation deepens further self-awareness disappears, this state is called absorption (*samādhi*).

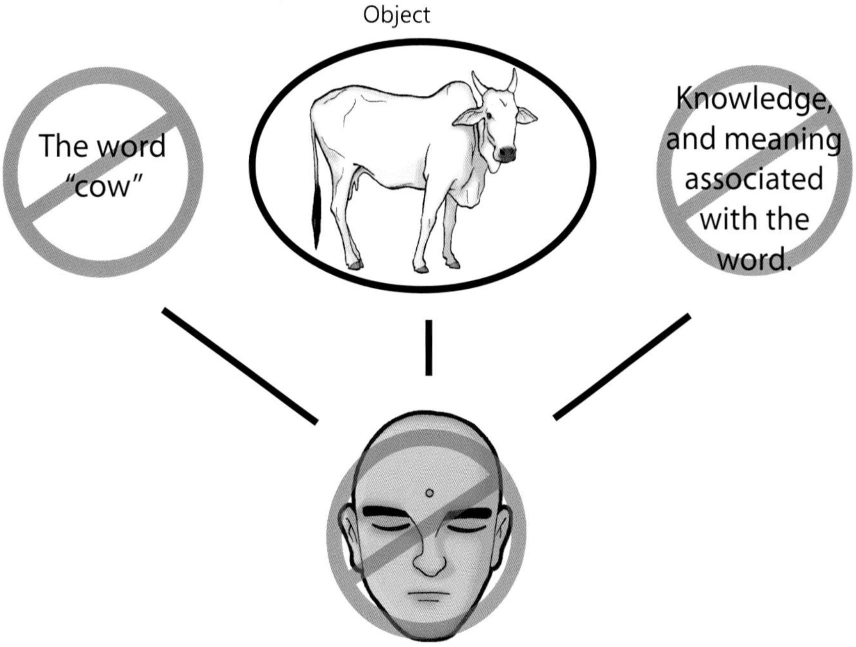

Object shining forth - devoid of the word and the knowledge.
Awareness of the self is also absent.

Saṁyama

त्रयमेकत्र संयमः ॥ ३.४ ॥
trayamekatra saṁyamaḥ ॥ 3.4 ॥

trayam = the three (dhāraṇā, dhyāna, and samādhi)
ekatra = at one place, together
saṁ-yamaḥ = all-round control, restraint, discipline, constraint

The three together are called all-round control [saṁyama].

Dhāraṇā, *dhyāna*, and *samādhi* together are called all-round control (*saṁyama*). *Saṁyama* is an important technical term. It is a state in which the mind is brought under complete control. On a practical basis it refers to the ability of a yogī to rapidly bring together all three stages of meditation — from initial fixing of attention through *samādhi* — as a unified act.

तज्जयात्प्रज्ञालोकः ॥ ३.५ ॥
tajjayātprajñālokaḥ ॥ 3.5 ॥

tat = that
jayāt = from mastering
prajñā = knowledge, wisdom
ā-lokaḥ = vision, light, insight

From mastering that [saṁyama] comes the light of knowledge.

When all-round control (*saṁyama*) is mastered, one attains the light of knowledge (*prajñāloka*). A yogī attains insight into whatever he or she wishes to know about.

तस्य भूमिषु विनियोगः ॥ ३.६ ॥
tasya bhūmiṣu viniyogaḥ ॥ 3.6 ॥

tasya = of that (saṁyama)
bhūmiṣu = in stages
viniyogaḥ = application, practice

It [saṁyama] should be applied in stages.

Saṁyama must be practiced on different objects or locations, and this should be done in the proper sequence. For example, concentration on gross objects should be achieved before attempting concentration on the subtle elements. The exception is that concentration on God can be done at any time.

Internal and External Limbs

त्रयमन्तरङ्गं पूर्वेभ्यः ॥ ३.७ ॥
trayamantaraṅgaṁ pūrvebhyaḥ ॥ 3.7 ॥

trayam = the three (dhāraṇā, dhyāna, samādhi)
antar-aṅgaṁ = internal limbs
pūrvebhyaḥ = from the previous (five limbs)

These three are internal limbs [in relation to] the previous.

The three limbs *dhāraṇā*, *dhyāna*, and *samādhi* are called the *internal* limbs (*antar-aṅgam*), because they focus on internal mental processes. The previous five limbs (*yama*, *niyama*, *āsana*, *prāṇayāma*, and *pratyāhāra*) regulate external actions, and so are called the "external" limbs (*bahir-aṅgam*).

तदपि बहिरङ्गं निर्बीजस्य ॥ ३.८ ॥
tadapi bahiraṅgaṁ nirbījasya ॥ 3.8 ॥

tat = that (inner limbs)
api = also, even, yet
bahir-aṅgaṁ = external limb
nir-bījasya = of the seedless one-pointed meditation (nirbīja samādhi)

Yet, those [the three] are external [in relation] to the seed-less [state].

Even the three inner limbs are considered *external* to the "seedless" type of absorption (*nirbījasamādhi*). In seedless absorption there is no object of meditation. The consciousness abides in itself. Seedless *samādhi* was described in sūtra 1.51. The opposite of seedless *samādhi* is *samādhi* with seed (*sabījasamādhi*) which has an object of meditation.

Sūtras 3.9-3.15: Transformations of the Mind and Objects

This method of meditation (*dhāraṇā*, *dhyāna*, and *samādhi*) results in the following transformations of the mind.

Restrained Transformation (Nirodha)

व्युत्थाननिरोधसंस्कारयोरभिभवप्रादुर्भावौ निरोधक्षणचित्तान्वयो निरोधपरिणामः ॥ ३.९ ॥
vyutthānanirodhasaṁskārayorabhibhavaprādurbhāvau nirodhakṣaṇacittānvayo nirodhapariṇāmaḥ ॥ 3.9 ॥

vyutthāna = rising up, out-going activity
nirodha = arresting, restraining
saṁskārayoḥ = of the impressions
abhibhava = defeating, overpowering
prādur-bhāvau = in manifesting, arising, emerging
nirodha = arrested, restrained
kṣaṇa = moment
citta = mind
anvayaḥ = connected
nirodha-pariṇāmaḥ = is called the "restrained-transformation" (pariṇāmaḥ)

When distracting impressions are overpowered and restrained impressions manifest, [the result] in that moment of the arrested state is called "restrained-transformation."

The word *pariṇāma* simply means "transformation." For example, if we churn milk and get butter, the milk has undergone a transformation. This sūtra uses the term *nirodha-pariṇāma* to refer to a particular change in mental state in which the mind becomes well-controlled. Because our thoughts change constantly, these moments (*kṣaṇa*) of control may be very brief. But, as our practice of meditation improves, our ability to hold on to these moments of control improves as well.

The word *vyutthāna* refers to the feelings and thoughts that arise in us. These distractions can be controlled by restraining impressions, which are generated by the practice of *dhāraṇā*, *dhyāna*, and *samādhi*. When the distracting impressions are overpowered by the restraining impressions, the resulting state of mind is called the "restrained transformation" (*nirodha-pariṇāma*). Restrained impressions cannot sprout into thoughts that distract us.

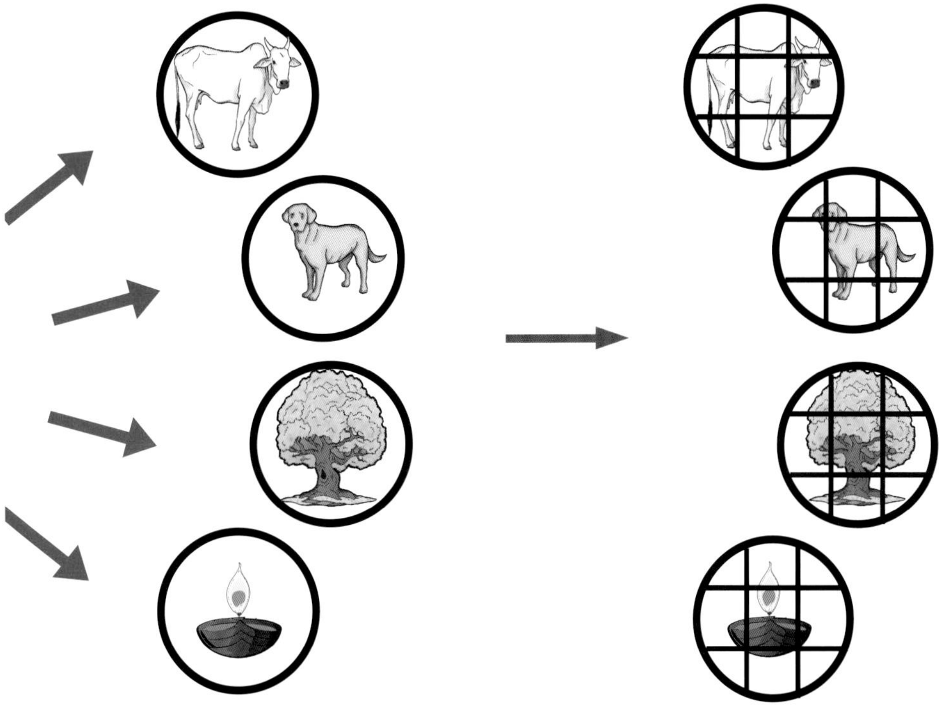

Active impressions becoming restrained impressions

तस्य प्रशान्तवाहिता संस्कारात् ॥ ३.१० ॥
tasya praśāntavāhitā saṁskārāt ॥ 3.10 ॥

tasya = of that (arrested state of mind "nirodhapariṇāma")
praśānta = calm, peaceful
vāhitā = flowing, current
saṁskārāt = due to impressions

[The arrested mind's] calm flow is due to the [restrained] impressions.

That arrested state of the mind becomes stable and continuous because of the impressions generated from it. The more you do anything, the better you get at it. Learning to control the mind is like learning to dance, or to swim. At first, you have to think about everything you do, and it doesn't feel fluid. But, with practice, things become automatic and feel natural. In physical activity, this is due to "muscle memory" — impressions generated by previous practice. The same thing happens when developing mental habits.

Absorption Transformation (Samādhi)

सर्वार्थतैकाग्रतयोः क्षयोदयौ चित्तस्य समाधिपरिणामः ॥ ३.११ ॥
sarvārthataikāgratayoḥ kṣayodayau cittasya samādhipariṇāmaḥ
॥ 3.11 ॥

sarva-arthatā = "many-object-ness," distractedness
eka-agratayoḥ = "one-pointed-ness," having a single focus
kṣaya = decay, dwindling
udayau = rising, emerging
cittasya = of the mind
samādhi-pariṇāmaḥ = (is called) "absorption-transformation"

The "absorption-transformation" of the mind is the decay of distractedness and the emergence of one-pointedness.

When concentration on many objects subsides and concentration on only one object emerges, that state is called "absorption transformation."

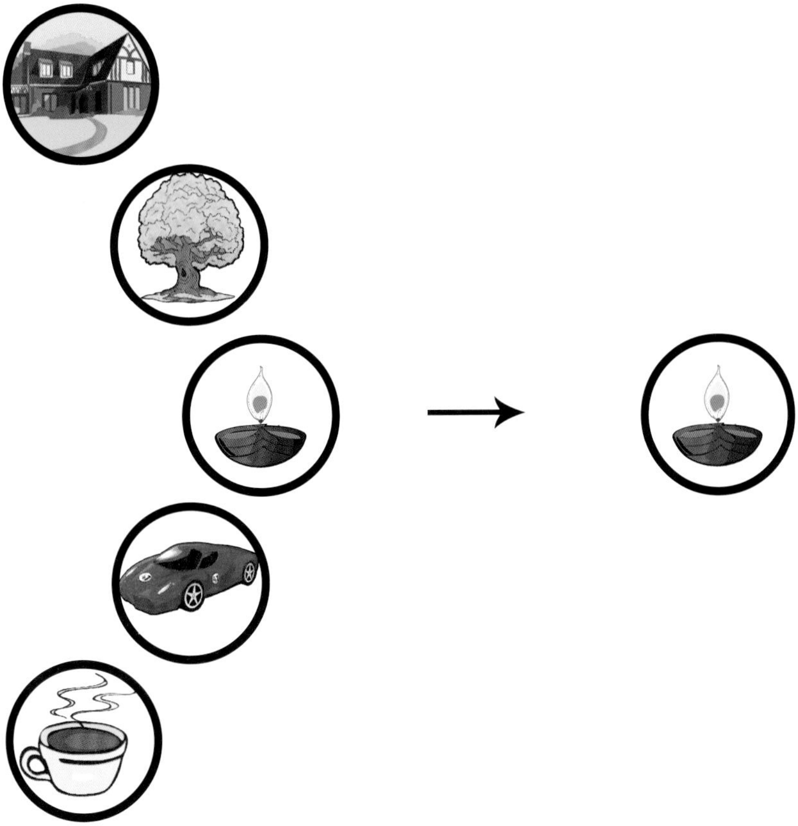

Emergence of one-pointedness

One-Pointed Transformation (Ekāgra)

ततः पुनः शान्तोदितौ तुल्यप्रत्ययौ चित्तस्यैकाग्रतापरिणामः ॥ ३.१२ ॥
tataḥ punaḥ śāntoditau tulyapratyayau cittasyaikāgratāpariṇāmaḥ ॥ 3.12 ॥

tataḥ = thence, from that
punaḥ = again
śānta = subsiding
uditau = in the arising
tulya = similar or same
pratyayau = thought, knowledge
cittasya = of the mind
ekāgratā-pariṇāmaḥ = one-pointed transformation.

The one-pointed transformation is when subsiding and arising thoughts are the same.

Like everything else in the universe, the mind is never constant — there is always a flux of impressions or thoughts. When one thought subsides, another arises. When the subsiding thought is the same as the emerging one, there is a continuous flow of that image. This is called the "one-pointed transformation" (*ekāgratā-pariṇāma*). *Eka* means one, and *agra* means the point or tip. The point of an arrow is an *agra*. One must learn to focus the mind and aim it like an archer shooting an arrow.

Thinking of the same thing in the past moment, the current moment, and the subsequent moment is called *ekāgratā-pariṇāma*. When you watch a movie, it's actually a collection of still images. If the camera stays fixed on one image, there may not appear to be any movement. However, many frames are in fact passing before your eyes very quickly. This is the model of awareness that this verse presents. Thoughts come and go, but since they are very similar (*tulya*) to one another, there is no apparent disruption in thinking. This is the one-pointed (*ekāgratā*) state of mind.

One-pointed transformation

Transformation of Objects and Instruments

एतेन भूतेन्द्रियेषु धर्मलक्षणावस्थापरिणामा व्याख्याताः ॥ ३.१३ ॥
etena bhūtendriyeṣu dharmalakṣaṇāvasthāpariṇāmā vyākhyātāḥ ॥ 3.13 ॥

etena = by this (the previous description of transformations)
bhūta-indriyeṣu = in the elements of nature, and our sense and motor instruments
dharma = characteristic, quality, property
lakṣaṇa = observable characteristic (in relation to time)
avasthā = state, condition
pariṇāmāḥ = transformations, changes
vyākhyātāḥ = are explained

By this, the characteristic, state, and conditional transformations of the elements of nature and the instruments [sense and motor instruments] are explained.

This sūtra describes three kinds of transformations that any object — animate or inanimate — can undergo just like the transformations that our mind undergoes. These are transformations of characteristic or form (*dharma*), state (temporal characteristic — *lakṣaṇa*), or condition (*avasthā*).

The word *dharma* has many different meanings. In the *Yoga Sūtras*, *dharma* is used as a technical term to mean a property or form of something. *Dharma* comes from the root *dhṛ*, which means to bear or to hold. The word *dharmī* means a "form-holder," possessing properties or forms (*dharmas*). For example, clay can take the form of a pot or a plate. So, the pot and the plate are *dharmas* that the clay can exhibit. Clay is the *dharmī* because it can hold different forms. The word "form" is not just limited to physical form — it can refer to any property of a thing.

This sūtra refers to the three changes (*pariṇāma*) that anything (again, animate or inanimate, including mental thoughts) can undergo.

- *Dharma-pariṇāma*: This is a change in the form of something — transformation of the *dharmī* from one form to another. For example, clay transforming from a lump into a pot is *dharma-pariṇāma*. Here, clay is transforming from its "lump" form to a "pot" form.
- *Lakṣaṇa-pariṇāma*: This type of change is primarily about state of an object in relation to time. The time-related states through which the clay progresses can be named "hasn't become a pot," "is a pot," and "was a pot," depending on what state it is in at any point.
- *Avasthā-pariṇāma*: This type of change is primarily about a change in the condition of an object. After taking on a particular form, the newly-formed object continues to change because nature (*prakṛti*) is never static — it is continually changing. A newly-

formed pot, even though it is a pot, undergoes decay. This process, through which an object changes its condition but does not acquire a new *dharma*, (it is still a pot) is called *avasthā-pariṇāma*.

A mind that was distracted by many objects but transforms into a fully-controlled mind — in which all mental activities are restrained — is called *dharma-pariṇāma*, because it has transformed from a wandering state to a restrained state. While transforming, at any given point of time, it can be in an intermediate or a final state (*lakṣaṇa-pariṇāma*). Even when the goal of the restrained state is achieved, that state undergoes changes in its condition (*avasthā-pariṇāma*) to slowly transform back to a wandering state. Over time, it becomes easier for a yogī to prevent the mind from wandering.

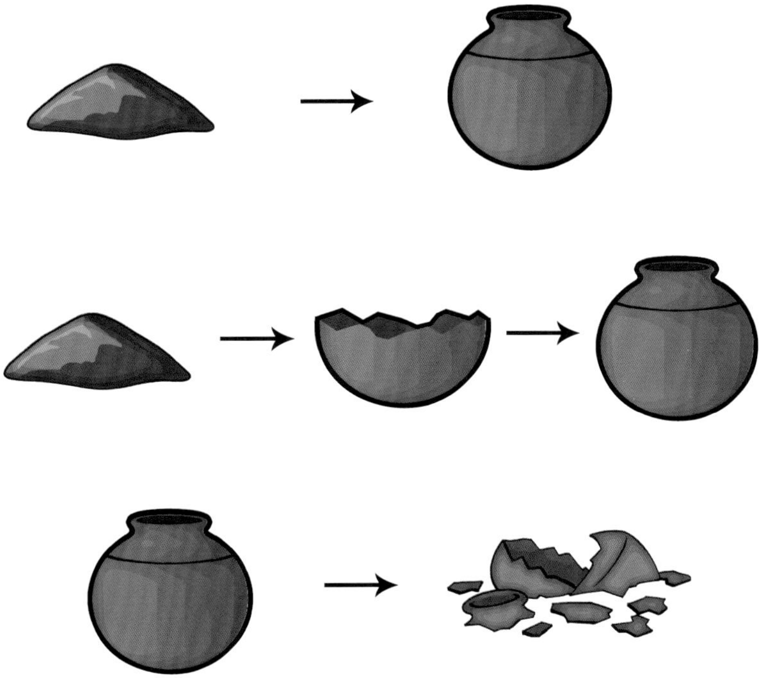

Dharma, lakṣaṇa, and avasthā transformations

Dharmī, the Substratum

शान्तोदिताव्यपदेश्यधर्मानुपाती धर्मी ॥ ३.१४ ॥
śāntoditāvyapadeśyadharmānupātī dharmī ॥ 3.14 ॥

śānta = quiescent, pacified (past)
udita = uprisen (present)
avyapadeśya = that which is not yet defined (future)
dharma = form, characteristic
anupātī = following as consequence
dhtarmī = property-holder, substratum, substance ("dharmī")

[That which] conforms to all past, present, and future forms is called the form-holder.

This is the formal definition of *dharmī*. The form-holder is the thing that is present in the past, the present, and the future forms of an object.

क्रमान्यत्वं परिणामान्यत्वे हेतुः ॥ ३.१५ ॥
kramānyatvaṁ pariṇāmānyatve hetuḥ ॥ 3.15 ॥

krama = sequence
anyatvaṁ = difference, other-ness
pariṇāma = transformation
anyatve = in the differentiation
hetuḥ = cause, reason

Difference in the sequence is the cause of difference in transformations.

Different processes of transformation result in the different forms of an object. In the case of a pot or a plate, clay must go through different processes or sequences of transformation to form these different types of containers. In this way, one *dharmī* may become multiple *dharmas*. Similarly, the same mind encompasses different states of concentration and different attainments because of different paths in meditation.

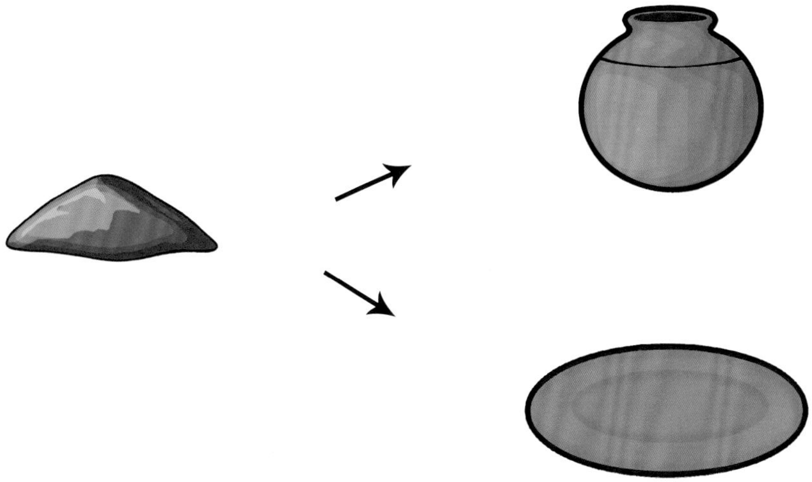

Difference in transformations

Sūtras 3.16-3.49: Siddhis, the Attainments Obtained Through Concentration

We now begin a series of verses that describe specific types of meditation that practitioners may wish to engage in. Each of these suggested meditations involves concentrating on a particular thing or topic. Depending on where and how you focus, the mind develops different insights and powers. The *Yoga Sūtras* uses the word *siddhi*, which means attainment, to refer to the benefits of these practices. Later Patañjali mentions that one should not become complacent with these intermediate achievements, as they themselves can become distractions to attaining the final goal of Yoga.

Knowledge of Past and Future

परिणामत्रयसंयमादतीतानागतज्ञानम् ॥ ३.१६ ॥
pariṇāmatrayasaṁyamādatītānāgatajñānam ॥ 3.16 ॥

pariṇāma-traya = the three kinds of transformations (described before as dharma, lakṣaṇa, and avasthā)
saṁyamāt = from practicing control (saṁyama)
atīta = that which is past
anāgata = that which is yet to come, the future
jñānam = knowledge

From practicing control [saṁyama] on the three types of transformations comes knowledge of the past and future.

Meditation on the *dharma*, *lakṣaṇa*, and *avasthā* transformations described in the previous verse results in a knowledge of the previous and future states of an object.

Word, Object, and Knowledge

शब्दार्थप्रत्ययानामितरेतराध्यासात्संकरस्तत्प्रविभागसंयमात्सर्वभूतरुतज्ञानम् ॥ ३.१७ ॥
śabdārthapratyayānāmitaretarādhyāsātsaṁkarastatpravibhāgasaṁyam ātsarvabhūtarutajñānam ॥ 3.17 ॥

śabda = word
ārtha = the object denoted or connoted by the word
pratyayānām = of the knowledge of the object, the concept
itaretara = one on the other
ādhyāsāt = due to overlap, overlaying, superimposition
saṁkaraḥ = confusion
tat = that
pravibhāga = division, distinction
saṁyamāt = from control (saṁyama)
sarva = all
bhūta = beings
ruta = language, saying, utterance
jñānam = knowledge

Due to the overlap of the word, the object implied, and the concept of the object, there arises confusion. By practicing control [saṁyama] over the differentiation, one gains a knowledge of the utterances of all beings.

This sūtra says that a yogī who can perform *saṁyama* on the distinction between a word, the object it signifies, and the knowledge of the object understands the utterances of all living beings.

A word is different from the object it refers to, and is also different from the knowledge of the object in our minds. In our minds, there is often an overlap of the three. There is a discussion in the commentaries elaborating on this distinction between the word, the object denoted, and the actual knowledge. It is presented below.

A physical word is simply a sequence of sounds, the individual consonants and vowels. For example, the word "cow" has the sound of the consonant "c" and of the vowel combining "o" and "w." Uttering the word consists of uttering the individual sounds in a sequence. Listening to the word consists of hearing the individual sounds and assembling them to form a complete word. After the sequence of sounds is heard, a non-physical, atomic word (say, the "mental word") is created in the mind of the listener. This mental word, called *sphoṭa*, is a single unit that does not have parts like the physical word, and which triggers impressions of the object in the mind of the listener. The word is different from the object it refers to, which is itself different from the knowledge of the object present in the mind. The physical word travels through the air and forms a mental word in the mind, while the object (cow) is seen in the fields. The knowledge of the word is conceptualized in the mind, and stays there. A cow can grow old, large, or thin, but the associated word and knowledge do not change along with the object. Clearly the word, object, and knowledge are different. A yogī who can practice concentration on the distinction between them can understand the utterances of all beings.

Also, it is said in the Vedic science of phonetics (*śikṣā*) that speaking a word or sound starts in the navel region. The mind, wishing to speak, excites the air in the navel region, which rises and takes an indecipherable form in the chest, is further refined in the throat, and then finally is expressed in full by the mouth. However, a yogī can understand the sound even when it is still in the chest and navel region.

There are many day-to-day implications of this sūtra. For example, while describing ourselves or our actions, we might use words like "success," "failure," and so forth. But, these words might not actually be correct. According to this sūtra, our qualities are not the same as the words used to describe them. Our bodies and minds are complex configurations of *sattva*, *rajas*, and *tamas* that no word can accurately capture. Investigating the true nature of something without being conditioned by the words of a language can replace our anxiety and fear with curiosity and confidence. Another implication of this sūtra relates to communication. Very often, the words people use have meanings in their minds that are different from the meanings we attach to them.

Understanding the utterances of all beings

It is interesting to note that the words and meanings, which are part of a language, are not any subtler than other impressions of objects in our minds. They too are mental activities. We are using one mental activity (word) to refer to another (meaning), which in turn points to another mental activity (object). So, language is just another group of mental fluctuations or activities in the mind. It is just that words are easily communicable over space and air, that we use them to refer to other things. Otherwise, the impression of coffee could as well be used to refer to a cow. In other words, the word "cow" is as different from the actual impression of the cow as the impression of coffee is.

Not only are the three activities (word, meaning, and object) different from one another, they have no bearing on our core self which is free from all the three mental activities.

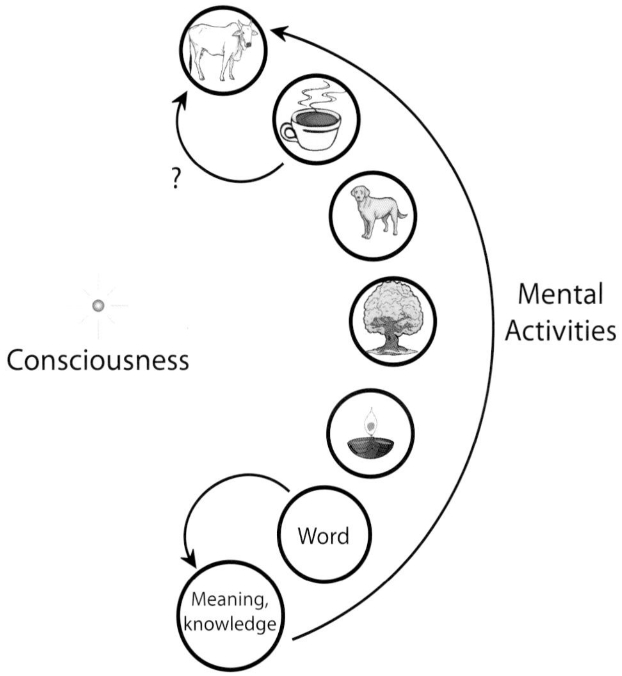

Knowledge of Previous Birth

संस्कारसाक्षात्करणात्पूर्वजातिज्ञानम् ॥ ३.१८ ॥
saṁskārasākṣatkaraṇātpūrvajātijñānam ॥ 3.18 ॥

saṁskāra = impression
sa-akṣāt-karaṇāt = from directly perceiving, seeing
pūrva = previous
jāti = birth
jñānam = knowledge

From directly seeing the impressions [saṁskāra] comes knowledge of previous births.

Every action is recorded on the mind as an impression (*saṁskāra*). By meditating on impressions and being able to perceive them, a yogī knows his or her previous lives. This sūtra is usually interpreted as referring to the doctrine of reincarnation.

Knowledge of Other's Feelings

प्रत्ययस्य परचित्तज्ञानम् ॥ ३.१९ ॥
pratyayasya paracittajñānam ॥ 3.19 ॥

pratyayasya = of cognition, of content of the mind
para-citta = another's mind
jñānam = knowledge

From another's cognition comes the knowledge of their mind.

By concentrating on the mind of another, a yogī gains the knowledge of that person's mind. The knowledge gained consists of the nature of thoughts the other person is having. One gets to know if the other person's thoughts are dominated by attachment or aversion etc. For a normal person, it is very difficult to know how to concentrate on another's mind or cognition. It can be inferred from the sūtras that one needs to go through the intermediate states of meditation — mastering *saṁyama* on gross objects — before attaining this capability.

न च तत्सालम्बनं तस्याविषयीभूतत्वात् ॥ ३.२० ॥
na ca tat sālambanaṁ tasyāviṣayībhūtatvāt ॥ 3.20 ॥

na = not
ca = and, but
tat = that
sa-ālambanaṁ = along with the support (object of thought)
tasya = of that
aviṣayī-bhūtatvāt = not being the subject

That [knowledge of another's mind] cannot reveal the object of thinking, because it is not the subject of the yogī's meditation.

Since the yogī meditates on the person's mind, and not on the object that the other mind is thinking of, the yogī gains knowledge of the mind but not of the object. Which implies that the a yogī gains the knowledge of that person's feelings. Some people are better than others in sensing or gauging other people's fealings. This power could be an enhancement of such a capability.

Invisibility

कायरूपसंयमात्तद्ग्राह्यशक्तिस्तम्भे चक्षुःप्रकाशासम्प्रयोगेऽन्तर्धनम् ॥ ३.२१ ॥
kāyarūpasaṁyamāttadgrāhyaśaktistambhe cakṣuḥprakāśāsamprayoge' ntardhānam ॥ 3.21 ॥

kāya-rūpa = form of the body
saṁyamāt = by practicing control
tad = that
grāhya-śakti = ability to be grasped (seen)
stambhe = in stopping, obstructing
cakṣuḥ = eye
prakāśa = light
asamprayoge = not in contact
antardhānam = being placed within (invisibility)

From control [saṁyama] on the form of the body, when light is not allowed to reach the eyes and the ability to be grasped is stopped, comes invisibility.

By meditating on the visible form of the body, a yogī can obstruct the reflective capacity of his or her form. As a result, the eyes of others will not come into contact with the reflected light, allowing the yogī to gain invisibility. From this, a similar phenomenon in other senses (sound, smell, touch, taste) is understood.

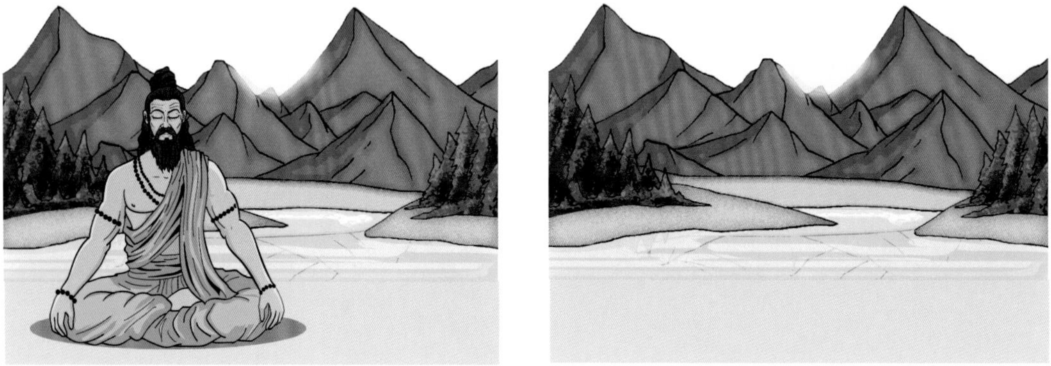

Invisibility

Knowledge of Death

सोपक्रमं निरुपक्रमं च कर्म तत्संयमादपरान्तज्ञानमरिष्टेभ्यो वा ॥ ३.२२ ॥
sopakramaṁ nirupakramaṁ ca karma tatsaṁyamādaparāntajñānamari ṣṭebhyo vā ॥ 3.22 ॥

sopakramaṁ = that which has commenced or is near
nirupakramaṁ = that which has not commenced
ca = and
karma = action
tat = that
saṁyamād = from control
aparānta = extreme end, death
jñānam = knowledge
ariṣṭebhyaḥ = from omens or portents
vā = or

Actions are fructifying, or non-fructifying. From practicing control, saṁyama, on that [fructification of actions], or through bad omens, comes the knowledge of death.

The word *fruit* is often used for "consequence" or "result" in Indian literature as it represents the result of the effort that has been put into tending a fruit-bearing tree. "Fructification of an action" is nothing but the development of consequences from a performed action. Actions are of three types based on the stage of fructification:

1. Currently being performed (*kriyamāṇa*)
2. Previously performed, the results of which are currently being experienced (*prārabdha*)
3. Previously performed, but the results of which are yet to be experienced (*sañcita*)

Sopakrama is another name for *prārabdha*, above, and *nirupakrama* is another name for *sañcita*. By concentrating on the fructification of his or her own karma, a yogī acquires a knowledge of consequences that are yet to be experienced. From this, the yogī knows the time of his or her own death. Time of death can also be inferred from bad omens (*ariṣṭaṁ*), the indicators of calamity and death. Many portents relating to health are described in *Āyurveda*, the Indian science of medicine. Some examples are the following:

- There is a star close to the Big Dipper called *Arundhatī*. When a person can no longer see that particular star although others can, death is imminent in a month.
- If one does not hear internal sounds when closing one's ears (the humming sound we hear normally), death is imminent within a few months.

The practical value of this sūtra is that by contemplating our own actions and thinking about their forthcoming consequences, we come to be able to understand what the final years of our life will be like. In this sūtra the word *aparānta* is often translated simply as "death"; but, literally, *aparānta* means "the final end" (*apara-anta*), which can be thought of to include the final years of our lives. For older people, contemplating what their final years will be like is often very important. And, by contemplating upon it for considerable amounts of time, they can understand what their circumstances will be in their final years.

Powers of Friendliness and Others

मैत्र्यादिषु बलानि ॥ ३.२३ ॥
maitryādiṣu balāni ॥ 3.23 ॥

maitrī = friendliness
ādiṣu = others, etc.
balāni = strengths, powers

From friendliness and others comes powers.

Maitrī-ādiṣu means "friendliness etc.," indicating that friendliness is the first in a list of things. Many undersand that list as the one given in verse 1.33, which includes friendliness, compassion, joyfulness, and forbearance. Friendship, compassion and joy are the three powers that need to be developed.

- By concentrating on friendliness, one attains the power of friendship, and can evoke a feeling of friendliness in any person.
- By concentrating on compassion, one attains the power of compassion. The presence of such a person can eliminate pain and sorrow in others.
- By concentrating on joyfulness, one attains the power to be joyful in any situation. A frustrated person will feel peaceful around such a yogī.

Forbearance toward the non-virtuous is not listed, as no power is attained through it. It is simply the absence of any kind of attitude towards the non-virtuous.

Strengths

बलेषु हस्तिबलादीनि ॥ ३.२४ ॥
baleṣu hastibalādīni ॥ 3.24 ॥

baleṣu = in strengths
hasti = elephant
bala = strength, power
ādīni = etc.

[Practicing saṁyama] on strengths [leads to] the strengths of an elephant and others.

The difference between this verse and the prior verse is that here we are talking about physical powers rather than mental powers. By concentrating on the strength of an elephant, one attains prodigious power. Similarly, concentrating on the force of the wind, one acquires that power, and so forth.

Knowledge of Imperceptible Things

प्रवृत्त्यालोकन्यासात्सूक्ष्मव्यवहितविप्रकृष्टज्ञानम् ॥ ३.२५ ॥
pravṛttyālokanyāsātsūkṣmavyavahitaviprakṛṣṭajñānam ॥ 3.25 ॥

pravṛtti = activity
āloka = light, vision, insight
nyāsāt = by casting, placing (here, to put one's mind on something)
sūkṣma = subtle, microscopic, intangible
vyavahita = concealed, covered
viprakṛṣṭa = distant
jñānam = knowledge

From focusing the power of insight comes a knowledge of subtle, covered, and distant objects.

This power of insight is an intensely-developed sense of discernment. The yogī gains knowledge of things not normally perceptible by focusing that power of insight on them. The power of the mind that gives that insight is variously refered to as *viśokā*, *jyotiṣmatī*, and *prajñāloka* in verses 1.36 and 3.5. This type of super-sensory perception is found in other sūtras as well.

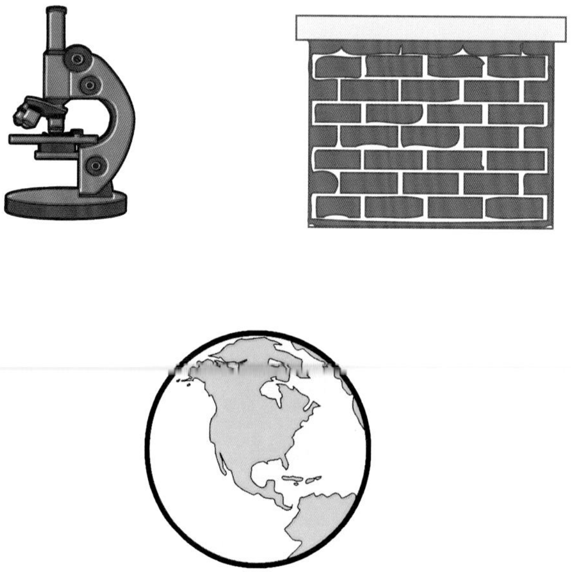

Knowledge of subtle, obstructed and distant objects

Knowledge of Celestial Objects

भुवनज्ञानं सूर्ये संयमात् ॥ ३.२६ ॥
bhuvanajñānaṁ sūrye saṁyamāt ॥ 3.26 ॥

bhuvana = world, region
jñānaṁ = knowledge
sūrye = on the sun
saṁyamāt = from control

From practicing saṁyama on the sun comes knowledge of the worlds.

In Indian tradition, there are multiple celestial and subterranean regions that are called "worlds." By practicing *saṁyama* on the sun, one gains the knowledge of these worlds.

चन्द्रे ताराव्यूहज्ञानम् ॥ ३.२७ ॥
candre tārāvyūhajñānam ॥ 3.27 ॥

candre = on the moon
tārā-vyūha = arrangements of stars, constellations
jñānam = knowledge

From practicing saṁyama on the moon comes knowledge of the arrangements of the stars.

This and the following sūtra are very straight forward.

ध्रुवे तद्गतिज्ञानम् ॥ ३.२८ ॥
dhruve tadgatijñānam ॥ 3.28 ॥

dhruve = on Polaris, the pole-star
tat = that (stars and constellations)
gati = movement
jñānam = knowledge

From concentrating on the pole-star comes knowledge of the movement [of the stars and constellations].

Knowledge of the Body

नाभिचक्रे कायव्यूहज्ञानम् ॥ ३.२९ ॥
nābhicakre kāyavyūhajñānam ॥ 3.29 ॥

nābhi = navel
cakre = center, circle, wheel
kāya = body
vyūha = arrangement
jñānam = knowledge

[From practicing saṁyama] on the navel center comes knowledge of the arrangement of the human body.

Arrangement of the body refers here to anatomy and the bodily systems. This includes their placement, growth, healthy functioning, and unhealthy aberrations. In traditional Indian medicine, there are three humors (*doṣa*):

- *vāta* = wind
- *pitta* = bile
- *śleṣma or kapha* = phlegm

There are also seven elements (*dhātu*) of the body:

1. skin
2. blood
3. flesh
4. tendon, nerve
5. bone
6. marrow
7. semen

This sūtra describes that one attains a knowledge of the above by practicing saṁyama on the center of the navel.

Doṣa

Our bodies are made of the five gross elements (earth, water, fire, air, space). Three combinations of these five gross elements are called "*doṣas*" which are recognized as the basic bodily elements or humors in *Ayurveda*. The three *doṣas* are *vāta*, *pitta*, and *kapha* (or *śleṣma*). *Vāta* has the qualities of air, *pitta* of fire, and *kapha* of water. A balanced composition and working of the three *doṣas* constitutes good health. This is a rather terse description of *doṣas*. Interested readers would greatly benefit from consulting related texts on *Ayurveda*.

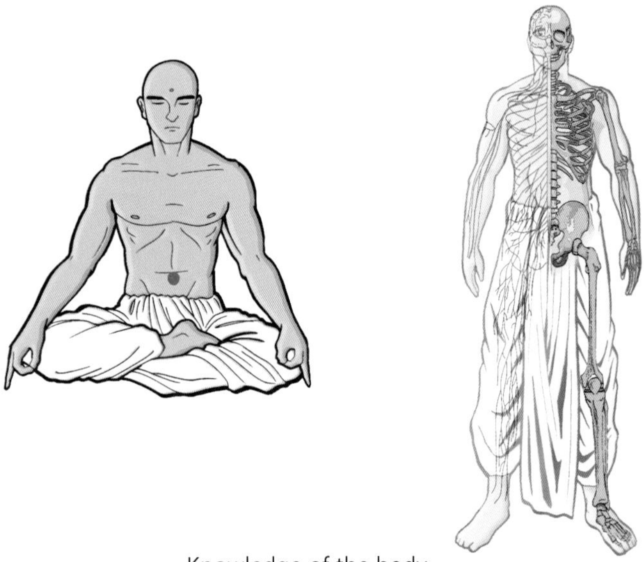

Knowledge of the body

Hunger

कण्ठकूपे क्षुत्पिपासानिवृत्तिः ॥ ३.३० ॥
kaṇṭhakūpe kṣutpipāsānivṛttiḥ ॥ 3.30 ॥

kaṇṭha = throat
kūpe = in the pit
kṣut = hunger
pipāsā = thirst
nivṛttiḥ = cessation

[From practicing saṁyama] on the pit of the throat comes the ability to suppress hunger and thirst.

Control over hunger

Stability of the Body

कूर्मनाड्यां स्थैर्यम् ॥ ३.३१ ॥
kūrmanāḍyāṁ sthairyam ॥ 3.31 ॥

kūrma = tortoise
nāḍyāṁ = on the tube, nerve, subtle channel
sthairyam = stability

[From practicing saṁyama] on the "tortoise tube" comes stability of mind and body.

Vyāsa takes "tortoise tube" to mean a structure shaped like a tortoise located below the pit of the throat mentioned in the previous sūtra. By concentrating on it, one gains stability of mind and body. Restlessness subsides and one becomes steady, like a serpent or an iguana. Reptiles are known for their ability to remain completely motionless.

Vision of the Siddhas

मूर्धज्योतिषि सिद्धदर्शनम् ॥ ३.३२ ॥
mūrdhajyotiṣi siddhadarśanam ॥ 3.32 ॥

mūrdha = head (or the highest)
jyotiṣi = on the light
siddha = the perfected ones, who have attained special powers
darśanam = vision

[From practicing saṁyama] on the light in the head comes the vision of the perfected ones.

Vyāsa mentions a point in the head that emanates subtle light. By practicing *saṁyama* on that light, one attains the vision of the *siddhas*, the accomplished yogīs.

Vision of accomplished yogis

प्रातिभाद्वा सर्वम् ॥ ३.३३ ॥
prātibhād vā sarvam ॥ 3.33 ॥

prātibhād = by intuition, prescience
vā = or
sarvam = everything, all the powers (siddhis)

Or, from intuition comes everything.

Through the special power of intuition (*prātibhā*), one attains all siddhis — all powers. Intuition is a type of awareness that is achieved before becoming one with pure consciousness. *Prātibhā* is mentioned again in verse 3.36.

हृदये चित्तसंवित् ॥ ३.३४ ॥
hṛdaye cittasaṁvit ॥ 3.34 ॥

hṛdaye = on the heart
citta = mind
saṁvit = knowledge, understanding

[From practicing saṁyama] on the heart comes the knowledge of the citta.

This nerve center is shaped like a lotus, although its exact location is unclear. Some refer to the heart-shaped region below the trachea, while others refer to heart as the space between the eyebrows. Concentrating on it, one gains the understanding of the mind. The mind includes all of the internal processes of the mind, including ego. One gets an understanding of one's own personality.

Knowledge of the Self

सत्त्वपुरुषयोरत्यन्तासंकीर्णयोः प्रत्ययाविशेषो भोगः परार्थत्वात्स्वार्थसंयमात्पुरुषज्ञानम्
॥ ३.३५ ॥
sattvapuruṣayoratyantāsaṁkīrṇayoḥ pratyayāviśeṣo bhogaḥ parārthatvāt svārthasaṁyamāt puruṣajñānam ॥ 3.35 ॥

sattva = intellect (buddhi)
puruṣayor = of consciousness
atyanta = extremely, completely
asaṁkīrṇayoḥ = not overlapping
pratyaya = cognition, perception, idea
aviśeṣaḥ = non-difference, similarity
bhogaḥ = experience
para-arthatvāt = due to the nature of being for another purpose
sva-artha = for own purpose
saṁyamāt = by control (saṁyama)
puruṣa-jñānam = knowledge of the consciousness

Worldly experience comes from a cognition of the non-differentiation of intellect and consciousness, [which are in fact] completely differentiated. Knowledge of consciousness [puruṣa] results from practicing saṁyama on one's own purpose, as opposed to purpose of the other [the prakṛti].

The word *sattva* has many meanings. It is one of the fundamental forces of the universe that is responsible for illumination and understanding. Another meaning of *sattva* is *buddhi*, the intellect. As *buddhi* increasingly clarifies, knowledge of *puruṣa* dawns. Like someone recognizing himself in a mirror, *buddhi* reflects the original *puruṣa*.

This gives an approximate understanding of the *puruṣa*, but true realization of the self can occur only with *nirvikalpa-samādhi*, where the *puruṣa* is completely detached from *buddhi*. Therefore, the knowledge that is discussed in this sūtra is the penultimate stage before *kaivalya*, complete independence or liberation.

ततः प्रातिभश्रावणवेदनादर्शास्वादवार्ता जायन्ते ॥ ३.३६ ॥
tataḥ prātibhaśrāvaṇavedanādarśāsvādavārtā jāyante ॥ 3.36 ॥

tataḥ = from that
prātibha = intuition
śrāvaṇa = hearing
vedanā = touch
ādarśa = seeing
āsvāda = taste
vārtā = smell
jāyante = are born

From that [knowledge of consciousness], intuitive hearing, touch, sight, taste, and smell are born.

As one's intuitive capacity increases, super-sensory capabilities are the result. The super-sensory capabilities mentioned in this sūtra are,

1. *shrāvaṇa*: extraordinary listening powers, such as listening from afar or to very quiet sounds, or knowing the sounds made by other beings
2. *vedanā*: a superior sense of touch
3. *ādarśa*: special vision
4. *āsvāda*: special powers of taste
5. *vārtā*: special powers of smell

Powers as Hindrances

ते समाधावुपसर्गा व्युत्थाने सिद्धयः ॥ ३.३७ ॥
te samādhāvupasargā vyutthāne siddhayaḥ ॥ 3.37 ॥

te = those (powers)
samādhau = in absorption, perfected meditation
upasargāḥ = obstacles
vyutthāne = outwardly-focused, distracted
siddhayaḥ = powers

Those [powers] are obstacles in the way of samādhi, but are powers in an outwardly-focused mind.

This sūtra advises a yogī to not to dwell on supernatural powers. They are distractions that prevent one from accomplishing the goal of yoga — liberation that results after attaining seedless *samādhi*. Feeling powerful is the indulgence of the ego. *Vyutthāna* is the word used in the verse to describe the state of mind associated with the powers; this is an extroverted state of consciousness. Rather than increasing attachment to external things, instead in yoga we learn to maintain detachment from them. We recognize that our true self is not dependent on anything outside of us.

Powers Continued...

बन्धकारणशैथिल्यात्प्रचारसंवेदनाच्च चित्तस्य परशरीरावेशः ॥ ३.३८ ॥
bandhakāraṇaśaithilyātpracārasaṁvedanācca cittasya paraśarīrāveśaḥ ॥ 3.38 ॥

bandha-kāraṇa = cause of bondage
śaithilyāt = from loosening, relaxation
pracāra = movement, operation
saṁvedanāt = from knowledge
ca = and
cittasya = of mind
para = other's
śarīra = body
āveśaḥ = entering

From the loosening of the causes of bondage and the experience of the movements of the mind comes [the power] of entering another's body.

By restraining the impressions of karma and rendering them impotent, a yogī is no longer bound to his or her body. Knowing the movements of the mind from concentration, one can withdraw the mind from the current body and enter another's.

उदानजयाज्जलपङ्ककण्टकादिष्वसङ्ग उत्क्रान्तिश्च ॥ ३.३९ ॥
udānajayājjalapaṅkakaṇṭakādiṣvasaṅga utkrāntiśca ॥ 3.39 ॥

udāna = the air that is present in the body from throat to the head (udāna is one of the vital airs)
jayāt = from mastering
jala = water
paṅka = mud, mire
kaṇṭaka = thorn
ādiṣu = in others
asaṅgaḥ = non-contact
utkrāntiḥ = moving upwards, levitation
ca = and

From mastering the vital air called udāna comes [the ability to be] untouched by water, mud, and thorns, and [the power of] levitation.

Our bodies have five vital airs (*prāṇas*) that are necessary for the proper functioning of the body. They are

1. *prāṇa*, the body of air extending from the tip of nose to the lungs. This is the air that is taken in.
2. *apāna*, the body of air extending from the stomach and navel to the feet, responsible for removing wastes from the body. This is the air that is pushed out.
3. *samāna*, the body of air going from the heart to the center of the stomach, responsible for digestion and sending nutrition to the different parts of the body.
4. *vyāna*, the body of air extending from head to feet and spread all over the body, including the blood.
5. *udāna*, the body of air from the throat to the head.

Upon attaining perfection in concentrating on the body of air called *udāna*, one gains the ability to be untouched by water, mud and thorns. Water, mud, thorns, and the like do not stick to the yogī while walking on them. A yogī attains the power of levitation as well.

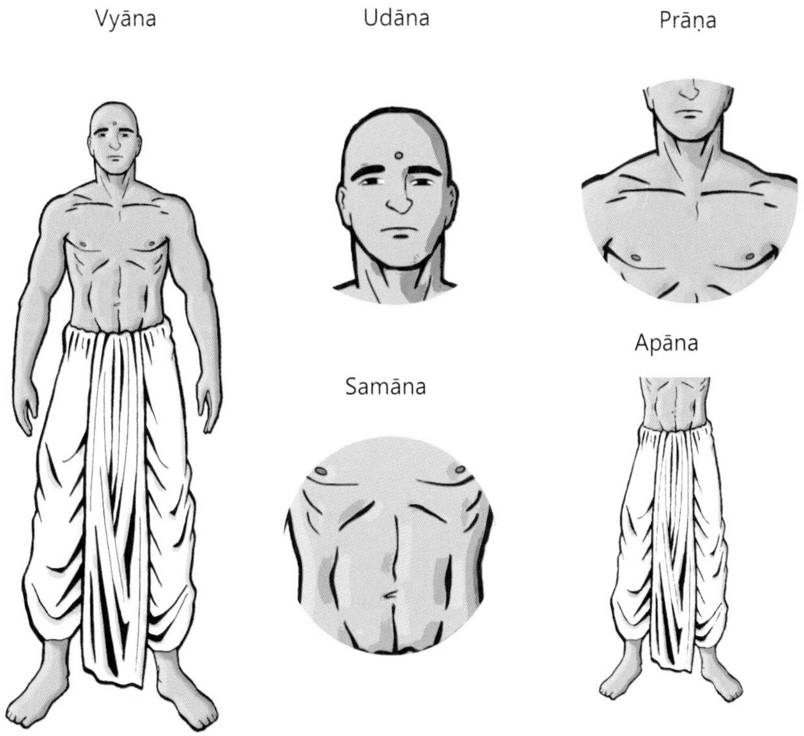

Ability to be untouched by water, and levitation

समानजयाज्ज्वलनम् ॥ ३.४० ॥
samānajayājjvalanam ॥ 3.40 ॥

samāna = vital air called samāna
jayāt = from mastering
prajvalanam = radiance, effulgent, blazing

From mastering the vital air called Samāna comes radiance.

The body of air from the heart to the stomach, responsible for digestion and sending nutrition to different parts of the body, is called *samāna*. By mastering samāna, a yogī's body becomes radiant.

श्रोत्राकाशयोः सम्बन्धसंयमाद्दिव्यं श्रोत्रम् ॥ ३.४१ ॥
śrotrākāśayoḥ saṁbandhasaṁyamāddivyaṁ śrotram ॥ 3.41 ॥

śrotra = ear
ākāśayoḥ = of space or ether, one of the five elements of nature
saṁbandha = relation, connection
saṁyamāt = by practicing control (saṁyama)
divyaṁ = divine, supernatural
śrotram = hearing

From practicing saṁyama on the relation between the ear and the ether comes supernatural hearing.

Ether (*ākāśa*) is produced from the *tanmātra* of the sound (the building block for space described as one of the evolutes of nature). Sound is the natural attribute of ether. The subtle sense of hearing can pick up sound from ethereal vibrations. This is not done with the external ear, but with the subtle sense of hearing. By concentrating on the relation between ether and the sense of hearing, a yogī can perceive any sound in the universe. Supernatural powers relating to vision, smell, touch, and taste are also similarly attained by concentrating on the relationship between the subtle sense and the corresponding *tanmātra*.

कायाकाशयोः सम्बन्धसंयमाल्लघुतूलसमापत्तेश्चाकाशगमनम् ॥ ३.४२ ॥
kāyākāśayoḥ saṁbandhasaṁyamāllaghutūlasamāpatteścākāśagamanam ॥ 3.42 ॥

kāya = body
ākāśayoḥ = of the ether
saṁbandha = relation, connection
saṁyamāt = from practicing control (saṁyama)
laghu = light
tūla = cotton
samāpatteḥ = from the state of completion, absorption (samādhi)
ca = and
ākāśa-gamanam = travel in space

From practicing saṁyama on the relation between the body and space and from obtaining samādhi on the lightness of cotton comes [the ability to] travel through space.

The meaning of this sūtra is quite straight forward. By practicing concentration (*saṁyama*) on the relation between the body and the space one attains the ability to travel through space. This power is also attained by obtaining *saṁyama* on the lightness of cotton.

बहिरकल्पिता वृत्तिर्महाविदेहा ततः प्रकाशावरणक्षयः ॥ ३.४३ ॥
bahirakalpitā vṛttirmahāvidehā tataḥ prakāśāvaraṇakṣayaḥ ॥ 3.43 ॥

bahiḥ = outside, external
a-kalpitā = not made, not fashioned, not formed, non-imaginary
vṛttiḥ = activity
mahā = great
videhā = without a body, body-less
tataḥ = from that
prakāśa = illumination
āvaraṇa = covering
kṣayaḥ = descrease, dwindling

There is a state of mind that is external and not imaginary, "the great bodyless-ness" (mahāvidehā). From that comes the dwindling of the covering of the light.

When we meditate on an object, we feel that our mind is still within our body. *Kalpita* normally means formed, and here it refers to how our mind is still in our bodily form. A yogī, on the other hand, can project the mind outside the body, and in this verse the term *akalpita* seems to refer to the fact that the consciousness is no longer limited to being within the body. The term *videha* means the state of being "without a body," or "body-less," and is used to describe a state of the mind (*vṛtti*). This *mahāvidehā* ("the great bodyless-ness") is a type of disembodied consciousness that is not dependent on being inside a physical form — it is a type of out-of-body experience. The benefit of this mode of consciousness is that the limitations on one's inner light are diminished.

स्थूलस्वरूपसूक्ष्मान्वयार्थवत्त्वसंयमाद्भूतजयः ॥ ३.४४ ॥
sthūlasvarūpasūkṣmānvayārthavattvasaṁyamādbhūtajayaḥ ॥ 3.44 ॥

sthūla = gross
sva-rūpa = own form
sūkṣma = subtle
anvaya = connected
artha-vat-tva = purposeful-ness
saṁyamāt = by practicing control (saṁyama)
bhūta-jayaḥ = mastery over the elements

From practicing saṁyama on the gross nature, inherent form, subtle nature, and their associations and their purposes, comes mastery over the elements.

The gross elements (*sthūlabhūtas*) have different aspects that the yogī can meditate on.

1. The gross (*sthūla*) state, which can be perceived by our external sense organs.
2. Their own form (*svarūpa*), referring to the state or characterisics they possess (solid vs. liquid).
3. Their subtle (*sūkṣma*) nature, referring to the subtle elements (the *tanmātras* of sound, touch, form, taste, and smell) from which the physical form (space, air, fire, water, and earth) originated.
4. Their association (*anvaya*), taken to mean their connections with the three *guṇas* found in all elements (*sattva*, *rajas*, and *tamas*).
5. Their purpose (*arthavattva*) or their functional roles.

ततोऽणिमादिप्रादुर्भावः कायसम्पत्तद्धर्मानभिघातश्च ॥ ३.४५ ॥
tato'ṇimādiprādurbhāvaḥ kāyasampattaddharmānabhighātaśca ॥ 3.45 ॥

tataḥ = from that, thence
aṇimanā = the supernatural power named aṇimā
ādi = and others, etc.
prādurbhāvaḥ = emergence, manifestation
kāya = body
sampat = attainment, perfection
tat = that
dharma = attribute, property
anabhighātaḥ = indestructible, invulnerable, unattacked
ca = and

From that [mastery over the elements] comes the manifestation of [the powers of] miniaturization and others, perfection of the body, and the invulnerability of its properties.

From mastery over the elements, one is said to attain a list of powers.

1. *Aṇimā*, the power of becoming small.
2. *Laghimā*, the power of making the body very light.
3. *Mahimā*, the power of making the body very large in size.
4. *Prāpti*, the power to reach everywhere, such as touching the moon with one's fingertips.
5. *Prākāmya*, the power of irresistible strength of will. For example, one can pass through earth as if it were water.
6. *Vaśitva*, the power of mastery over anything.
7. *Īśitva*, the power of supremacy or lordship.
8. *Yatrakāmāvasāyitva*, the power to fulfill any wish.

In addition to these powers, the yogī attains the *kāyasampat* — the "perfection of the body," which is explained in the coming verse. The yogī's body becomes invulnerable.

रूपलावण्यबलवज्रसंहननत्वानि कायसम्पत् ॥ ३.४६ ॥
rūpalāvaṇyabalavajrasaṁhananatvāni kāyasampat ॥ 3.46 ॥

rūpa = form, beauty of form
lāvaṇya = charm, gracefulness
bala = strength
vajra = diamond-hard, adamantine
saṁhananatva = robust, strongly-built
kāya = body
sampat = perfection

Perfection of the body [consists of] beauty, gracefulness, strength, and the hardness of a diamond.

This is the definition of the term *kāyasampat*, used in previous sūtra.

ग्रहणस्वरूपास्मितान्वयार्थवत्त्वसंयमादिन्द्रियजयः ॥ ३.४७ ॥
grahaṇasvarūpāsmitānvayārthavattvasaṁyamādindriyajayaḥ ॥ 3.47 ॥

grahaṇa = grasping, perception
sva-rūpa = own form, character, nature
asmitā = "I-am-ness"
anvaya = succession
arthavattva = purposfulness
saṁyamād = by practicing control (saṁyama)
indriya = sense organs, intruments
jayaḥ = mastery

From practicing saṁyama on aspects of grasping, essential character, the sense of ego, succession, and purposefulness of senses comes mastery over the senses.

This sūtra describes concentration on the five different aspects of the sense instruments.

- Grasping: This is the aspect in which the senses perceive the sensory data received by each sense. This consists of not just the general sense (for example, sound) but also the specific sense (different pitches, loudness, and so on).
- Essential nature: The luminous (sensing) nature of the components of the mind and the instruments is due to the element of *sattva*. Since *buddhi* is the first evolute and is present in all subsequent evolutes, *buddhi* is indirectly the building block of all sense instruments. The illuminating nature of *buddhi* (*sattva*) is present in all senses. The dif-

ferences between sense instruments are due to the presense of a different combination of *buddhi* in each. Thus, the general and specific nature of a sense instrument is formed out of *buddhi*.

- Sense of "I": Similar to *buddhi*, *ahaṅkāra* is present in all instruments. From *buddhi* forms *ahaṅkāra*, and from *ahaṅkāra* all the senses are formed. It is due to *ahaṅkāra* that all perceptions are geared towards the "I."
- Succession: This refers to the succession of evolution of the sense instruments from the primordial elements (*sattva*, *rajas*, and *tamas*). Because of this, the qualities of those three elements (illumination, movement, and stability) are present in each of the instruments.
- Purposefulness: This is the ultimate purpose of sense instruments — to serve as the objects (possessions) of consciousness to bring about experience and liberation.

Concentrating on these aspects of the senses gives a yogī mastery over them.

ततो मनोजवित्वं विकरणभावः प्रधानजयश्च ॥ ३.४८ ॥
tato manojavitvaṁ vikaraṇabhāvaḥ pradhānajayaśca ॥ 3.48 ॥

tato = from that (mastery over the senses)
manas = mind
javitvaṁ = speed
vi-karaṇa = without organs
bhāvaḥ = condition, existence
pradhāna = primary, the primordial nature (a synonym for prakṛti)
jaya = mastery
ca = and

From that [mastering the senses] comes fleetness like that of the mind, a condition of independence from the senses, and mastery over primordial matter.

By mastering the senses, a yogī can move at the speed of the mind. Further, the senses can work without the external gross organs or body, and the yogī gains control over primordial matter (*prakṛti*). *Pradhāna* is a synonym for the primordial matter.

सत्त्वपुरुषान्यताख्यातिमात्रस्य सर्वभावाधिष्ठातृत्वं सर्वज्ञातृत्वं च ॥ ३. ४९ ॥
sattvapuruṣānyatākhyātimātrasya sarvabhāvādhiṣṭhātṛtvaṁ sarvajñātṛtvaṁ ca ॥ 3.49 ॥

sattva = reality, differentiating intellect (buddhi)
puruṣa = consciousness, self
anyatā = difference
khyāti = vision, insight
mātrasya = of only, merely
sarva-bhāva = all states, conditions, beings
adhiṣṭhātṛtvaṁ = command over
sarva-jñātṛtvaṁ = omniscience
ca = and

Only from insight [into] the difference between sattva (buddhi) and puruṣa comes mastery over all states [of existence], and omniscience.

When a yogī comes to the point of clearly seeing the distinction between the intellect (*buddhi*) and consciousness (*puruṣa*), he or she can see all states of the *guṇas* in the formation of any object. One gains the knowledge of the past, present, and future of that object. This power is called *viśokā*. After attaining this, a yogī becomes free from all afflictions (*kleśas*).

Sūtras 3.50-3.55: Discriminating Wisdom and Liberation

Autonomy of the Self

तद्वैराग्यादपि दोषबीजक्षये कैवल्यम् ॥ ३.५० ॥
tadvairāgyādapi doṣabījakṣaye kaivalyam ॥ 3.50 ॥

tad = that
vairāgyāt = from detatchment
api = also, even
doṣa = defect, imperfection
bīja = seed
kṣaye = in dwindling, wearing away
kaivalyam = alone-ness, isolation, independence, autonomy

Due to detachment even from that [insight], upon the wearing away of the seed of defects comes isolation [of the consciousness].

After the seeds of imperfection are worn away, a yogī realizes that discriminating knowledge is also a characteristic of the *buddhi*, which is a product of the *prakṛti* and so must be renounced. This results in the yogī merging into the pure, immutable essense of *puruṣa*. *Buddhi* dissolves into its components (*sattva*, *rajas*, and *tamas*) and the consciousness abides in itself.

Behavior of a Yogī

स्थान्युपनिमन्त्रणे सङ्गस्मयाकरणं पुनरनिष्टप्रसङ्गात् ॥ ३.५१ ॥
sthānyupanimantraṇe saṅgasmayākaraṇaṁ punaḥ aniṣṭaprasaṅgāt ॥ 3.51 ॥

sthāni = anyone holding a higher position in society, or celestial beings with powers
upanimantraṇe = on invitation
saṅga = attachment
smaya = pride, conceit, arrogance
akaraṇaṁ = not doing
punaḥ = again
aniṣṭa = not desired
prasaṅgāt = due to contact, inclination, attachment, indulgence

When invited by the highly-placed ones, [a yogī] should have no cause for attachment and pride due to renewal of inclination towards undesirables.

When invited by people in the high ranks of society (*sthānin*), a yogī should not become egotistical, as this might lead to undesirable actions and their consequences. The word *sthānin* also means celestial beings — temporarily-liberated beings who exist without the external body.

There are four categories of yogīs described in the commentaries:

1. *prathamakalpika*: Yogis at this stage are practicing yoga such that supernatural perception is just beginning to manifest.
2. *madhubhūmika*: Yogis at this stage have attained truth-bearing (*ṛtambharā*) wisdom.
3. *prajñājyoti*: Yogis at this stage have mastered the elements of nature (*bhūtas*) and sense organs, and are engaged in achieving further attainments.
4. *atikrāntabhāvanīya*: Yogis at this stage are beyond attaining any achievements, and are waiting for the *buddhi* to dissolve into *prakṛti*.

Madhubhūmika yogīs are susceptible to feeling egotistical when invited to consort with people in positions of power or celestial beings. Here, they are advised not to fall into such behavior, as this can lead them back to the bondage of the world.

Discriminating Wisdom

क्षणतत्क्रमयोः संयमाद्विवेकजं ज्ञानम् ॥ ३.५२ ॥
kṣaṇatatkramayoḥ saṁyamādvivekajaṁ jñānam ॥ 3.52 ॥

kṣaṇa = moment
tat-kramayoḥ = sequence or transition of that
saṁyamāt = from practicing control (saṁyama)
viveka-jaṁ = born out of discernment
jñānam = knowledge

From practicing saṁyama on the moment and its sequence comes discriminating knowledge.

A moment is not a real thing; it is only a mental concept. All objects in the universe undergo constant transformation. The transition of one moment into another is called *krama*, or sequence. By practicing *saṁyama* on this sequence, a yogī attains discriminating wisdom. In Vyāsa's commentary, a moment of time that cannot be further divided is called *kṣaṇa*.

The present is only the current moment. The previous moment and the future moment cannot coexist with it. The past and the future are dependent on the constant change in *prakṛti*. If there is no change, there is no future or past (and so no concept of a moment passing away).

जातिलक्षणदेशैरन्यतानवच्छेदात्तुल्ययोस्ततः प्रतिपत्तिः ॥ ३.५३ ॥
jātilakṣaṇadeśairanyatānavacchedāt tulyayostataḥ pratipattiḥ ॥ 3.53 ॥

jāti = birth, species, class, kind
lakṣaṇa = characteristic
deśaiḥ = by location
anyatā = difference
anavacchedāt = not being divided, not differentiated
tulyayoḥ = of similar, of the ones that are same
tataḥ = from that, thence
pratipattiḥ = perception, ascertainment

From that [practicing saṁyama] comes the differentiation of two similar things that are not distinguishable by class, characteristics, or location.

Two objects can be differentiated if their class or category is different (like a cow and a horse), or if their perceptible characteristics are different (like two cows of different color), or if their location is different (like two identical cows in different locations). On the other hand, if two objects are identical in category, characteristics, and location, it would be impossible to tell the difference. For example, if two identical plums are in different locations but their position is switched while the observer is not looking, the observer may not be able to notice the diffference. A yogī with discriminating wisdom will be able to tell the difference.

तारकं सर्वविषयं सर्वथाविषयमक्रमं चेति विवेकजं ज्ञानम् ॥ ३.५४ ॥
tārakaṁ sarvaviṣayaṁ sarvathāviṣayamakramaṁ ceti vivekajaṁ jñānam ॥ 3.54 ॥

tārakaṁ = that which liberates, deliverer
sarva-viṣayaṁ = of all objects
sarvathā-viṣayam = in every way, at all times
akramaṁ = with no sequence
ca = and
iti = like this, thus
viveka-jaṁ = born out of discernment
jñānam = knowledge

Knowledge born of discernement is the deliverer. It relates to all objects in every way, and is non-sequential.

Knowledge born of discrimination is the great deliverer. Vyāsa says that such knowledge is obtained independently, without any instruction from others. It relates to all objects, in every way, and has no sequence (that is, is independent of time — the past, present, and future states of objects are known).

सत्त्वपुरुषयोः शुद्धिसाम्ये कैवल्यमिति ॥ ३.५५ ॥
sattvapuruṣayoḥ śuddhisāmye kaivalyam iti ॥ 3.55 ॥

sattva = buddhi
puruṣayoḥ = of consciousness
śuddhi = purity
sāmye = in equality
kaivalyam = alone-ness, isolation, independence, autonomy
iti = like this, thus

When the purity of sattva [buddhi] and puruṣa are equal, this is kaivalya.

The word *sattva* in this verse refers to *buddhi*; it does not mean *sattva-guṇa* (one of the three *guṇas*). The verse says that when the *buddhi* is as pure as *puruṣa*, that state is called *kaivalya*. This definition hinges on the word "purity." In this context, "pure" means not to be contaminated by anything else. That is, consciousness no longer identifies with any of the characteristics of *prakṛti*. This is the state of complete independence — *kaivalya*.

The *guṇas* that compose the mind have fulfilled their purpose, and there is nothing left for *puruṣa* to experience. The absence of experiencing pain or pleasure and being established in its own form is *puruṣa*'s purity.

Kaivalyapādaḥ (Independence)

Sūtras 4.1-4.6: Powers and Transformations

Causes that Lead to Powers

जन्मौषधिमन्त्रतपःसमाधिजाः सिद्धयः ॥ ४.१ ॥
janmauṣadhimantratapaḥsamādhijāḥ siddhayaḥ ॥ 4.1 ॥

janma = birth
oṣadhi = medicinal herbs
mantra = mystical verse, incantation, secret
tapaḥ = austerity
samādhi = perfected concentration, absorption
jāḥ = born of
siddhayaḥ = powers (siddhis), attainments

Attainments result from birth, medicinal herbs, incantations, austerity, and samādhi.

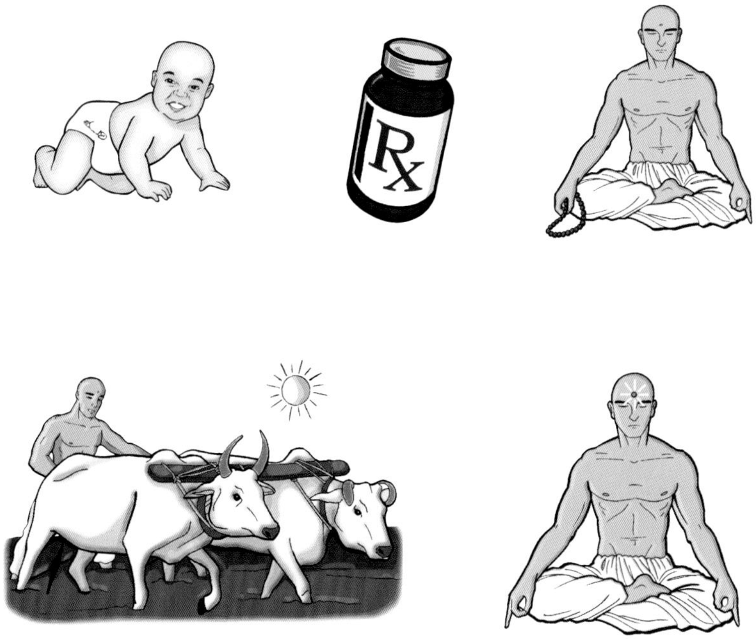

Methods of obtaining powers: birth, medicinal herbs, incantation, austerity (hard work), and samādhi

This sūtra mentions methods of acquiring powers (*siddhis*). Examples of powers obtained by each of the items above include the following:

Birth:

- Dogs have an extraordinary sense of smell by birth.
- Some people have inborn artistic or intellectual capabilities from birth. This is due to the effort in previous life.

Medicinal herbs:

- Strength and physical beauty can be gained through different herbs, ointments, etc.

Incantations:

- Repetitive recitation of mantras can induce a meditative state of mind. Ancient Indians believed that special powers can be attained through chanting of *mantras* or Vedic hymns. The word *mantra* can also mean a secret.

Austerity:

- Through austerity, hard work, and persistence one gains strength and success.

Concentration:

- All powers can be obtained through *samādhi*.

Of all of the methods, only the powers acquired through *samādhi* do not result in any stock of karma (sūtra 4.6).

The Role of Nature in Transformations

जात्यन्तरपरिणामः प्रकृत्यापूरात् ॥ ४.२ ॥
jātyantarapariṇāmaḥ prakṛtyāpūrāt ॥ 4.2 ॥

jāti = birth, category, class
antara = difference, another
pariṇāmaḥ = transformation, change
prakṛti = the primordial matter
āpūrāt = from the completion, from the filling, from overflowing of nature, superabundance

Transformation from one kind to another results from the abundance of prakṛti (or the filling in of prakṛti).

Jātyantarapariṇāma means transformation between any two states. In this sūtra the term refers to the transformation from one body to another, as when one takes birth in another body after death. It can also be any kind of transformation within a particular life. For example, a physically weak person becoming strong, a dull person becoming enlightened, etc.

This verse says that all transformations are brought about by the combination of elements of *prakṛti*. *Prakṛti* responds with consequences based on our stock of karma. The new body that a soul enters, such as an elephant or an ant, is formed based on the combination of our past virtuous and non-virtuous actions. Due to its abundant nature, *prakṛti* is capable of responding with all kinds of transformations. It is this specific capability of *prakṛti* that this sūtra refers to. The word *āpūra* can mean "fullness" or "filling in." The idea is that nature is "full of" possibilities, or it "fills in" with proper combinations of its elements to manifest the consequences.

निमित्तमप्रयोजकं प्रकृतीनां वरणभेदस्तु ततः क्षेत्रिकवत् ॥ ४.३ ॥
nimittamaprayojakaṁ prakṛtīnāṁ varaṇabhedastu tataḥ kṣetrikavat ॥ 4.3 ॥

nimittam = instrumental cause, efficient cause
aprayojakaṁ = non-mover (it does not move the elements of nature)
prakṛtīnāṁ = of the elements of nature
varaṇa = barrier, mound, obstacle
bhedaḥ = breaking through, piercing
tu = but, instead, on the other hand
tataḥ = from that
kṣetrika-vat = like a farmer

The instrumental cause is not the mover of nature [in bringing about transformation]. Instead, it breaks through obstacles [to transformation] like a farmer.

This sūtra describes the role of our actions in bringing about transformations. Although the transformation it refers to is the transformation from one body to another — as when one takes birth in another body after death — it can also mean any transformation or result that we experience as a consequence of our actions. So, all consequences come under "transformations" that we bring about with our actions. We think that our actions *directly* create the results that we experience. However, this sūtra teaches that the role of our actions in creating results is not as direct as we perceive. The role of our actions is like that of a farmer who does not personally carry the water between parts of the land he wishes to irrigate. Instead, he just breaks down the mound that would otherwise prevent the water from flowing. The idea is that water will naturally flow from a higher level to a lower level. The farmer just makes use of that phenomenon. Similarly, our actions do not directly bring about the transformations of things. *Prakṛti* is constantly changing due to its inherent nature in bringing about transformations. Our actions, virtuous or non-virtuous, do not actually create the consequences — they simply remove obstacles to consequences. The actual consequences and experiences in all their peculiarities are brought about by *prakṛti*.

The point made by this sūtra is very subtle, and gives considerable insight into how we perform actions in reality. We normally tend to ignore the role of *prakṛti* in performing actions. We say, "The farmer has irrigated the land," but we make an inaccurate assessment of that action and do not mention the role of water and its inherent nature to flow, which allowed the farmer to irrigate the land in the first place. This is one of the many ways we confuse the abilities and functions of our core consciousness with those of our mind and body, which leads to incorrect knowledge resulting in frustration and misery.

In order to emphasize the role of *prakṛti* in performing actions, Sāṅkhya calls *prakṛti* the "performer" of the actions, and considers the soul as the source of the actions. This has led to a lot of misunderstanding about Sāṅkhya which will be clarified in the coming section.

To understand this concept better, consider the analogy of a car. In order to accelerate the car, the driver only presses the accelerator — the car's machinery and fuel are the ones that really propel the car. In this analogy, the driver acts like the soul, the car acts like *prakṛti*, and "accelerating the car" is the action. Although the driver is the originator of the action and the experiencer of its consequences, it is the car that is actually carrying out the action. We can say *puruṣa* (soul) performs the "internal action" while *prakṛti* (mind and body) perform the visible "external action." *Puruṣa* is more of a director than a performer of any action.

The role of *prakṛti* is present in all actions, including mundane day-to-day activities, but it may not be obvious. For example, while raising a hand we do not know exactly how our body orchestrates the movement of all the muscles, ligaments, and bones etc. Similarly in a simple mental act, like remembering what we had for lunch yesterday, our mind's mechanisms of recalling are unknown to us. We just *initiate* the action and our minds and bodies carry out the action for us. Sometimes, the role of *prakṛti* is readily observable. Consider the healing of a person who has a bone fracture — a doctor can provide support for the bone to heal, but ultimately the bone repairs itself. The doctor's role is to diminish obstacles to that healing.

This sūtra has many day-to-day implications. Sometimes we may do everything right to bring about a particular result, but the result may nonetheless not be as we expect. This is because our role in creating the result is limited. Ignoring the role of *prakṛti* in performing actions and creating results can lead to frustration. In that frustration, we may wrongly evaluate our actions, which can be detrimental in our future pursuits. Understanding the roles of nature and of our own selves can alleviate some of that frustration, and help us to approach situations with a healthier attitude.

Prakṛti is not a sentient being. Yet, how can it give us the results based on our actions? *Prakṛti* behaves according to its intrinsic nature, just like a stone falls to the ground due to gravity. The natural law of karma that *prakṛti* follows is established by God (*Īśvara*) utilizing the attributes of *prakṛti*.

Nimitta

The word *nimitta* used in this sūtra is a technical term in philosophy. It is an efficient or instrumental cause, in the sense of something that enables an event but is not responsible for all of the factors involved in the event. In the case of making a pot, the potter is the efficient or the instrumental cause, as opposed to the clay, which is the material cause.

Originator of Actions and Experiencer of Consequences in Sāṅkhya

There is some misunderstanding regarding the originator of actions and free will in Sāṅkhya. The view of Sāṅkhya is the same as that of Yoga as expressed in the previous sūtra. Sāṅkhya states that the actions are performed by our minds and bodies (that is, by the three *guṇas* present in the mind and body), but makes it clear that the soul or consciousness is the originator of these actions. As the originator of its actions, the *puruṣa* is also the experiencer of the consequences (of its actions).

अहङ्कारः कर्ता न पुरुषः ॥

ahaṅkāraḥ kartā na puruṣaḥ ॥ *Sāṅkhya-darśana* 6.54 ॥
"*Ahaṅkāra* is the performer, not the consciousness."

उपरागात् कर्तृत्वं चित्सान्निध्यात् चित्सान्निध्यात् ॥

uparāgāt kartṛtvaṁ citsānnidhyāt citsānnidhyāt ॥ *Sāṅkhya-darśana* 1.164 ॥
"Agency [of the mind] is derived from the superimposition of consciousness, due to its (mind's) proximity with consciousness."

चिदवसानो भोगः ॥

cidavasāno bhogaḥ ॥ *Sāṅkhya-darśana* 1.104 ॥
"The consciousness is the final receptacle of experience."

Cit means consciousness. Consciousness only initiates an action, the action itself is carried out by *prakṛti* as explained in the last sūtra (4.3). In order to emphasize this, Sāṅkhya calls *ahaṅkāra* ("ego," which is part of mind) the performer of the action. But, this does not mean that consciousness lacks free will, any more than the driver of a car lacks free will — it is the consciousness that gives the power of "agency" to the mind, and therefore the consciousness has free will. Sāṅkhya clarifies the initiation of action by consciousness in the Sāṅkhya-sūtra 1.164 above.

Because of this free will of the consciousness, actions differ from one soul to another, and nature responds with varied consequences.

कर्मवैचित्र्यात् सृष्टिवैचित्र्यम् ॥

karmavaicitryāt sṛṣṭivaicitryam ॥ *Sāṅkhya-darśana* 6.41 ॥
"Variation in nature is due to variation in actions [of individual souls]."

A complete discussion of related sūtras can be found in *Sāṅkhya-darśanam* by Acharya Ananda Prakash.

निर्माणचित्तान्यस्मितामात्रात् ॥ ४.४ ॥
nirmāṇacittānyasmitāmātrāt ॥ 4.4 ॥

nirmāṇa = constructed, transformed
cittāni = minds
asmitā = ego (ahaṅkāra)
mātrāt = from only

Transformed minds are [made] from ego alone.

Vyāsa mentions that one power of a yogī (not mentioned in the *Yoga Sūtras*) is that a yogī can create multiple minds and bodies to consume the stock of karma (*karmāśaya*) that is yet to be experienced. The word *nirmāṇacitta* is taken to mean artificial minds that are created by a yogī. This clarification about a power to create bodies and minds that is not mentioned in the *Yoga Sūtras* seems quite odd. Patañjali mentions in the last sūtra (4.3) that consciousness is not the mover or manipulator of *prakṛti*. In addition, such powers are not supported by other *darśanas*. For these reasons some scholars do not agree with Vyāsa's commentary on this sūtra and the next, suggesting possible interpolations that may have crept into the commentaries over many centuries.

A better interpretation of the sūtra that fits the context is given by the eminent scholar Swami Satyapati Parivrajaka of Gurukul Rojad, Gujrat. The word *nirmāṇacitta* means the "transformed mind" that is attained through the five methods described in sūtra 4.1. This sūtra clarifies that all powers are obtained through the transformation of the ego material (*ahaṅkāra*) that makes up the mind. It should also be kept in mind that a yogī does not manipulate the material but acts only as the director as mentioned in the sūtra 4.3.

प्रवृत्तिभेदे प्रयोजकं चित्तमेकमनेकेषाम् ॥ ४.५ ॥
pravṛttibhede prayojakaṁ cittamekamanekeṣām ॥ 4.5 ॥

pravṛtti = activity, action
bhede = in the difference
prayojakaṁ = mover, director
cittam = mind
ekam = one
anekeṣām = of the many

Although the activities are different, the one mind is the performer of the many [activities].

Vyāsa's commentary interprets this sūtra to mean that the mind of the yogī controls the other minds that manage the many bodies he or she creates. As noted, some modern scholars do not accept the commentary to this sūtra as accurately representing Patañjali's principles for there is no mention of creating multiple bodies anywhere in the *Yoga Sūtras*. It can be inferred that the activities mentioned in this sūtra are the activities related to the powers (or transformed minds) obtained through the five methods described in sūtra 4.1. It simply means one mind can display various powers depending on how it is transformed.

The Superiority of Powers Obtained through Meditation

तत्र ध्यानजमनाशयम् ॥ ४.६ ॥
tatra dhyānajamanāśayam ॥ 4.6 ॥

tatra = among, there (in the transformed minds, in the powers attained)
dhyānajam = that which is born out of meditation (dhyāna)
anāśayam = without deposit, impressions of karma, "stock of karma"

Among [the transformed minds], that which is born out of meditation is without the stock of karma.

Sūtra 4.1 described different ways one could obtain the powers (*siddhis*). This sūtra says that only when the powers are obtained from meditation are they free of karmic deposits (*karmāśaya*). Those attained by other means create impressions of karma that result in consequences. For example, a person trying to gain strength through exercise could incur injuries, and one trying to experience an altered state of mind through the use of drugs could become addicted. Therefore, meditation is the best method for acquiring powers as it does not create any stock of karma. It was explained in sūtra 4.1 that powers can be obtained in five ways:

1. birth
2. medicinal herbs
3. mystical verses, incantations
4. austerity or hard work, and
5. *samādhi*, perfected meditation.

In this sūtra the word *dhyāna* (meditation) is used which I take to mean *samādhi.*

Meditation-born powers are free of the stock of karma that leads to consequences (represented as "baggage")

Sūtras 4.7-4.11: Actions, Impressions, and Consequences

कर्माशुक्लाकृष्णं योगिनस्त्रिविधमितरेषाम् ॥ ४.७ ॥
karmāśuklākṛṣṇaṁ yoginastrividhamitareṣām ॥ 4.7 ॥

karma = action
aśukla = non-white (not virtuous)
akṛṣṇaṁ = non-black (virtuous)
yoginaḥ = of a yogī
trividham = three kinds
itareṣām = of the others

The action of a yogī are neither black nor white. For other people, it is of three kinds.

The actions of a yogī do not produce a stock of karma. However, for other people the actions are either virtuous, non-virtuous, or a mixture of both. Commentators list the following four types of actions:

1. Non-virtuous actions cause harm to others.
2. Virtuous actions are mostly internal and self-directed, such as acts of austerity, introspection, and meditation. They are mental and do not injure others.
3. Virtuous and non-virtuous actions are those that cause both happiness and suffering to others.
4. Actions that are neither virtuous nor non-virtuous are those performed by yogīs. Actions without the influence of afflictions (ignorance, ego, attachment, aversion, and clinging to physical life) are considered neither good nor bad because they do not result in consequences.

Three kinds of actions

Impressions That Result from Actions

ततस्तद्विपाकानुगुणानामेवाभिव्यक्तिर्वासनानाम् ॥ ४.८ ॥
tatastadvipākānuguṇānāmevābhivyaktirvāsanānām ॥ 4.8 ॥

tataḥ = thence, from that
tad = that
vipāka = maturation, fruition, ripening
anuguṇānām = favorable conditions, accordingly, having corresponding attributes
eva = only
abhivyaktiḥ = manifestation
vāsanānām = scents, subconscious impressions, inclinations

From that [three kinds of actions], manifestation [activation] occurs only of subliminal impressions where conditions are favorable for ripening.

As explained before, when we perform actions (virtuous, non-virtous, and mixed), the impressions relating to those actions are stored in our mind. Such impressions need proper circumstances to fructify. When we take birth in a particular body, not all of the impressions can fructify — some of them might need another kind of body to provide the right circumstances. Therefore, only those impressions that can fructify in a particular body are "activated" when we enter that body. The rest remain "latent" — meaning they will remain dormant until we are reborn in another body. The goal of yoga is to prevent impressions from fructifying by completely restraining them.

जातिदेशकालव्यवहितानामप्यानन्तर्यं स्मृतिसंस्कारयोरेकरूपत्वात् ॥ ४.९ ॥
jātideśakālavyavahitānāmapyānantaryaṁ smṛtisaṁskārayorekarūpatvāt ॥ 4.9 ॥

jāti = birth, category, species
deśa = place
kāla = time
vyavahitānām = interrupted, separated, discontinuous
api = also, even, although
ānantaryaṁ = without interval, successive, uninterrupted
smṛti = memory
saṁskārayoḥ = of the impressions
eka-rūpatvāt = due to one-ness of form, due to similarity

There is an uninterrupted identity of memory and impressions, even though they are separated by birth, place, and time.

Impressions stored in the mind are reactivated when the circumstances for reactivating them arise in the future. The reactivated memory is identical to the impression recorded. This means that impressions lodged in the mind do not vanish, even after many births — no matter how much time has passed or how far the place where such impressions were recorded.

If a person performs actions that require one to be born as a cat in order to experience the consequences, then the impressions of such actions will remain latent until being born as a cat at some point in the future. When that occurs, those impressions are reactivated without loss, even if separated by hundreds of intervening births in other bodies. A subset of impressions relating to previous births as a cat, many lives ago, is also reactivated, which helps in experiencing the consequences in a cat's life. This allows for that soul to gain the behavior of a cat, to conduct the life of a cat and experience the consequences of cat-like actions.

We may ask the question, "What about the time we were born as a cat for the first time? There would have been no cat-related impressions in the mind then. How can one function in a cat body if there are no such impressions?" The answer to this question is that God (*Īśvara*), individual souls (*puruṣa*), and nature (*prakṛti*) are eternal. There is no beginning or end to them. Creation and dissolution happen continuously. Consequently, there is no "first birth as a cat." Our minds have the impressions relating to all creatures at all times, only some of them are active in a particular birth. The only time when our minds do not contain such impressions is when the *prakṛti* dissolves at the end of a creation cycle and our minds dissolve into the primordial elements (of *prakṛti*). Even then, the impressions are not lost. The knowledge of all impressions remains in God. When the cycle of creation begins again, our minds are created with residual impressions from the previous creation.

तासामनादित्वं चाशिषो नित्यत्वात् ॥ ४.१० ॥
tāsāmanāditvaṁ cāśiṣo nityatvāt ॥ 4.10 ॥

tāsām = of those
anāditvaṁ = beginning-less
ca = and
āśiṣaḥ = of will, desire, hope, wish
nityatvāt = due to the nature of persisting forever.

They [these memories and impressions] are beginning-less, as the will is eternal.

This is an explanation for why impressions remain forever — the will to survive is eternal. Even a newborn baby shows a fear of death. That fear of death is not developed from knowledge obtained through inference or verbal testimony; the impressions of fear of death have persisted from previous births.

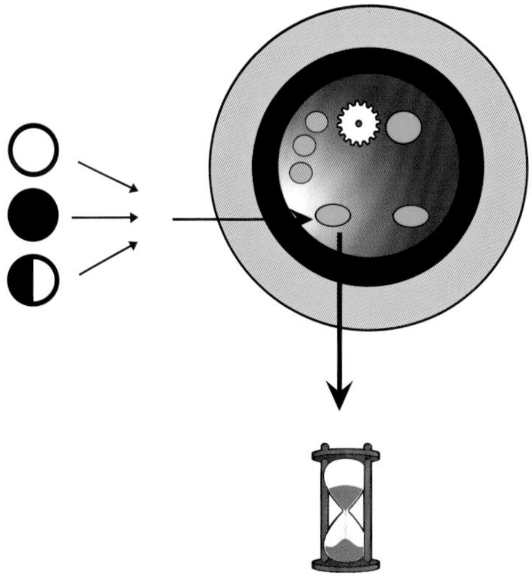

Durable impressions formed by the actions

हेतुफलाश्रयालम्बनैः संगृहीतत्वादेषामभावे तदभावः ॥ ४.११ ॥
hetuphalāśrayālambanaiḥ saṁgṛhītatvādeṣāmabhāve tadabhāvaḥ ॥ 4.11 ॥

hetu = cause
phala = fruit, result
āśraya = seat, basis, shelter, dwelling
ālambanaiḥ = by support, dependency
saṁgṛhītatvāt = due to being held together, connectedness
eṣām = of these
abhāve = in the absence, disappearance
tad = that
abhāvaḥ = absence, disappearance

Because of the connections between cause, result, seat, and dependency, when these cease, they [the impressions also] cease.

What are cause, result, seat, and dependency?

- Cause means virtue or vice which results in pleasure or pain.
- Result is the consequence of any action. The consequences of both virtuous and non-virtuous karma must be experienced — there is no escape from it. As long as the consequences of actions have not been experienced, impressions (*saṁskāra*) remain.
- Seat refers to the mind, which holds impressions. Impressions remain as long as the mind exists.
- Dependency refers to the objects of the senses. As long as the objects of desire or hate exist, impressions have the potential to sprout into activities.

As long as these four things exist, impressions exist. If all four are eliminated, impressions are also eliminated.

Sūtras 4.12-4.15: Objects and Perception of them

Past, Present, and Future Forms of Objects (Vastu)

अतीतानागतं स्वरूपतोऽस्त्यध्वभेदाद्धर्माणाम् ॥ ४.१२ ॥
atītānāgataṁ svarūpato'styadhvabhedāddharmāṇām ॥ 4.12 ॥

atīta = past
anāgataṁ = yet to come, future
sva-rūpataḥ = from the own form
asti = it is, exists
adhva = course, path
bhedāt = due to difference
dharmāṇām = of the forms, properties, characteristics

The past and future exist due to the different courses of manifestations taken by properties [of an object].

The past is an already-manifested form, while the future is a yet-to-be-manifested form. Both exist in an object. All objects are considered to be *dharmīs* because they have properties or forms (*dharmas*) that manifest at different times. Considering both the past and the future forms as being always present in an object is the basis of a principle called *Satkārya*, which Sāṅkhya and Yoga follow. The principle of *Satkārya* is that the effect is already present in the cause (as a potentiality), and may manifest over time. For example, fire is considered to be present in a matchstick. That fire manifests when the appropriate circumstances arise.

ते व्यक्तसूक्ष्मा गुणात्मानः ॥ ४.१३ ॥
te vyaktasūkṣmā guṇātmānaḥ ॥ 4.13 ॥

te = these (the past and future)
vyakta = manifest
sūkṣmāḥ = subtle
guṇa = the three elements, forces (sattva, rajas, and tamas)
ātmānaḥ = made of

These [the past and future] — manifest or latent — are made of the three guṇas.

Past and future (and by implication, the present) are simply the result of the transformation of the *guṇas*. In this sūtra, the fundamental principle of Sāṅkhya is revisited — that everything we experience is brought about by constant changes in the combination of the three primordial elements of nature. For more information, please read the chapter on Sāṅkhya philosophy at the beginning of this book.

Perceptions of an Object (Vastu)

परिणामैकत्वाद्वस्तुतत्त्वम् ॥ ४.१४ ॥
pariṇāmaikatvādvastutattvam ॥ 4.14 ॥

pariṇāma = transformation, change
ekatvāt = due to being one
vastu = object
tattvam = nature

From the uniqueness of its transformation comes the nature of an object.

Sāṅkhya teaches that *prakṛti* is in a state of continuous change — the three *guṇas* constantly interact with one another. Objects (*vastu*) seem solid and permanent, but they are really transitory and impermanent. This is the first of four verses that discuss the nature of objects. This verse describes how what we perceive as an object is in reality simply a unique confluence of transformations (*pariṇāma*). All objects have the properties of *sattva*, *rajas*, and *tamas* even though they still form a single unique object. Each of the three *guṇas* plays its particular role in an object being perceptible.

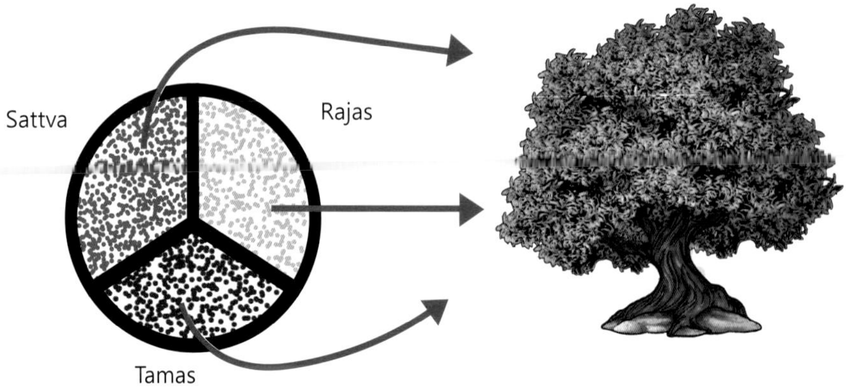

Sattva, rajas and tamas transforming into an object

वस्तुसाम्ये चित्तभेदात्तयोर्विभक्तः पन्थाः ॥ ४.१५ ॥
vastusāmye cittabhedāttayorvibhaktaḥ panthāḥ ॥ 4.15 ॥

vastu = object
sāmye = being the same, same-ness
citta-bhedāt = due to difference in minds, multiplicity of minds
tayor = of the two
vibhaktaḥ = divided, different, separated
panthāḥ = path

While the object is the same, due to difference in minds, the difference in the two [the object known, and the knowledge or perception of it] is due to the separate paths of the minds.

The previous sūtra said that the objects (*vastu*) are unique transformations of elements of nature. This sūtra is meant to offer proof that objects really do exist, as opposed to the view of some who maintain that objects do not exist and are merely imagined by the mind. Multiple minds perceive a single object in different ways. For example, an object can evoke a feeling of pleasure in one person and pain in another.

If an object is assumed to be merely a creation of the mind, then there arises the question of which mind created the object. If one mind created it, how could it influence the other minds? The object must exist on its own but is perceived differently by different minds.

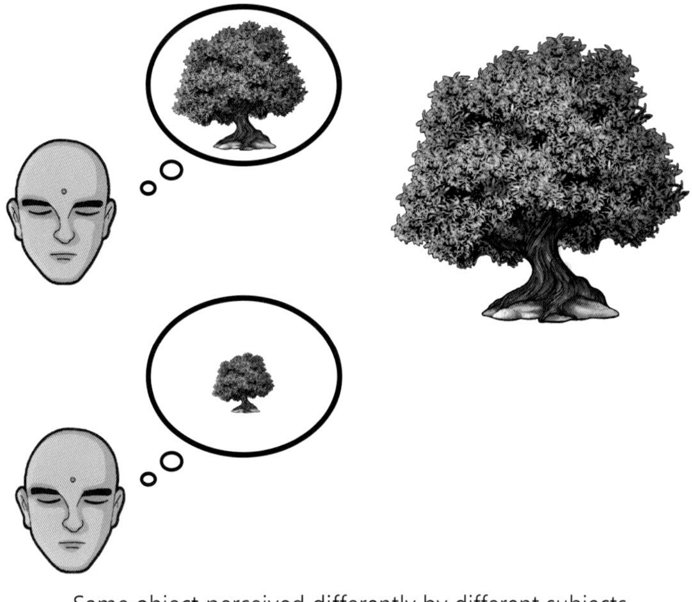

Same object perceived differently by different subjects

Sūtras 4.16-4.24: Distinctness of the Mind (seen) and the Consciousness (seer)

Nature is Independent of Consciousness

न चैकचित्ततन्त्रं चेद्वस्तु तदप्रमाणकं तदा किं स्यात् ॥ ४.१६ ॥
na caikacittatantraṁ cedvastu tadapramāṇakaṁ tadā kiṁ syāt ॥ 4.16 ॥

na = not
ca = and
eka-citta = one mind
tantraṁ = dependent
cet = if
vastu = object
tat = that
apramāṇakaṁ = unprovable, not perceived, unwitnessed
tadā = then
kiṁ = what
syāt = could be, will be

An object is not dependent on a single mind. If it were not perceived [by that single mind], then what would the it be (or become)?

This sūtra questions the notion maintained by some philosophies that objects are not real, and are just the imagination of the mind. If the existence of an object is dependent on a single mind, then what will happen when that mind is not thinking about it? When that mind is thinking of something else or is in a state of *samādhi*, will the object cease to exist? Will others be unable to perceive it? For example, when one is perceiving or imagining a pot, what will happen to all the other things that are not being imagined, such as the home, a tree, the ground, etc. Do they cease to exist? If you see a person's front side, does it mean that the person's back does not exist?

This sūtra is consistent with the view that objects exist in reality and are perceived differently by various minds depending on their stock of karma (*karmāśaya*). It is important to recall here that the *karmāśaya* influences every perception of the mind.

Objects exist even when not being perceived by a subject

तदुपरागापेक्षित्वाच्चित्तस्य वस्तु ज्ञाताज्ञातम् ॥ ४.१७ ॥
taduparāgāpekṣitvāccittasya vastu jñātājñātam ॥ 4.17 ॥

tat = that
uparāga = coloring
apekṣitvāt = depending on, requirement
cittasya = of the mind
vastu = object
jñātā = known
ajñātam = unknown

An object is known or not known depending on the coloring of mind by it.

When the senses come into contact with an object, they convey sensory information to the mind. Mind takes on the form of that sensory data as if it were "colored" by it. This coloring is witnessed by the consciousness. This is how consciousness perceives things. If the mind is not colored by an object, we don't perceive it.

सदा ज्ञाताश्चित्तवृत्तयस्तत्प्रभोः पुरुषस्यापरिणामित्वात् ॥ ४.१८ ॥
sadā jñātāścittavṛttayastatprabhoḥ puruṣasyāpariṇāmitvāt ॥ 4.18 ॥

sadā = always
jñātāḥ = known
citta = mind
vṛttayaḥ = the activities
tat = that
prabhoḥ = of the superior, master
puruṣasya = of the consciousness
apariṇāmitvāt = due to immutability, unchanging nature

The activities of the mind are always known, because the lord of the mind, puruṣa, is unchangeable.

In Sāṅkhya philosophy, *puruṣa* is eternal and unchanging. *Puruṣa* is called "constant eternal" (*kūṭasthanitya*). *Prakṛti* is called "changing eternal" (*pariṇāmanitya*). It constantly changes but is eternal. Both *puruṣa* and *prakṛti* are neither created nor destroyed.

The previous five verses described the changeable nature of phenomenal reality and explained how these transformations affect our mind. This verse uses the word *prabhu* which literally means a superior or a master. The verse is referring to *puruṣa* in its pure form, which is not the same as our mind. Patañjali describes yoga as regulation of the operations of *citta* (sūtra 1.2). The same phrase *cittavṛtti* reappears here. This sūtra says that all of these operations of a mind are known (*jñāta*) by its owner (*prabhu*), the consciousness. *Puruṣa* is always aware of the mind's activities. If *puruṣa* changed, then it would not be aware of the things it was aware of before changing.

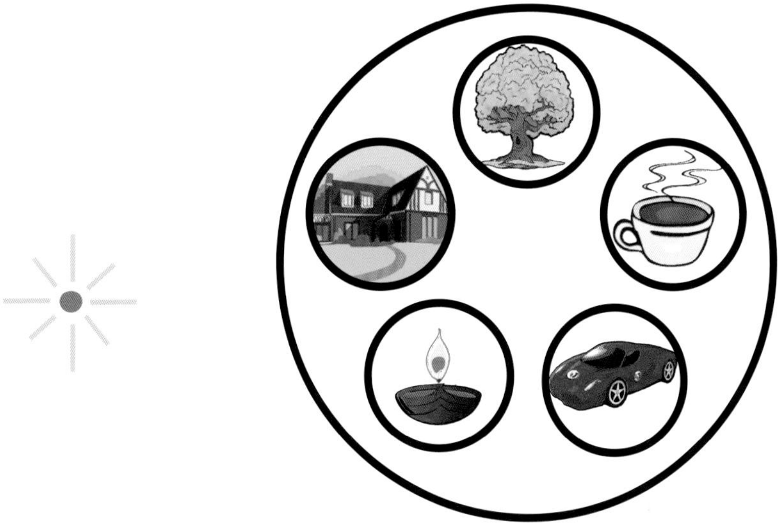

Consciousness perceives the mind colored by the objects

न तत्स्वभासं दृश्यत्वात् ॥ ४.१९ ॥
na tat svābhāsaṁ dṛśyatvāt ॥ 4.19 ॥

na = not
tat = that (mind)
svābhāsaṁ = self luminous or self knowing
dṛśyatvāt = due to being seen, "seen-ness," due to being objectified

That [mind] is not self-luminous due to it being an object [of perception].

Just as the sense organs, through which we perceive things, do not sense themselves, the mind does not sense or know itself. We can see that the mind is knowable, because we are able to describe emotions such as "I am afraid," "I am angry," "I like this" and so on. The mind is the object of consciousness. Consciousness is the real subject that experiences the mind (the object).

The term *svābhāsaṁ* deserves a comment. *Ābhāsam* means luminous. In this context it means knowing. *Sva* means "self" — thus *svābhāsam* means "self-knowing."

एकसमये चोभयानवधारणम् ॥ ४.२० ॥
ekasamaye cobhayānavadhāraṇam ॥ 4.20 ॥

eka-samaye = in the same moment, simultaneously
ca = and
ubhaya = both
ānavadhāraṇam= not determining, not distinguishing

Both [the mind and its object] cannot be perceived at the same time.

This verse is a follow-up for the previous verse, which said that mind is itself an object and not self-luminous. This verse says that the subject and object cannot be both known or perceived simultaneously. The mind cannot be aware of itself directly. Verse 4.17 described mind as simply taking on the color of what is around it. Consciousness perceives this colored mind and identifies with it. The pure nature of consciousness must be separated out from the characteristics of the mind.

Some schools of philosophy propound that everything in the universe is imaginary and momentary. Even perception is momentary. Everything exists for a moment, and in the subsequent moment everything is created anew: our bodies, minds, and objects that seem to exist for more than a moment are only appearances of continuity because the subsequent moments produce perceptions similar to those of the previous moments. Every object, including your self ("I"), is new in the subsequent moment — it is not the same as the one in the previous moment, which completely disappears after a moment. This is the principle of *kṣaṇikavāda*.

This sūtra refutes such a theory by citing that we experience perceptions like "I saw the pot" or "I know the pot," in which there is awareness of both "I" and the "pot." If everything (including "I" and the "pot") were momentary, then we could not have such perceptions. In one moment I perceive the pot and in the second moment I cannot say "I saw the pot," because in the second moment a new "I" is born. The new "I" will have to sense the pot again to know the pot in the second moment. In the third moment I still cannot say that I saw the pot, because the "I" that existed in the second moment does not exist any more — a new "I" is created. This continues forever, and we can never have perceptions like "I saw a pot" in reality if *kṣaṇikavāda* argument holds.

The word *kṣaṇikavāda* is taken to mean Buddhism by many commentators. *Kṣaṇikavāda* could also be a generic name for a theory that is subscribed to by many followers of different philosophies. *Śaṅkara on Yoga Sūtras* by Trevor Leggett is a great source for readers who are interested in the debate between the Yoga and *kṣaṇikavāda* followers.

चित्तान्तरदृश्ये बुद्धिबुद्धेरतिप्रसङ्गः स्मृतिसङ्करश्च ॥ ४.२१ ॥
cittāntaradṛśye buddhibuddheratiprasaṅgaḥ smṛtisaṁkaraśca ॥ 4.21 ॥

citta = mind
antara = other, another
dṛśye = in being seen, perceived
buddhi = knowing
buddheḥ = of knowing
atiprasaṅgaḥ = excessive occurrence, recursive, excessive interconnections
smṛti = memory
saṁkaraḥ = confusion
ca = and

[If] mind were perceived by another [mind], there would be recursion of perceptions by perceptions, and confusion of memory.

The previous sūtra refuted the *kṣaṇikavāda* philosophy by noting that there could never be the perception of the subject and the object at the same time — perceptions like "I know the pot." There is, however, an explanation given for that kind of phenomenon by the *kṣaṇikavāda* followers. It is offered that the mind that perceives the object in the first moment creates a mind in the second moment that is aware of the first mind. This sūtra elucidates the flaw in this proposition.

If the mind in the subsequent moment is the knower of the mind in the previous moment, then there would be no end to the recursive cognitions. The mind in the second moment will be aware of the mind in the first moment. The mind in the third moment will be aware of the mind in the second moment, and therefore also the mind in the first moment. The mind in the fourth moment knows the third, the second, and first, and this regression continues infinitely. For example, when the mind sees a tree, it knows that it has seen the tree. The mind in the second moment knows that it knows that it has seen a tree. The mind, in the third moment, knows that it knows that it knows that it has seen a tree, and so on. *Kṣaṇikavāda* thoery will lead to this kind of recursive perception. Also, when we perceive something, there is an impression of memory created in the mind. The infinite perceptions of a single thing demonstrated above would make recollection of memory confusing, or perhaps impossible.

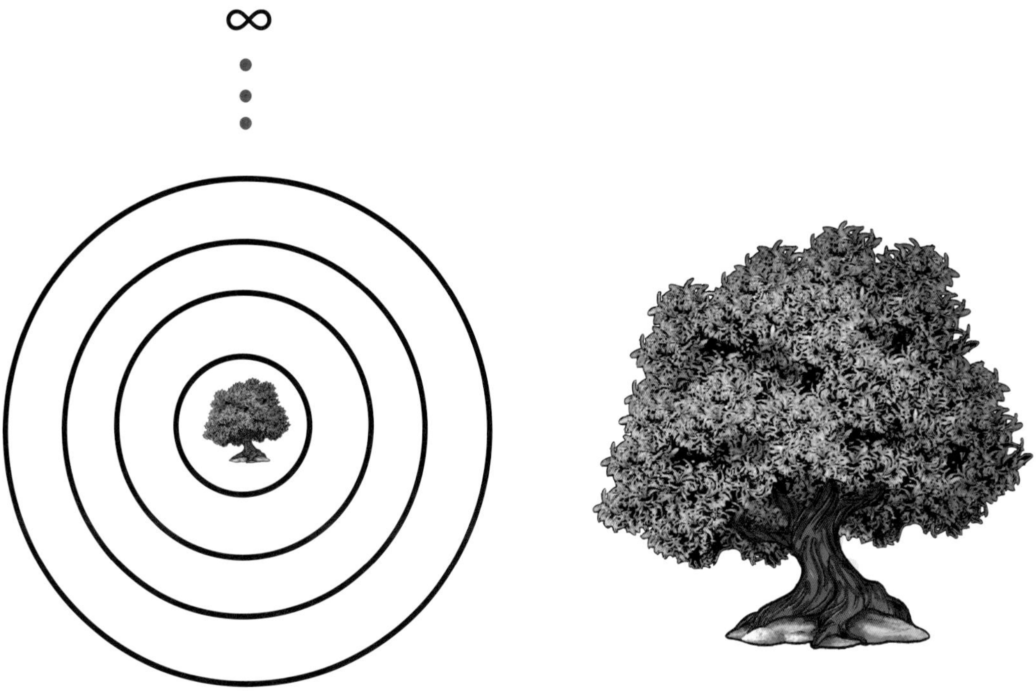

Recursive perceptions resulting from a mind perceiving another mind (or even itself)

चितेरप्रतिसंक्रमायास्तदाकारापत्तौ स्वबुद्धिसंवेदनम् ॥ ४.२२ ॥
citerapratisaṁkramāyāstadākārāpattau svabuddhisaṁvedanam ॥ 4.22 ॥

citeḥ = of the mind
apratisaṁkramāyāḥ = of the unchanging, of the immobile
tat = that (that object)
ākāra = form
āpattau = occuring, entering into a state
sva = own
buddhi = mind, intellect
saṁvedanam = feeling, knowing

The unchanging consciousness becomes aware of intellect when it [the intellect] takes the form of [an object].

When *buddhi* takes the form of an object, *puruṣa* can know *buddhi* along with its activities. For example, when we see a tree, the impression of the tree is formed on the mind. *Puruṣa* experiences the mind and becomes aware of the tree along with the thinking activity happening in the mind. It is because of this experience that we feel like we are a person, male or female, that is perceiving the tree. But our souls are distinct from the male and female bodies or minds.

The verse uses the word experience (*saṁvedanam*) to describe the relationship that *puruṣa* has with *buddhi*'s activities. That is, *puruṣa* is the experiencer of the operations of *buddhi*. The goal of yoga is for *puruṣa* to know itself without being confused with *buddhi*.

द्रष्टृदृश्योपरक्तं चित्तं सर्वार्थम् ॥ ४.२३ ॥
draṣṭṛdṛśyoparaktaṁ cittaṁ sarvārtham ॥ 4.23 ॥

draṣṭṛ = the seer
dṛśya = the seen
uparaktaṁ = colored
cittaṁ = mind
sarva-artham = for all purposes, for any purpose, various purposes

Mind, colored by both the seer and the seen, has various purposes.

Mind (*citta*) acts like a mirror that reflects both ways. It can show the external objects to the *puruṣa* as well as *puruṣa*'s own reflection (metaphorically speaking). Mind is colored by the external objects. That is how *puruṣa* is aware of them. Mind is also colored or influenced by the *puruṣa*. That is how *puruṣa* can know itself through mind. It is mind that is colored by the objects and not *puruṣa*.

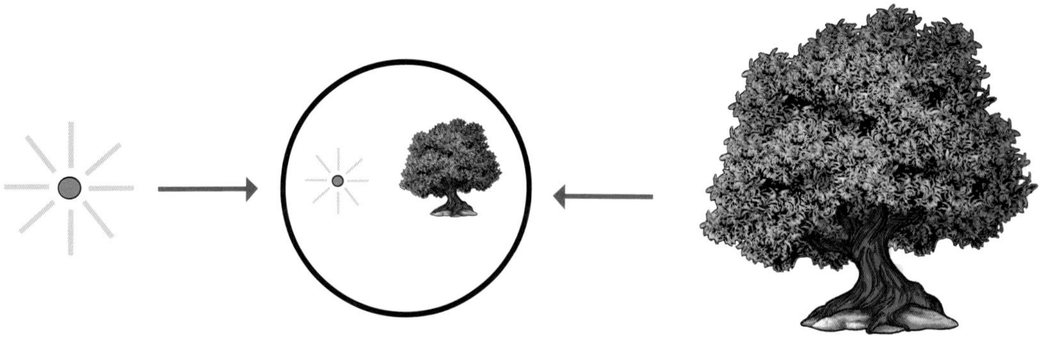

Various purposes of the mind

Consciousness is Independent of Nature

तदसंख्येयवासनाभिश्चित्रमपि परार्थं संहत्यकारित्वात् ॥ ४.२४ ॥
tadasaṁkhyeyavāsanābhiścitramapi parārthaṁ saṁhatyakāritvāt ॥ 4.24 ॥

tat = that (citta)
asaṁkhyeya = innumerable, countless
vāsanābhiḥ = by the impressions
citram = spotted, imprinted
api = even
parārthaṁ = for the purpose of another
saṁhatya = put together from components, combined
kāritvāt = due to working, activity

Being imprinted with innumerable impressions, the mind is for the purpose of another [not for itself], because it works with many components.

There is an important principle in Indian philosophy which states that anything that is made of, or functions due to, a combination of multiple elements exists for a purpose other than itself. For example, a chair — made of legs, a base, and a back support — cannot be for itself. The purpose of a chair is for someone to sit in. In that sense, a chair does not exist "for itself." A chair does not sit on itself, it exists for its user. In the same way, the mind is a collection of elements which serves the purpose of "another," which is *puruṣa*. The mind cannot be for itself because it is made of components (i.e. *sattva*, *rajas*, *tamas*, intellect, ego, mental impressions and activities, and so on) and it works with other entities like the sense organs. The mind does not experience itself, it is the soul that experiences the mind.

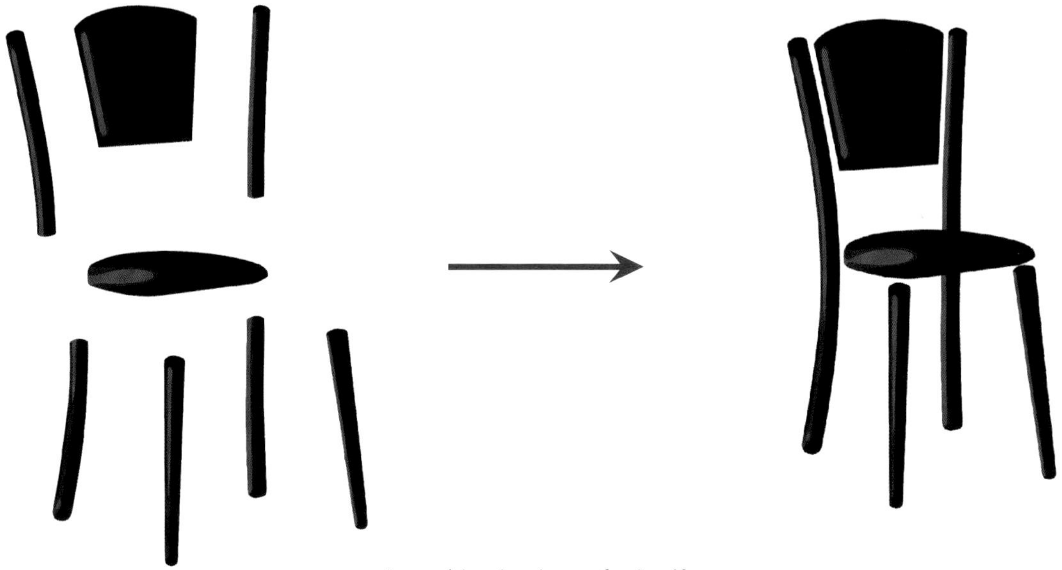

A combination is not for itself

Sūtras 4.24-4.34: Final Stages

विशेषदर्शिन आत्मभावभावनाविनिवृत्तिः ॥ ४.२५ ॥
viśeṣadarśina ātmabhāvabhāvanāvinivṛttiḥ ॥ 4.25 ॥

viśeṣa = distinct, particular
darśinaḥ = of the seer
ātma-bhāva = meaning of self, sense of self
bhāvanā = thinking about, contemplation
vinivṛttiḥ = cessation

For the one who has the vision of the distinctness [of puruṣa and buddhi] contemplation on the nature of the self ceases.

For those who have gained awareness of the difference between the mind and pure consciousness (*puruṣa*), questions such as "who am I?," "where did I come from?," and "what is the purpose of life?," etc., cease to concern them. People who have practiced yoga in their previous lives are drawn to such questions. This kind of self-examination is important as we learn about how our minds work. But at some point the vision of how the mind is different from pure consciousness (*puruṣa*) becomes very clear and we no longer worry about things that used to concern us. We simple know the truth and no longer speculate about it.

तदा विवेकनिम्नं कैवल्यप्राग्भारश्चित्तम् ॥ ४.२६ ॥
tadā vivekanimnaṁ kaivalyaprāgbhāraṁ cittam ॥ 4.26 ॥

tadā = then
viveka = discernment, discrimination
nimnaṁ = leaning toward, inclined
kaivalya = alone-ness, isolation, independence, autonomy
prāgbhāram = gravitating toward, laden with
cittam = mind

Then, the mind inclined toward discrimination gravitates toward isolation.

This sūtra uses the word *kaivalya* to describe the state the yogī is moving toward. The word *kaivalya* is derived from the word *kevala* which means "alone" or "by itself." *Kaivalya* is the state of being "by itself." The idea is that in *kaivalya* the yogī is no longer under the influence of external forces and no longer identifies with things that are not part of the true self. *Kaivalya* is often translated as "isolation" or "alone-ness" which are attempts to capture this idea. It is also sometimes translated as "liberation" but in Sanskrit the word more often used for that concept is *mokṣa*. The word *kaivalya* is a technical term in this literature for the specific state of independence from outside forces that is the result of yogic practice.

तच्छिद्रेषु प्रत्ययान्तराणि संस्कारेभ्यः ॥ ४.२७ ॥
tacchidreṣu pratyayāntarāṇi saṁskārebhyaḥ ॥ 4.27 ॥

tat = that
chidreṣu = in the intervals
pratyaya = thought, knowledge, conception
āntarāṇi = other things
saṁskārebhyaḥ = from the impressions

During the intervals [between discriminating wisdom], the perception of other things arises due to latent impressions.

When the yogī is not in *samādhi*, various thoughts may arise due to latent mental impressions that have not yet been restrained. This is how people who have achieved the goal of yoga are also able to function in day-to-day life. The verse says something about the way yoga is actually practiced that is worth noting. It assumes that the yogī will go in and out of the state of mental absorption that we call *samādhi*. That is, a yogī even at very high levels of practice is not always completely absorbed. Many people when they are first learning about yoga think of *samādhi* as an "all or nothing" experience. But, in fact, Patañjali describes several different kinds of *samādhi* in the text and emphasizes the importance of the subliminal impressions that are left behind when the yogī comes out of *samādhi*. That model of repetitively entering and exiting from the yogic state of mind underlies this sūtra.

हानमेषां क्लेशवदुक्तम् ॥ ४.२८ ॥
hānameṣāṁ kleśavaduktam ॥ 4.28 ॥

hānam = removal, abandoning
eṣāṁ = these (latent impressions)
kleśavat = like the afflictions (kleśa)
uktam = is said to be, described

It is said that these [latent impressions] should be eliminated like the afflictions (kleśas).

With the fire of true knowledge, even the latent impressions (*saṁskāras*) are burnt up and are made unproductive. The impressions created by true knowledge, on the other hand, are helpful in restraining the activities of our minds. They too will dissolve into *prakṛti* when the mind stops functioning completely after the dissociation of the *puruṣa* and *citta* at death. This happens naturally and without effort.

प्रसंख्यानेऽप्यकुसीदस्य सर्वथा विवेकख्यातेर्धर्ममेघस्समाधिः ॥ ४.२९ ॥
prasaṁkhyāne'pyakusīdasya sarvathāvivekakhyāterdharmameghaḥ samādhiḥ ॥ 4.29 ॥

prasaṁkhyāne = in the special knowledge (obtained from meditation)
api = also, even
akusīdasya = of the one who has no interest, of the disinterested one
sarvathā = completely
vivekakhyāteḥ = of the discriminating
dharmameghaḥ = dharma-cloud
samādhiḥ = perfected concentration, absorption

For the one who is disinterested in meditative knowledge, and [having] a complete vision of discernment, [there is] dharmamegha-samādhiḥ.

When a yogī becomes disinterested even in the powers of meditation and the knowledge it brings, and has a thorough discriminating wisdom, the state of *samādhi* they attain is called *dharmamegha*. The word *dharmamegha* is used here as a technical term to refer to a name of a particular kind of *samādhi* that is the penultimate state before *kaivalya*.

ततः क्लेशकर्मनिवृत्तिः ॥ ४.३० ॥
tataḥ kleśakarmanivṛttiḥ ॥ 4.30 ॥

tataḥ = from that
kleśa = affliction
karma = action
nivṛttiḥ = cessation

From that [results] the cessation of afflictions and actions.

In that *dharmamegha-samādhi*, all five *kleśas* (ignorance, ego, attachment, hate, clinging to physical life) are eliminated. The *karmāśaya*, or stock of impressions, arising from the three kinds of actions (virtuous, non-virtuous, and mixed) are also eliminated.

तदा सर्वावरणमलापेतस्य ज्ञानस्यानन्त्याज्ज्ञेयमल्पम् ॥ ४.३१ ॥
tadā sarvāvaraṇamalāpetasya jñānasyānantyājjñeyamalpam ॥ 4.31 ॥

tadā = then
sarva = all
āvaraṇa = covering, veil
mala = impurity
apetasya = of the gone, removed
jñānasyā = of the knowledge
ānantyāt = from the limitlessness, from the inifinity
jñeyam = which is to be known
alpam = little

Because the knowledge obtained when all the impurities are removed is limitless, little remains to be known.

Knowledge becomes unlimited when impurities of the mind such as *kleśas* are eliminated. A yogī can know everything that he or she wants to know. Thus, very little remains to be known.

ततः कृतार्थानां परिणामक्रमसमाप्तिगुणानाम् ॥ ४.३२ ॥
tataḥ kṛtārthānāṁ pariṇāmakramasamāptirguṇānām ॥ 4.32 ॥

tataḥ = from that (dharmameghasamādhi)
kṛta-arthānāṁ = of the ones who have fulfilled their goals
pariṇāma = change, transformation
krama = sequence
samāptir = end, termination
guṇānām = of the guṇas (of the fundamental elements sattva, rajas and tamas)

From that [dharmamegha-samādhi], comes the end of the sequence of transformation of the guṇas, which have fulfilled their purpose.

When the goals of the *guṇas* are achieved, their sequence of mutation (*krama*) stops. The goals of the *guṇas* are experience (*bhoga*) and liberation (*apavarga*). The meaning of this sūtra will become clearer after the definition of the word *krama* is given in the following sūtra.

Krama, the Perceptible Change

क्षणप्रतियोगी परिणामापरान्तनिर्ग्राह्यः क्रमः ॥ ४.३३ ॥
kṣaṇapratiyogī pariṇāmāparāntanirgrāhyaḥ kramaḥ ॥ 4.33 ॥

kṣaṇa = moment
pratiyogī = that which is related, connected, correlated
pariṇāma = change, transformation
apara-anta = the other end, the terminus
nirgrāhyaḥ = perceptible, graspable
kramaḥ = sequence

Connected with moments, the transformation that is perceptible at their end is "sequence" (krama).

This verse defines the word *krama* which was used in the previous sūtra. Every object is undergoing continuous change. When a table gets old in a year, it has been undergoing change at every moment. In other words, aging doesn't happen all at once. This kind of continuous change, which happens at every moment and is only perceivable when it has progressed significantly, is called *krama*. In other words "perceptible change" can be called *krama*.

The previous sūtra states that when the goals of the *guṇas* are achieved, the mutations of the *guṇas* do not stop — only the perceptible changes in the *guṇas* stop. In other words, the mutations of the *guṇas* become so subtle that they are imperceptible.

Kaivalya

पुरुषार्थशून्यानां गुणानां प्रतिप्रसवः कैवल्यं स्वरूपप्रतिष्ठा वा चितिशक्तिरिति ॥ ४.३४ ॥
puruṣārthaśūnyānāṁ guṇānāṁ pratiprasavaḥ kaivalyaṁ svarūpapratiṣṭhā vā citiśaktiriti ॥ 4.34 ॥

puruṣa-artha = goal of consciousness
śūnyānāṁ = of the ones who are devoid of
guṇānāṁ = of the guṇas (sattva, rajas and tamas)
prati-prasavaḥ = reverse flow, re-absorption, dissolution
kaivalyaṁ = alone-ness, isolation, independence, autonomy, liberation, one-ness with self
sva-rūpa = own form
pratiṣṭhā = establishment
vā = or
citi-śakteḥ = the power of conciousness
iti = thus, the end, finis

One-ness with self or complete liberation (kaivalya) is when the guṇas are devoid of purpose for puruṣa, and are re-absorbed. Or [it is] the establishement of the power of consciousness in its own form.

The transformation of the *guṇas* to provide experience (*bhoga*) and liberation (*apavarga*) to the *puruṣa* stops. Having fulfilled their purpose, the *guṇas* are of no further use to the *puruṣa*. The yogī's mind is re-absorbed into its constituent elements of nature. Consciousness, having detached from the mind, remains in its own form. This is true liberation and independence from the mutations of nature.

The nature still exists and undergoes transformations for those individuals who have not yet attained complete liberation. With this, Patañjali marks the end of the *Yoga Sūtras*. Before concluding this book, I will briefly present some information on the nature of liberation.

The Nature and Span of Liberation

In liberation, one is said to be free from the many provocations of the mind — the consciousness is pervaded by the omniscience of God, and so experiences uninterrupted bliss, freedom, and independence. There are many theories describing how exactly the state of liberation is experienced. This is elaborated in Svami Dayananda Sarasvati's *Satyārthaprakāsh*. Some propound that such a consciousness is free from all elements of nature (*prakṛti*) — that is, it is free from the subtle body. Others say that consciousness is still attached to another kind of subtle body, with which it experiences bliss. There are also differences of opinion on the time-span of liberation — some say that the period for which the soul experiences bliss is unlimited, eternal, while others maintain that it expires after a set period. Much of Vedic and Upanishadic literature mentions that souls return from emancipation to re-enter the worldly cycle. The period before this, during which one enjoys liberation, is called *Parāntakāla* (*Mundakopaniṣad 3.2.6*). The *Parāntakāla* consists of 100 Brahma-years. A Brahma-day consists of 4,320 million years — the amount of time that this current universe persists. The dissolution of creation takes the same amount of time — 4,320 million years — and it is called a Brahma-night. One Brahma-day-night therefore consists of 8,640 million years. 360 of such days comprise one Brahma-year. 100 such brahma-years is the time-span of *Parāntakāla*, of liberation — 311,040,000 million years, or 311.04 trillion years.

Need for a Holistic Approach to Darśanas

The *Yoga Sūtras* consists of only 195 lines, and although they are packed with an immense amount of information, they do not answer every question. Like all the authors of the *darśanas*, Patañjali quite sensibly avoided redundancy by not repeating what is treated in other works. The six *darśanas* together present a cohesive model of life, but none of them individually explains all the questions one can have about life. Together, however, the six *darśanas* give a comprehensive picture of life as presented by the Indian rishis. Each of the *darśanas* is therefore best studied in conjunction with the others; interpreting a *darśana* independent of the others amounts to taking it out of context. Such one-track approaches have led to misinterpretation, and to an overemphasis on some *darśanas* and marginalization of others. This has not fostered a productive atmosphere for understanding the Vedic way of life. It is important to take a more holistic approach to understanding these six great *śāstras*. I encourage readers to take a look at other *darśanas*, and not to be limited to only the *Yoga Sūtras*.

Concluding thoughts

As much as I personally advocate the usefulness of Sāṅkhya and Yoga in understanding the mind and the self, no body of knowledge can claim to be complete. It goes without saying that this is true with Sāṅkhya and Yoga as well. Many people have gained discernment and insights into life without being conscious of Sāṅkhya and Yoga, and their methods of obtaining knowledge are all valid. As Patañjali says, God is the source of all true knowledge and inspiration. May people from all cultures come together to enhance knowledge and happiness, and help shed misconceptions to eliminate misery.

यत्र विश्वं भवत्येकनीडम्

Where the whole world is one nest.

- *Yajurveda* 32.8

Appendix
Yoga Sūtras: Text & Translation

अथ योगानुशासनम् ॥ १.१ ॥
atha yogānuśāsanam ॥ 1.1 ॥
Now begins the re-enunciation of the principles of yoga. *Page 51*

योगश्चित्तवृत्तिनिरोधः ॥ १.२ ॥
yogaścittavṛttinirodhaḥ ॥ 1.2 ॥
Yoga means restraining the activities of the mind. *Page 52*

तदा द्रष्टुः स्वरूपेऽवस्थानम् ॥ १.३ ॥
tadā draṣṭuḥ svarūpe'vasthānam ॥ 1.3 ॥
Then, the seer is established in his own form. *Page 59*

वृत्तिसारूप्यमितरत्र ॥ १.४ ॥
vṛttisārūpyamitaratra ॥ 1.4 ॥
At other times, it (the seer, consciousness) takes the same form as its [mind's] activities. *Page 60*

वृत्तयः पञ्चतय्यः क्लिष्टाक्लिष्टाः ॥ १.५ ॥
vṛttayaḥ pañcatayyaḥ kliṣṭākliṣṭāḥ ॥ 1.5 ॥
There are five kinds of activities, which are either afflicting or non-afflicting. *Page 61*

प्रमाणविपर्ययविकल्पनिद्रास्मृतयः ॥ १.६ ॥
pramāṇaviparyayavikalpanidrāsmṛtayaḥ ॥ 1.6 ॥
They [the mental activities] are proof, misconception, imagination, sleep, and memory. *Page 62*

प्रत्यक्षानुमानागमाः प्रमाणानि ॥ १.७ ॥
pratyakṣānumānāgamāḥ pramāṇāni ॥ 1.7 ॥
Valid proofs are 1) direct perception through senses, 2) inference or deduction, and 3) reliable testimony. *Page 62*

विपर्ययो मिथ्याज्ञानमतद्रूपप्रतिष्ठम् ॥ १.८ ॥
viparyayo mithyājñānamatadrūpapratiṣṭham ॥ 1.8 ॥
Incorrect perception is perceiving a thing to be what it is not. *Page 64*

शब्दज्ञानानुपाती वस्तुशून्यो विकल्पः ॥ १.९ ॥
śabdajñānānupātī vastuśūnyo vikalpaḥ ॥ 1.9 ॥
Imagination follows from verbal knowledge devoid of a real object. *Page 65*

अभावप्रत्ययालम्बना वृत्तिर्निद्रा ॥ १.१० ॥
abhāvapratyayālambanā vṛttirnidrā ॥ 1.10 ॥
Sleep is a mental activity that depends on the absence of cognition. *Page 66*

अनुभूतविषयासंप्रमोषः स्मृतिः ॥ १.११ ॥
anubhūtaviṣayāsampramoṣaḥ smṛtiḥ ॥ 1.11 ॥
Memory is the non-loss of [the impressions of] objects of experience. *Page 67*

अभ्यासवैराग्याभ्यां तन्निरोधः ॥ १.१२ ॥
abhyāsavairāgyābhyāṁ tannirodhaḥ ॥ 1.12 ॥
Restraint of these [activities of mind] is achieved through practice and detachment. *Page 68*

तत्र स्थितौ यत्नोऽभ्यासः ॥ १.१३ ॥
tatra sthitau yatno'bhyāsaḥ ॥ 1.13 ॥
Practice is the effort to remain steady. *Page 68*

स तु दीर्घकालनैरन्तर्यसत्कारासेवितो दृढभूमिः ॥ १.१४ ॥
sa tu dīrghakālanairantaryasatkārāsevito dṛḍhabhūmiḥ ॥ 1.14 ॥
This [practice] becomes firmly established when conducted for a long time with devotion and without interruption. *Page 69*

दृष्टानुश्रविकविषयवितृष्णस्य वशीकारसंज्ञा वैराग्यम् ॥ १.१५ ॥
dṛṣṭānuśravikaviṣayavitṛṣṇasya vaśīkārasaṁjñā vairāgyam ॥ 1.15 ॥
Completely mastered detachment is thirstless-ness towards objects experienced through senses or objects that are heard or learned from reading. *Page 70*

तत्परं पुरुषख्यातेर्गुणवैतृष्ण्यम् ॥ १.१६ ॥
tatparaṁ puruṣakhyātergunavaitṛṣṇyam ॥ 1.16 ॥
Beyond that [detachment] is the thirstless-ness towards the three guṇas [sattva, rajas, and tamas], obtained through the realization of the self. *Page 70*

वितर्कविचारानन्दास्मितारूपानुगमात्सम्प्रज्ञातः ॥ १.१७ ॥
vitarkavicārānandāsmitārūpānugamāt samprajñātaḥ ॥ 1.17 ॥
[Samādhi] with awareness is accompanied by gross thought, subtle thought, bliss, and the feeling of "I." *Page 72*

विरामप्रत्ययाभ्यासपूर्वः संस्कारशेषोऽन्यः ॥ १.१८ ॥
virāmapratyayābhyāsapūrvaḥ saṁskāraśeṣo'nyaḥ ॥ 1.18 ॥
The other [kind of samādhi] results from the cessation of activities of the mind and [leaves] impressions as a remainder. *Page 74*

भवप्रत्ययो विदेहप्रकृतिलयानाम् ॥ १.१९ ॥
bhavapratyayo videhaprakṛtilayānām ॥ 1.19 ॥
[The samādhi] obtained by the body-less and those who have dissolved into the

elements of nature has birth as its cause. *Page 75*

श्रद्धावीर्यस्मृतिसमाधिप्रज्ञापूर्वक इतरेषाम् ॥ १.२० ॥
śraddhāvīryasmṛtisamādhiprajñāpūrvaka itareṣām ॥ 1.20 ॥
The prerequisites for others are devotion, courage, memory, perfected concentration, and wisdom. *Page 76*

तीव्रसंवेगानामासन्नः ॥ १.२१ ॥
tīvrasaṁvegānāmāsannaḥ ॥ 1.21 ॥
It [Samādhi] is obtained by those who practice with intense vigor and persistence. *Page 78*

मृदुमध्याधिमात्रत्वात्ततोऽपि विशेषः ॥ १.२२ ॥
mṛdumadhyādhimātratvāttato'pi viśeṣaḥ ॥ 1.22 ॥
Difference in result is due to mild, medium, and intense [practices]. *Page 78*

ईश्वरप्रणिधानाद्वा ॥ १.२३ ॥
īśvarapraṇidhānādvā ॥ 1.23 ॥
Or, mental activities can also be restrained by meditating on or practicing devotion to God. *Page 79*

क्लेशकर्मविपाकाशयैरपरामृष्टः पुरुषविशेष ईश्वरः ॥ १.२४ ॥
kleśakarmavipākāśayairaparāmṛṣṭaḥ puruṣaviśeṣa īśvaraḥ ॥ 1.24 ॥
God is a special kind of consciousness that is untouched by afflictions, actions, fruition, and the repository of impressions. *Page 79*

तत्र निरतिशयं सर्वज्ञबीजम् ॥ १.२५ ॥
tatra niratiśayaṁ sarvajñabījam ॥ 1.25 ॥
In Īśvara, the seed of omniscience is unexcellable. *Page 80*

पूर्वेषामपि गुरुः कालेनानवच्छेदात् ॥ १.२६ ॥
pūrveṣāmapi guruḥ kālenānavacchedāt ॥ 1.26 ॥
Īśvara is the teacher of former teachers as well, because He is not delimited by time. *Page 80*

तस्य वाचकः प्रणवः ॥ १.२७ ॥
tasya vācakaḥ praṇavaḥ ॥ 1.27 ॥
Īśvara's signifier is "Oṁ." *Page 82*

तज्जपस्तदर्थभावनम् ॥ १.२८ ॥
tajjapastadarthabhāvanam ॥ 1.28 ॥
The repetition of it [praṇava] and contemplation of its meaning [should be done]. *Page 83*

ततः प्रत्यक्चेतनाधिगमोऽप्यन्तरायाभावश्च ॥ १.२९ ॥
tataḥ pratyakcetanādhigamo'pyantarāyābhāvaśca ॥ 1.29 ॥
From that, one attains the realization of inner consciousness and the cessation of obstacles. *Page 85*

व्याधिस्त्यानसंशयप्रमादालस्याविरतिभ्रान्तिदर्शनालब्धभूमिकत्वानवस्थितत्वानि चित्तविक्षेपास्तेऽन्तरायाः ॥ १.३० ॥
vyādhistyānasaṁśayapramādālasyāviratibhrāntidarśanālabdhabhūmikatvānavasthitatvāni cittavikṣepāste'ntarāyāḥ ॥ 1.30 ॥
The obstacles — the distractors of the mind — are sickness, lethargy, doubt, negligence, sloth, lack of detachment, confusion, failure to attain a stage, and instability. *Page 86*

दुःखदौर्मनस्याङ्गमेजयत्वश्वासप्रश्वासा विक्षेपसहभुवः ॥ १.३१ ॥
duḥkhadaurmanasyāṅgamejayatvaśvāsapraśvāsā vikṣepasahabhuvaḥ ॥ 1.31 ॥
Sorrow, dejection, trembling, inhalation, and exhalation accompany the distractions. *Page 88*

तत्प्रतिषेधार्थमेकतत्त्वाभ्यासः ॥ १.३२ ॥
tatpratiṣedhārthamekatattvābhyāsaḥ ॥ 1.32 ॥
To counter them [the obstacles and their accompaniments], practice on one principle. *Page 89*

मैत्रीकरुणामुदितोपेक्षाणां सुखदुःखपुण्यापुण्यविषयाणां भावनातश्चित्तप्रसादनम् ॥ १.३३ ॥
maitrīkaruṇāmuditopekṣāṇāṁ sukhaduḥkhapuṇyāpuṇyaviṣayāṇāṁ bhāvanātaścittaprasādanam ॥ 1.33 ॥
Clarity of mind results from practicing friendliness toward those who are happy, compassion toward those in pain, joy toward the virtuous, and disinterest toward the non-virtuous. *Page 90*

प्रच्छर्दनविधारणाभ्यां वा प्राणस्य ॥ १.३४ ॥
pracchardanavidhāraṇābhyāṁ vā prāṇasya ॥ 1.34 ॥
Or by exhaling and holding the breath [the mind can be stilled]. *Page 92*

विषयवती वा प्रवृत्तिरुत्पन्ना मनसः स्थितिनिबन्धिनी ॥ १.३५ ॥
viṣayavatī vā pravṛttirutpannā manasaḥ sthitinibandhinī ॥ 1.35 ॥
Or when a sensory perception arises, it can cause steadiness of the mind. *Page 93*

विशोका वा ज्योतिष्मती ॥ १.३६ ॥
viśokā vā jyotiṣmatī ॥ 1.36 ॥
Or a sorrow free, luminous state of mind [can also cause steadiness of the mind]. *Page 94*

वीतरागविषयं वा चित्तम् ॥ १.३७ ॥
vītarāgaviṣayaṁ vā cittam ॥ 1.37 ॥

Or contemplating on one who is free from desire [can also cause steadiness of the mind]. *Page 95*

स्वप्ननिद्राज्ञानालम्बनं वा ॥ १.३८ ॥
svapnanidrājñānālambanaṁ vā ॥ 1.38 ॥
Or using knowledge obtained from a dream or sleep as the basis of meditation [can also cause steadiness of the mind]. *Page 96*

यथाभिमतध्यानाद्वा ॥ १ ३९ ॥
yathābhimatadhyānādvā ॥ 1.39 ॥
Or concentrating on any object one likes [can also cause steadiness of the mind]. *Page 97*

परमाणुपरममहत्त्वान्तोऽस्य वशीकारः ॥ १.४० ॥
paramāṇuparamamahattvānto'sya vaśīkāraḥ ॥ 1.40 ॥
The yogī's mastery [extends from] the most minute objects to the largest. *Page 98*

क्षीणवृत्तेरभिजातस्येव मणेर्ग्रहीतृग्रहणग्राह्येषु तत्स्थतदञ्जनता समापत्तिः ॥ १.४१ ॥
kṣīṇavṛtterabhijātasyeva maṇergrahītṛgrahaṇagrāhyeṣu tatsthatadañjanatā samāpattiḥ ॥ 1.41 ॥
Completion [samāpatti] is [the state] in which the activities of the mind are attenuated and [the mind] takes on the form of the grasper, grasping, and the grasped like a transparent jewel takes on color [from its surroundings]. *Page 99*

तत्र शब्दार्थज्ञानविकल्पैः संकीर्णा सवितर्का समापत्तिः ॥ १.४२ ॥
tatra śabdārthajñānavikalpaiḥ saṁkīrṇā savitarkā samāpattiḥ ॥ 1.42 ॥
Samādhi with conceptualization has the concepts of word, meaning, and knowledge mixed together. *Page 100*

स्मृतिपरिशुद्धौ स्वरूपशून्येवार्थमात्रनिर्भासा निर्वितर्का ॥ १.४३ ॥
smṛtipariśuddhau svarūpaśūnyevārthamātranirbhāsā nirvitarkā ॥ 1.43 ॥
Samādhi without conceptualization occurs when the memory is purified, [the meditation is] devoid of its own form, and the object alone manifests. *Page 101*

एतयैव सविचारा निर्विचारा च सूक्ष्मविषया व्याख्याता ॥ १.४४ ॥
etayaiva savicārā nirvicārā ca sūkṣmaviṣayā vyākhyātā ॥ 1.44 ॥
In a similar manner [to savitarkā and nirvitarkā], the concentration with subtle reflection and the concentration without subtle reflection on subtle objects (savichārā and nirvichārā) are explained. *Page 101*

सूक्ष्मविषयत्वं चालिङ्गपर्यवसानम् ॥ १.४५ ॥
sūkṣmaviṣayatvaṁ cāliṅgaparyavasānam ॥ 1.45 ॥
This subtlety extends down to undifferentiated [nature]. *Page 102*

ता एव सबीजः समाधिः ॥ १.४६ ॥
tā eva sabījaḥ samādhiḥ ॥ 1.46 ॥
These [previously described four samādhis], indeed, are samādhis with seed [bīja]. *Page 103*

निर्विचारवैशारद्येऽध्यात्मप्रसादः ॥ १.४७ ॥
nirvicāravaiśāradye'dhyātmaprasādaḥ ॥ 1.47 ॥
Clarity about self is gained when proficiency is attained in the samādhi without subtle reflection [nirvicāra]. *Page 104*

ऋतम्भरा तत्र प्रज्ञा ॥ १.४८ ॥
ṛtambharā tatra prajñā ॥ 1.48 ॥
In that state [nirvicāra], the knowledge is truth bearing [knowledge reveals truth]. *Page 104*

श्रुतानुमानप्रज्ञाभ्यामन्यविषया विशेषार्थत्वात् ॥ १.४९ ॥
śrutānumānaprajñābhyāmanyaviṣayā viśeṣārthatvāt ॥ 1.49 ॥
This [true knowledge] is different from the knowledge obtained from scriptures and inference due to its special nature. *Page 105*

तज्जः संस्कारोऽन्यसंस्कारप्रतिबन्धी ॥ १.५० ॥
tajjaḥ saṁskāro'nyasaṁskārapratibandhī ॥ 1.50 ॥
The impression born from that [nirvicāra-samādhi] becomes the restrainer of other impressions. *Page 106*

तस्यापि निरोधे सर्वनिरोधान्निर्बीजः समाधिः ॥ १.५१ ॥
tasyāpi nirodhe sarvanirodhānnirbījaḥ samādhiḥ ॥ 1.51 ॥
When such impressions are restrained, having restrained everything [one attains] samādhi without seed. *Page 107*

तपःस्वाध्यायेश्वरप्रणिधानानि क्रियायोगः ॥ २.१ ॥
tapaḥsvādhyāyeśvarapraṇidhānāni kriyāyogaḥ ॥ 2.1 ॥
Austerity, study of scriptures, and devotion to God constitute yoga of action. *Page 109*

समाधिभावनार्थः क्लेशतनूकरणार्थश्च ॥ २.२ ॥
samādhibhāvanārthaḥ kleśatanūkaraṇārthaśca ॥ 2.2 ॥
It [yoga of action] is for bringing about samādhi and the attenuation of afflictions. *Page 110*

अविद्यास्मितारागद्वेषाभिनिवेशाः क्लेशाः ॥ २.३ ॥
avidyāsmitārāgadveṣābhiniveśāḥ kleśāḥ ॥ 2.3 ॥
Incorrect knowledge, ego, attachment, aversion, and clinging to physical life are the five afflictions. *Page 111*

अविद्या क्षेत्रमुत्तरेषां प्रसुप्ततनुविच्छिन्नोदाराणाम् ॥ २.४ ॥

avidyā kṣetramuttareṣāṁ prasuptatanuvicchinnodārāṇām ॥ 2.4 ॥
Incorrect knowledge is the ground for the rest [of the afflictions], which can be in dormant, attenuated, interrupted, or fully-active states. *Page 112*

अनित्याशुचिदुःखानात्मसु नित्यशुचिसुखात्मख्यातिरविद्या ॥ २.५ ॥
anityāśuciduḥkhānātmasu nityaśucisukhātmakhyātiravidyā ॥ 2.5 ॥
Perceiving the temporary as eternal, the impure as pure, misery as joy, or the non-self as the self is called incorrect knowledge. *Page 114*

दृग्दर्शनशक्त्योरेकात्मतेवास्मिता ॥ २.६ ॥
dṛgdarśanaśaktyorekātmatevāsmitā ॥ 2.6 ॥
I-ness is to consider the power of the seer [consciousness] to be the power of seeing [the intellect, the mind]. *Page 114*

सुखानुशयी रागः ॥ २.७ ॥
sukhānuśayī rāgaḥ ॥ 2.7 ॥
Attachment is that which follows pleasure. *Page 115*

दुःखानुशयी द्वेषः ॥ २.८ ॥
duḥkhānuśayī dveṣaḥ ॥ 2.8 ॥
Aversion is that which follows misery. *Page 116*

स्वरसवाही विदुषोऽपि तथारूढोऽभिनिवेशः ॥ २.९ ॥
svarasavāhī viduṣo'pi tathārūḍho'bhiniveśaḥ ॥ 2.9 ॥
The instinct to preserve oneself is established even in the learned. *Page 117*

ते प्रतिप्रसवहेयाः सूक्ष्माः ॥ २.१० ॥
te pratiprasavaheyāḥ sūkṣmāḥ ॥ 2.10 ॥
These subtle afflictions are overcome by reverse-flow [of the mind toward its components]. *Page 118*

ध्यानहेयास्तद्वृत्तयः ॥ २.११ ॥
dhyānaheyāstadvṛttayaḥ ॥ 2.11 ॥
Those mental activities [afflictions] are overcome by the practice of meditation. *Page 118*

क्लेशमूलः कर्माशयो दृष्टादृष्टजन्मवेदनीयः ॥ २.१२ ॥
kleśamūlaḥ karmāśayo dṛṣṭādṛṣṭajanmavedanīyaḥ ॥ 2.12 ॥
The stock of karma having afflictions as the root is seen in the present life or the future. *Page 120*

सति मूले तद्विपाको जात्यायुर्भोगाः ॥ २.१३ ॥
sati mūle tadvipāko jātyāyurbhogāḥ ॥ 2.13 ॥
In the presence of the root [of afflictions], the fruitions of karma result in birth, lifespan, and experience. *Page 122*

ते ह्लादपरितापफलाः पुण्यापुण्यहेतुत्वात् ॥ २.१४ ॥
te hlādaparitāpaphalāḥ puṇyāpuṇyahetutvāt ॥ 2.14 ॥
Due to virtue and non-virtue, they [birth, lifespan, and experience] are either pleasurable or miserable. *Page 124*

परिणामतापसंस्कारदुःखैर्गुणवृत्तिविरोधाच्च दुःखमेव सर्वं विवेकिनः ॥ २.१५ ॥
pariṇāmatāpasaṁskāraduḥkhairguṇavṛttivirodhācca duḥkhameva sarvaṁ vivekinaḥ ॥ 2.15 ॥
Because of sorrows due to change, hardships, impressions, and the conflicting operations of the guṇas, all experiences are sorrowful to a discerning person. *Page 126*

हेयं दुःखमनागतम् ॥ २.१६ ॥
heyaṁ duḥkhamanāgatam ॥ 2.16 ॥
Misery that has not yet come should be avoided. *Page 128*

द्रष्टृदृश्ययोः संयोगो हेयहेतुः ॥ २.१७ ॥
draṣṭṛdṛśyayoḥ saṁyogo heyahetuḥ ॥ 2.17 ॥
The union of the seer and the seen is the cause of misery. *Page 128*

प्रकाशक्रियास्थितिशीलं भूतेन्द्रियात्मकं भोगापवर्गार्थं दृश्यम् ॥ २.१८ ॥
prakāśakriyāsthitiśīlaṁ bhūtendriyātmakaṁ bhogāpavargārthaṁ dṛśyam ॥ 2.18 ॥
The nature of the "seen" is illumination, movement, and stability. It is composed of the instruments of perception and the objects made from the natural elements. Its purpose is enjoyment and liberation. *Page 130*

विशेषाविशेषलिङ्गमात्रालिङ्गानि गुणपर्वाणि ॥ २.१९ ॥
viśeṣāviśeṣaliṅgamātrāliṅgāni guṇaparvāṇi ॥ 2.19 ॥
The states of the guṇas are 1) particularized 2) unparticularized 3) indicatory, and 4) non-indicatory *Page 132*

द्रष्टा दृशिमात्रः शुद्धोऽपि प्रत्ययानुपश्यः ॥ २.२० ॥
draṣṭā dṛśimātraḥ śuddho'pi pratyayānupaśyaḥ ॥ 2.20 ॥
The seer, is only [the power of] seeing. Although pure, it experiences the content of the mind. *Page 133*

तदर्थ एव दृश्यस्यात्मा ॥ २. २१ ॥
tadartha eva dṛśyasyātmā ॥ 2.21 ॥
The essence of the seen is only for that purpose [of consciousness]. *Page 133*

कृतार्थं प्रति नष्टमप्यनष्टं तदन्यसाधारणत्वात् ॥ २.२२ ॥
kṛtārthaṁ prati naṣṭamapyanaṣṭaṁ tadanyasādhāraṇatvāt ॥ 2.22 ॥
Although the object ceases to exist for the one whose purpose has been accomplished, it nevertheless remains in existence because of its commonality. *Page 134*

स्वस्वामिशक्त्योः स्वरूपोपलब्धिहेतुः संयोगः ॥ २.२३ ॥

svasvāmiśaktyoḥ svarūpopalabdhihetuḥ saṁyogaḥ ॥ 2.23 ॥
The union of the ability of the owner (the power to see) and the ability of the owned (the power to be seen) is for the purpose of obtaining an understanding of true nature. *Page 134*

तस्य हेतुरविद्या ॥ २.२४ ॥
tasya heturavidyā ॥ 2.24 ॥
The cause of this [union] is ignorance. *Page 135*

तदभावात्संयोगाभावो हानं तद्दृशेः कैवल्यम् ॥ २.२५ ॥
tadabhāvātsaṁyogābhāvo hānaṁ taddṛśeḥ kaivalyam ॥ 2.25 ॥
The absence of the union [of seer and seen] results from the absence of that [ignorance]. That [cessation is] the isolation of the seer. *Page 136*

विवेकख्यातिरविप्लवा हानोपायः ॥ २.२६ ॥
vivekakhyātiraviplavā hānopāyaḥ ॥ 2.26 ॥
Unwavering discerning vision is the means of cessation. *Page 136*

तस्य सप्तधा प्रान्तभूमिः प्रज्ञा ॥ २.२७ ॥
tasya saptadhā prāntabhūmiḥ prajñā ॥ 2.27 ॥
[One who has obtained clear, discriminating knowledge] his knowledge is of seven kinds. *Page 137*

योगाङ्गानुष्ठानादशुद्धिक्षये ज्ञानदीप्तिराविवेकख्यातेः ॥ २.२८ ॥
yogāṅgānuṣṭhānādaśuddhikṣaye jñānadīptirāvivekakhyāteḥ ॥ 2.28 ॥
By practicing the limbs of yoga, knowledge is kindled extending to the point of discriminating vision while impurities subside. *Page 138*

यमनियमासनप्राणायामप्रत्याहारधारणाध्यानसमाधयोऽष्टावङ्गानि ॥ २.२९॥
yamaniyamāsanaprāṇāyāmapratyāhāradhāraṇādhyānasamādhayo'ṣṭāvaṅgāni ॥ 2.29 ॥
The eight limbs of yoga are, 1. yama (restraint), 2. niyama (observance), 3. āsana (posture), 4. prāṇāyāma (regulation, expansion of breath), 5. pratyāhāra (withdrawal of the senses), 6. dhāraṇā (placing attention, focusing on something), 7. dhyāna (maintaining continued focus on something, meditation), 8. samādhi (absorption) *Page 139*

अहिंसासत्यास्तेयब्रह्मचर्यापरिग्रहा यमाः ॥ २.३० ॥
ahiṁsāsatyāsteyabrahmacaryāparigrahā yamāḥ ॥ 2.30 ॥
Non-harming, truthfulness, non-stealing, celibacy, and non-accumulation of objects of senses are the restraints. *Page 140*

जातिदेशकालसमयानवच्छिन्नाः सार्वभौमा महाव्रतम् ॥ २.३१ ॥
jātideśakālasamayānavacchinnāḥ sārvabhaumā mahāvratam ॥ 2.31 ॥
[Practicing these restraints] in all spheres — regardless of species, place, time, and circumstance — is the Great Vow. *Page 142*

शौचसंतोषतपःस्वाध्यायेश्वरप्रणिधानानि नियमाः ॥ २.३२ ॥
śaucasaṁtoṣatapaḥsvādhyāyeśvarapraṇidhānāni niyamāḥ ॥ 2.32 ॥
Cleanliness, contentment, austerity, study of scriptures, and devotion to God are the observances. *Page 144*

वितर्कबाधने प्रतिपक्षभावनम् ॥ २.३३ ॥
vitarkabādhane pratipakṣabhāvanam ॥ 2.33 ॥
When one is bothered by transgressing thoughts, oppositional thinking should be practiced. *Page 144*

वितर्का हिंसादयः कृतकारितानुमोदिता लोभक्रोधमोहपूर्वका मृदुमध्याधिमात्रा दुःखाज्ञानानन्तफला इति प्रतिपक्षभावनम् ॥ २.३४ ॥
vitarkā hiṁsādayaḥ kṛtakāritānumoditā lobhakrodhamohapūrvakā mṛdumadhyādhimātrā duḥkhājñānānantaphalā iti pratipakṣabhāvanam ॥ 2.34 ॥
Oppositional thinking is cultivating [the attitude] that transgressing thoughts, such as harming and the rest — done, caused to be done, or approved; arising from greed, anger, or delusion; minor, moderate, or excessive — result in unending fruits of misery and ignorance. *Page 146*

अहिंसाप्रतिष्ठायां तत्सन्निधौ वैरत्यागः ॥ २.३५ ॥
ahiṁsāpratiṣṭhāyāṁ tatsannidhau vairatyāgaḥ ॥ 2.35 ॥
Enmity is abandoned in the presence of a well-established practice of non-harming. *Page 148*

सत्यप्रतिष्ठायां क्रियाफलाश्रयत्वम् ॥ २.३६ ॥
satyapratiṣṭhāyāṁ kriyāphalāśrayatvam ॥ 2.36 ॥
When truthfulness is established, [the yogī] becomes the basis for the fruitfulness of actions. *Page 149*

अस्तेयप्रतिष्ठायां सर्वरत्नोपस्थानम् ॥ २.३७ ॥
asteyapratiṣṭhāyāṁ sarvaratnopasthānam ॥ 2.37 ॥
When non-stealing is established, the best of any kind of object (ratna) will become available. *Page 149*

ब्रह्मचर्यप्रतिष्ठायां वीर्यलाभः ॥ २.३८ ॥
brahmacaryapratiṣṭhāyāṁ vīryalābhaḥ ॥ 2.38 ॥
When celibacy is established, one gains power. *Page 150*

अपरिग्रहस्थैर्ये जन्मकथन्तासम्बोधः ॥ २.३९ ॥
aparigrahasthairye janmakathantāsambodhaḥ ॥ 2.39 ॥
When non-grasping is established, the knowledge of births past, present, and future arises. *Page 150*

शौचात्स्वाङ्गजुगुप्सा परैरसंसर्गः ॥ २.४० ॥

śaucātsvāṅgajugupsā parairasaṁsargaḥ ॥ 2.40 ॥
From practicing cleanliness, one gains dislike for one's own body and refrains from coming into contact with others. *Page 151*

सत्त्वशुद्धिसौमनस्यैकाग्र्येन्द्रियजयात्मदर्शनयोग्यत्वानि च ॥ २.४१ ॥
sattvaśuddhisaumanasyaikāgryendriyajayātmadarśanayogyatvāni ca ॥ 2.41 ॥
[From cleanliness], one also achieves clarity of mind, pleasantness, one-pointed concentration, control over the senses, and the capability to attain knowledge of the self. *Page 151*

सन्तोषादनुत्तमसुखलाभः ॥ २.४२ ॥
santoṣādanuttamasukhalābhaḥ ॥ 2.42 ॥
From contentment, one attains unexcelled happiness. *Page 152*

कायेन्द्रियसिद्धिरशुद्धिक्षयात्तपसः ॥ २.४३ ॥
kāyendriyasiddhiraśuddhikṣayāttapasaḥ ॥ 2.43 ॥
From the practice of austerities, impurities are attenuated. This results in the perfection of the body and the senses. *Page 152*

स्वाध्यायादिष्टदेवतासम्प्रयोगः ॥ २.४४ ॥
svādhyāyādiṣṭadevatāsamprayogaḥ ॥ 2.44 ॥
From practicing the study of scriptures and introspection one receives the revelation of the desired luminous personalities (iṣṭadevatā). *Page 153*

समाधिसिद्धिरीश्वरप्रणिधानात् ॥ २.४५ ॥
samādhisiddhirīśvarapraṇidhānāt ॥ 2.45 ॥
From devotion to God, one attains perfected concentration. *Page 153*

स्थिरसुखमासनम् ॥ २.४६ ॥
sthirasukhamāsanam ॥ 2.46 ॥
Posture is a stable and comfortable position. *Page 154*

प्रयत्नशैथिल्यानन्तसमापत्तिभ्याम् ॥ २.४७ ॥
prayatnaśaithilyānantasamāpattibhyām ॥ 2.47 ॥
[Perfection in āsana] is obtained from relaxation of effort and meditation on the infinite. *Page 156*

ततो द्वन्द्वानभिघातः ॥ २.४८ ॥
tato dvandvānabhighātaḥ ॥ 2.48 ॥
From that [stable posture], one is not assailed by opposing pairs of dualities. *Page 157*

तस्मिन्सति श्वासप्रश्वासयोर्गतिविच्छेदः प्राणायामः ॥ २.४९ ॥
tasminsati śvāsapraśvāsayorgativicchedaḥ prāṇāyāmaḥ ॥ 2.49 ॥
In that [stable posture], interrupting the movement of inhalation and exhalation is called praṇāyāma, or breath control. *Page 158*

बाह्याभ्यन्तरस्तम्भवृत्तिर्देशकालसंख्याभिः परिदृष्टो दीर्घसूक्ष्मः ॥ २.५० ॥
bāhyābhyantarastambhavṛttirdeśakālasaṁkhyābhiḥ paridṛṣṭo dīrghasūkṣmaḥ ॥ 2.50 ॥
Prāṇāyāma has external, internal, and arrested activities of breath. When observed through place, time, and number, these are long and subtle. *Page 159*

बाह्याभ्यन्तरविषयाक्षेपी चतुर्थः ॥ २.५१ ॥
bāhyābhyantaraviṣayākṣepī caturthaḥ ॥ 2.51 ॥
The fourth kind of prāṇāyāma transcends external and internal operations. *Page 160*

ततः क्षियते प्रकाशावरणम् ॥ २.५२ ॥
tataḥ kṣīyate prakāśāvaraṇam ॥ 2.52 ॥
From that practice [praṇāyāma], the veil over illumination is thinned. *Page 160*

धारणासु च योग्यता मनसः ॥ २.५३ ॥
dhāraṇāsu ca yogyatā manasaḥ ॥ 2.53 ॥
And also [from praṇāyāma] comes the ability to focus the mind, dhāraṇā. *Page 161*

स्वविषयासम्प्रयोगे चित्तस्य स्वरूपानुकार इवेन्द्रियाणां प्रत्याहारः ॥ २.५४ ॥
svaviṣayāsamprayoge cittasya svarūpānukāra ivendriyāṇāṁ pratyāhāraḥ ॥ 2.54 ॥
Withdrawal of the senses [pratyāhāra] is, as it were, an imitation by the senses of the mind in disconnecting from objects. *Page 162*

ततः परमा वश्यतेन्द्रियाणाम् ॥ २.५५ ॥
tataḥ paramā vaśyatendriyāṇām ॥ 2.55 ॥
From this comes supreme mastery over the senses. *Page 164*

देशबन्धश्चित्तस्य धारणा ॥ ३.१ ॥
deśabandhaścittasya dhāraṇā ॥ 3.1 ॥
Fixing the mind on a point is called concentration, dhāraṇā. *Page 167*

तत्र प्रत्ययैकतानता ध्यानम् ॥ ३.२ ॥
tatra pratyayaikatānatā dhyānam ॥ 3.2 ॥
Maintaining the continuity of a single thought is called contemplation, dhyāna. *Page 169*

तदेवार्थमात्रनिर्भासं स्वरूपशून्यमिव समाधिः ॥ ३.३ ॥
tadevārthamātranirbhāsaṁ svarūpaśūnyamiva samādhiḥ ॥ 3.3 ॥
Absorption [samādhi] is that [contemplation] in which only the object shines forth as if it [the meditator] has lost its own form. *Page 170*

त्रयमेकत्र संयमः ॥ ३.४ ॥
trayamekatra saṁyamaḥ ॥ 3.4 ॥
The three together are called all-round control [saṁyama]. *Page 172*

तज्जयात्प्रज्ञालोकः ॥ ३.५ ॥

tajjayātprajñālokaḥ ॥ 3.5 ॥
From mastering that [saṁyama] comes the light of knowledge. *Page 172*

तस्य भूमिषु विनियोगः ॥ ३.६ ॥
tasya bhūmiṣu viniyogaḥ ॥ 3.6 ॥
It [saṁyama] should be applied in stages. *Page 172*

त्रयमन्तरङ्गं पूर्वेभ्यः ॥ ३.७ ॥
trayamantaraṅgaṁ pūrvebhyaḥ ॥ 3.7 ॥
These three are internal limbs [in relation to] the previous. *Page 173*

तदपि बहिरङ्गं निर्बीजस्य ॥ ३.८ ॥
tadapi bahiraṅgaṁ nirbījasya ॥ 3.8 ॥
Yet, those [the three] are external [in relation] to the seed-less [state]. *Page 173*

व्युत्थाननिरोधसंस्कारयोरभिभवप्रादुर्भावौ निरोधक्षणचित्तान्वयो निरोधपरिणामः ॥ ३.९ ॥
vyutthānanirodhasaṁskārayorabhibhavaprādurbhāvau nirodhakṣaṇacittānvayo nirodhapariṇāmaḥ ॥ 3.9 ॥
When distracting impressions are overpowered and restrained impressions manifest, [the result] in that moment of the arrested state is called "restrained-transformation." *Page 174*

तस्य प्रशान्तवाहिता संस्कारात् ॥ ३.१० ॥
tasya praśāntavāhitā saṁskārāt ॥ 3.10 ॥
[The arrested mind's] calm flow is due to the [restrained] impressions. *Page 176*

सर्वार्थतैकाग्रतयोः क्षयोदयौ चित्तस्य समाधिपरिणामः ॥ ३.११ ॥
sarvārthataikāgratayoḥ kṣayodayau cittasya samādhipariṇāmaḥ ॥ 3.11 ॥
The "absorption-transformation" of the mind is the decay of distractedness and the emergence of one-pointedness. *Page 176*

ततः पुनः शान्तोदितौ तुल्यप्रत्ययौ चित्तस्यैकाग्रतापरिणामः ॥ ३.१२ ॥
tataḥ punaḥ śāntoditau tulyapratyayau cittasyaikāgratāpariṇāmaḥ ॥ 3.12 ॥
The one-pointed transformation is when subsiding and arising thoughts are the same. *Page 178*

एतेन भूतेन्द्रियेषु धर्मलक्षणावस्थापरिणामा व्याख्याताः ॥ ३.१३ ॥
etena bhūtendriyeṣu dharmalakṣaṇāvasthāpariṇāmā vyākhyātāḥ ॥ 3.13 ॥
By this, the characteristic, state, and conditional transformations of the elements of nature and the instruments [sense and motor instruments] are explained. *Page 180*

शान्तोदिताव्यपदेश्यधर्मानुपाती धर्मी ॥ ३.१४ ॥
śāntoditāvyapadeśyadharmānupātī dharmī ॥ 3.14 ॥
[That which] conforms to all past, present, and future forms is called the form-holder. *Page 182*

क्रमान्यत्वं परिणामान्यत्वे हेतुः ॥ ३.१५ ॥
kramānyatvaṁ pariṇāmānyatve hetuḥ ॥ 3.15 ॥
Difference in the sequence is the cause of difference in transformations. *Page 182*

परिणामत्रयसंयमादतीतानागतज्ञानम् ॥ ३.१६ ॥
pariṇāmatrayasaṁyamādatītānāgatajñānam ॥ 3.16 ॥
From practicing control [saṁyama] on the three types of transformations comes knowledge of the past and future. *Page 184*

शब्दार्थप्रत्ययानामितरेतराध्यासात्संकरस्तत्प्रविभागसंयमात्सर्वभूतरुतज्ञानम् ॥ ३.१७ ॥
śabdārthapratyayānāmitaretarādhyāsātsaṁkarastatpravibhāgasaṁyamātsarvabhūtarutajñān am ॥ 3.17 ॥
Due to the overlap of the word, the object implied, and the concept of the object, there arises confusion. By practicing control [saṁyama] over the differentiation, one gains a knowledge of the utterances of all beings. *Page 185*

संस्कारसाक्षात्करणात्पूर्वजातिज्ञानम् ॥ ३.१८ ॥
saṁskārasākṣatkaraṇātpūrvajātijñānam ॥ 3.18 ॥
From directly seeing the impressions [saṁskāra] comes knowledge of previous births. *Page 188*

प्रत्ययस्य परचित्तज्ञानम् ॥ ३.१९ ॥
pratyayasya paracittajñānam ॥ 3.19 ॥
From another's cognition comes the knowledge of their mind. *Page 188*

न च तत्सालम्बनं तस्याविषयीभूतत्वात् ॥ ३.२० ॥
na ca tat sālambanaṁ tasyāviṣayībhūtatvāt ॥ 3.20 ॥
That [knowledge of another's mind] cannot reveal the object of thinking, because it is not the subject of the yogī's meditation. *Page 189*

कायरूपसंयमात्तद्ग्राह्यशक्तिस्तम्भे चक्षुःप्रकाशासम्प्रयोगेऽन्तर्धनम् ॥ ३.२१ ॥
kāyarūpasaṁyamāttadgrāhyaśaktistambhe cakṣuḥprakāśāsamprayoge'ntardhānam ॥ 3.21 ॥
From control [saṁyama] on the form of the body, when light is not allowed to reach the eyes and the ability to be grasped is stopped, comes invisibility. *Page 189*

सोपक्रमं निरुपक्रमं च कर्म तत्संयमादपरान्तज्ञानमरिष्टेभ्यो वा ॥ ३.२२ ॥
sopakramaṁ nirupakramaṁ ca karma tatsaṁyamādaparāntajñānamariṣṭebhyo vā ॥ 3.22 ॥
Actions are fructifying, or non-fructifying. From practicing control, saṁyama, on that [fructification of actions], or through bad omens, comes the knowledge of death. *Page 191*

मैत्र्यादिषु बलानि ॥ ३.२३ ॥
maitryādiṣu balāni ॥ 3.23 ॥
From friendliness and others comes powers. *Page 192*

बलेषु हस्तिबलादीनि ॥ ३.२४ ॥
baleṣu hastibalādīni ॥ 3.24 ॥
[Practicing saṁyama] on strengths [leads to] the strengths of an elephant and others. *Page 193*

प्रवृत्त्यालोकन्यासात्सूक्ष्मव्यवहितविप्रकृष्टज्ञानम् ॥ ३.२५ ॥
pravṛttyālokanyāsātsūkṣmavyavahitaviprakṛṣṭajñānam ॥ 3.25 ॥
From focusing the power of insight comes a knowledge of subtle, covered, and distant objects. *Page 194*

भुवनज्ञानं सूर्ये संयमात् ॥ ३.२६ ॥
bhuvanajñānaṁ sūrye saṁyamāt ॥ 3.26 ॥
From practicing saṁyama on the sun comes knowledge of the worlds. *Page 195*

चन्द्रे ताराव्यूहज्ञानम् ॥ ३.२७ ॥
candre tārāvyūhajñānam ॥ 3.27 ॥
From practicing saṁyama on the moon comes knowledge of the arrangements of the stars. *Page 195*

ध्रुवे तद्गतिज्ञानम् ॥ ३.२८ ॥
dhruve tadgatijñānam ॥ 3.28 ॥
From concentrating on the pole-star comes knowledge of the movement [of the stars and constellations]. *Page 195*

नाभिचक्रे कायव्यूहज्ञानम् ॥ ३.२९ ॥
nābhicakre kāyavyūhajñānam ॥ 3.29 ॥
[From practicing saṁyama] on the navel center comes knowledge of the arrangement of the human body. *Page 196*

कण्ठकूपे क्षुत्पिपासानिवृत्तिः ॥ ३.३० ॥
kaṇṭhakūpe kṣutpipāsānivṛttiḥ ॥ 3.30 ॥
[From practicing saṁyama] on the pit of the throat comes the ability to suppress hunger and thirst. *Page 198*

कूर्मनाड्यां स्थैर्यम् ॥ ३.३१ ॥
kūrmanāḍyāṁ sthairyam ॥ 3.31 ॥
[From practicing saṁyama] on the "tortoise tube" comes stability of mind and body. *Page 198*

मूर्धज्योतिषि सिद्धदर्शनम् ॥ ३.३२ ॥
mūrdhajyotiṣi siddhadarśanam ॥ 3.32 ॥
[From practicing saṁyama] on the light in the head comes the vision of the perfected ones. *Page 199*

प्रातिभाद्वा सर्वम् ॥ ३.३३ ॥

prātibhād vā sarvam ॥ 3.33 ॥
Or, from intuition comes everything. *Page 200*

हृदये चित्तसंवित् ॥ ३.३४ ॥
hṛdaye cittasaṁvit ॥ 3.34 ॥
[From practicing saṁyama] on the heart comes the knowledge of the citta. *Page 200*

सत्त्वपुरुषयोरत्यन्तासंकीर्णयोः प्रत्ययाविशेषो भोगः परार्थत्वात्स्वार्थसंयमात्पुरुषज्ञानम् ॥ ३.३५ ॥
sattvapuruṣayoratyantāsaṁkīrṇayoḥ pratyayāviśeṣo bhogaḥ parārthatvāt svārthasaṁyamāt puruṣajñānam ॥ 3.35 ॥
Worldly experience comes from a cognition of the non-differentiation of intellect and consciousness, [which are in fact] completely differentiated. Knowledge of consciousness [puruṣa] results from practicing saṁyama on one's own purpose, as opposed to purpose of the other [the prakṛti]. *Page 201*

ततः प्रातिभश्रावणवेदनादर्शास्वादवार्ता जायन्ते ॥ ३.३६ ॥
tataḥ prātibhaśrāvaṇavedanādarśāsvādavārtā jāyante ॥ 3.36 ॥
From that [knowledge of consciousness], intuitive hearing, touch, sight, taste, and smell are born. *Page 202*

ते समाधावुपसर्गा व्युत्थाने सिद्धयः ॥ ३.३७ ॥
te samādhāvupasargā vyutthāne siddhayaḥ ॥ 3.37 ॥
Those [powers] are obstacles in the way of samādhi, but are powers in an outwardly-focused mind. *Page 203*

बन्धकारणशैथिल्यात्प्रचारसंवेदनाच्च चित्तस्य परशरीरावेशः ॥ ३.३८ ॥
bandhakāraṇaśaithilyātpracārasaṁvedanācca cittasya paraśarīrāveśaḥ ॥ 3.38 ॥
From the loosening of the causes of bondage and the experience of the movements of the mind comes [the power] of entering another's body. *Page 203*

उदानजयाज्जलपङ्ककण्टकादिष्वसङ्ग उत्क्रान्तिश्च ॥ ३.३९ ॥
udānajayājjalapaṅkakaṇṭakādiṣvasaṅga utkrāntiśca ॥ 3.39 ॥
From mastering the vital air called udāna comes [the ability to be] untouched by water, mud, and thorns, and [the power of] levitation. *Page 204*

समानजयाज्ज्वलनम् ॥ ३.४० ॥
samānajayājjvalanam ॥ 3.40 ॥
From mastering the vital air called Samāna comes radiance. *Page 206*

श्रोत्राकाशयोः सम्बन्धसंयमाद्दिव्यं श्रोत्रम् ॥ ३.४१ ॥
śrotrākāśayoḥ saṁbandhasaṁyamāddivyaṁ śrotram ॥ 3.41 ॥
From practicing saṁyama on the relation between the ear and the ether comes supernatural hearing. *Page 206*

कायाकाशयोः सम्बन्धसंयमाल्लघुतूलसमापत्तेश्चाकाशगमनम् ॥ ३.४२ ॥

kāyākāśayoḥ saṁbandhasaṁyamāllaghutūlasamāpatteścākāśagamanam ॥ 3.42 ॥
From practicing saṁyama on the relation between the body and space and from obtaining samādhi on the lightness of cotton comes [the ability to] travel through space. *Page 207*

बहिरकल्पिता वृत्तिर्महाविदेहा ततः प्रकाशावरणक्षयः ॥ ३.४३ ॥
bahirakalpitā vṛttirmahāvidehā tataḥ prakāśāvaraṇakṣayaḥ ॥ 3.43 ॥
There is a state of mind that is external and not imaginary, "the great bodyless-ness" (mahāvidehā). From that comes the dwindling of the covering of the light. *Page 207*

स्थूलस्वरूपसूक्ष्मान्वयार्थवत्त्वसंयमाद्भूतजयः ॥ ३.४४ ॥
sthūlasvarūpasūkṣmānvayārthavattvasaṁyamādbhūtajayaḥ ॥ 3.44 ॥
From practicing saṁyama on the gross nature, inherent form, subtle nature, and their associations and their purposes, comes mastery over the elements. *Page 208*

ततोऽणिमादिप्रादुर्भावः कायसम्पत्तद्धर्मानभिघातश्च ॥ ३.४५ ॥
tato'ṇimādiprādurbhāvaḥ kāyasampattaddharmānabhighātaśca ॥ 3.45 ॥
From that [mastery over the elements] comes the manifestation of [the powers of] miniaturization and others, perfection of the body, and the invulnerability of its properties. *Page 209*

रूपलावण्यबलवज्रसंहननत्वानि कायसम्पत् ॥ ३.४६ ॥
rūpalāvaṇyabalavajrasaṁhananatvāni kāyasampat ॥ 3.46 ॥
Perfection of the body [consists of] beauty, gracefulness, strength, and the hardness of a diamond. *Page 210*

ग्रहणस्वरूपास्मितान्वयार्थवत्त्वसंयमादिन्द्रियजयः ॥ ३.४७ ॥
grahaṇasvarūpāsmitānvayārthavattvasaṁyamādindriyajayaḥ ॥ 3.47 ॥
From practicing saṁyama on aspects of grasping, essential character, the sense of ego, succession, and purposefulness of senses comes mastery over the senses. *Page 210*

ततो मनोजवित्वं विकरणभावः प्रधानजयश्च ॥ ३.४८ ॥
tato manojavitvaṁ vikaraṇabhāvaḥ pradhānajayaśca ॥ 3.48 ॥
From that [mastering the senses] comes fleetness like that of the mind, a condition of independence from the senses, and mastery over primordial matter. *Page 211*

सत्त्वपुरुषान्यताख्यातिमात्रस्य सर्वभावाधिष्ठातृत्वं सर्वज्ञातृत्वं च ॥ ३. ४९ ॥
sattvapuruṣānyatākhyātimātrasya sarvabhāvādhiṣṭhātṛtvaṁ sarvajñātṛtvaṁ ca ॥ 3.49 ॥
Only from insight [into] the difference between sattva (buddhi) and puruṣa comes mastery over all states [of existence], and omniscience. *Page 212*

तद्वैराग्यादपि दोषबीजक्षये कैवल्यम् ॥ ३.५० ॥
tadvairāgyādapi doṣabījakṣaye kaivalyam ॥ 3.50 ॥
Due to detachment even from that [insight], upon the wearing away of the seed of defects comes isolation [of the consciousness]. *Page 213*

स्थान्युपनिमन्त्रणे सङ्गस्मयाकरणं पुनरनिष्टप्रसङ्गात् ॥ ३.५१ ॥
sthānyupanimantraṇe saṅgasmayākaraṇaṁ punaḥ aniṣṭaprasaṅgāt ॥ 3.51 ॥
When invited by the highly-placed ones, [a yogī] should have no cause for attachment and pride due to renewal of inclination towards undesirables. *Page 214*

क्षणतत्क्रमयोः संयमाद्विवेकजं ज्ञानम् ॥ ३.५२ ॥
kṣaṇatatkramayoḥ saṁyamādvivekajaṁ jñānam ॥ 3.52 ॥
From practicing saṁyama on the moment and its sequence comes discriminating knowledge. *Page 215*

जातिलक्षणदेशैरन्यतानवच्छेदात्तुल्ययोस्ततः प्रतिपत्तिः ॥ ३.५३ ॥
jātilakṣaṇadeśairanyatānavacchedāt tulyayostataḥ pratipattiḥ ॥ 3.53 ॥
From that [practicing saṁyama] comes the differentiation of two similar things that are not distinguishable by class, characteristics, or location. *Page 215*

तारकं सर्वविषयं सर्वथाविषयमक्रमं चेति विवेकजं ज्ञानम् ॥ ३.५४ ॥
tārakaṁ sarvaviṣayaṁ sarvathāviṣayamakramaṁ ceti vivekajaṁ jñānam ॥ 3.54 ॥
Knowledge born of discernement is the deliverer. It relates to all objects in every way, and is non-sequential. *Page 216*

सत्त्वपुरुषयोः शुद्धिसाम्ये कैवल्यमिति ॥ ३.५५ ॥
sattvapuruṣayoḥ śuddhisāmye kaivalyam iti ॥ 3.55 ॥
When the purity of sattva [buddhi] and puruṣa are equal, this is kaivalya. *Page 217*

जन्मौषधिमन्त्रतपःसमाधिजाः सिद्धयः ॥ ४.१ ॥
janmauṣadhimantratapaḥsamādhijāḥ siddhayaḥ ॥ 4.1 ॥
Attainments result from birth, medicinal herbs, incantations, austerity, and samādhi. *Page 219*

जात्यन्तरपरिणामः प्रकृत्यापूरात् ॥ ४.२ ॥
jātyantarapariṇāmaḥ prakṛtyāpūrāt ॥ 4.2 ॥
Transformation from one kind to another results from the abundance of prakṛti (or the filling in of prakṛti). *Page 221*

निमित्तमप्रयोजकं प्रकृतीनां वरणभेदस्तु ततः क्षेत्रिकवत् ॥ ४.३ ॥
nimittamaprayojakaṁ prakṛtīnāṁ varaṇabhedastu tataḥ kṣetrikavat ॥ 4.3 ॥
The instrumental cause is not the mover of nature [in bringing about transformation]. Instead, it breaks through obstacles [to transformation] like a farmer. *Page 222*

निर्माणचित्तान्यस्मितामात्रात् ॥ ४.४ ॥
nirmāṇacittānyasmitāmātrāt ॥ 4.4 ॥
Transformed minds are [made] from ego alone. *Page 225*

प्रवृत्तिभेदे प्रयोजकं चित्तमेकमनेकेषाम् ॥ ४.५ ॥

pravṛttibhede prayojakaṁ cittamekamanekeṣām ॥ 4.5 ॥
Although the activities are different, the one mind is the performer of the many [activities]. *Page 226*

तत्र ध्यानजमनाशयम् ॥ ४.६ ॥
tatra dhyānajamanāśayam ॥ 4.6 ॥
Among [the transformed minds], that which is born out of meditation is without the stock of karma. *Page 226*

कर्माशुक्लाकृष्णं योगिनस्त्रिविधमितरेषाम् ॥ ४.७ ॥
karmāśuklākṛṣṇaṁ yoginastrividhamitareṣām ॥ 4.7 ॥
The action of a yogī are neither black nor white. For other people, it is of three kinds. *Page 228*

ततस्तद्विपाकानुगुणानामेवाभिव्यक्तिर्वासनानाम् ॥ ४.८ ॥
tatastadvipākānuguṇānāmevābhivyaktirvāsanānām ॥ 4.8 ॥
From that [three kinds of actions], manifestation [activation] occurs only of subliminal impressions where conditions are favorable for ripening. *Page 229*

जातिदेशकालव्यवहितानामप्यानन्तर्यं स्मृतिसंस्कारयोरेकरूपत्वात् ॥ ४.९ ॥
jātideśakālavyavahitānāmapyānantaryaṁ smṛtisaṁskārayorekarūpatvāt ॥ 4.9 ॥
There is an uninterrupted identity of memory and impressions, even though they are separated by birth, place, and time. *Page 229*

तासामनादित्वं चाशिषो नित्यत्वात् ॥ ४.१० ॥
tāsāmanāditvaṁ cāśiṣo nityatvāt ॥ 4.10 ॥
They [these memories and impressions] are beginning-less, as the will is eternal. *Page 231*

हेतुफलाश्रयालम्बनैः संगृहीतत्वादेषामभावे तदभावः ॥ ४.११ ॥
hetuphalāśrayālambanaiḥ saṁgṛhītatvādeṣāmabhāve tadabhāvaḥ ॥ 4.11 ॥
Because of the connections between cause, result, seat, and dependency, when these cease, they [the impressions also] cease. *Page 232*

अतीतानागतं स्वरूपतोऽस्त्यध्वभेदाद्धर्माणाम् ॥ ४.१२ ॥
atītānāgataṁ svarūpato'styadhvabhedāddharmāṇām ॥ 4.12 ॥
The past and future exist due to the different courses of manifestations taken by properties [of an object]. *Page 233*

ते व्यक्तसूक्ष्मा गुणात्मानः ॥ ४.१३ ॥
te vyaktasūkṣmā guṇātmānaḥ ॥ 4.13 ॥
These [the past and future] — manifest or latent — are made of the three guṇas. *Page 233*

परिणामैकत्वाद्वस्तुतत्त्वम् ॥ ४.१४ ॥

pariṇāmaikatvādvastutattvam ॥ 4.14 ॥
From the uniqueness of its transformation comes the nature of an object. *Page 234*

वस्तुसाम्ये चित्तभेदात्तयोर्विभक्तः पन्थाः ॥ ४.१५ ॥
vastusāmye cittabhedāttayorvibhaktaḥ panthāḥ ॥ 4.15 ॥
While the object is the same, due to difference in minds, the difference in the two [the object known, and the knowledge or perception of it] is due to the separate paths of the minds. *Page 235*

न चैकचित्ततन्त्रं चेद्वस्तु तदप्रमाणकं तदा किं स्यात् ॥ ४.१६ ॥
na caikacittatantraṁ cedvastu tadapramāṇakaṁ tadā kiṁ syāt ॥ 4.16 ॥
An object is not dependent on a single mind. If it were not perceived [by that single mind], then what would the it be (or become)? *Page 236*

तदुपरागापेक्षित्वाच्चित्तस्य वस्तु ज्ञाताज्ञातम् ॥ ४.१७ ॥
taduparāgāpekṣitvāccittasya vastu jñātājñātam ॥ 4.17 ॥
An object is known or not known depending on the coloring of mind by it. *Page 238*

सदा ज्ञाताश्चित्तवृत्तयस्तत्प्रभोः पुरुषस्यापरिणामित्वात् ॥ ४.१८ ॥
sadā jñātāścittavṛttayastatprabhoḥ puruṣasyāpariṇāmitvāt ॥ 4.18 ॥
The activities of the mind are always known, because the lord of the mind, puruṣa, is unchangeable. *Page 238*

न तत्स्वभासं दृश्यत्वात् ॥ ४.१९ ॥
na tat svābhāsaṁ dṛśyatvāt ॥ 4.19 ॥
That [mind] is not self-luminous due to it being an object [of perception]. *Page 240*

एकसमये चोभयानवधारणम् ॥ ४.२० ॥
ekasamaye cobhayānavadhāraṇam ॥ 4.20 ॥
Both [the mind and its object] cannot be perceived at the same time. *Page 240*

चित्तान्तरदृश्ये बुद्धिबुद्धेरतिप्रसङ्गः स्मृतिसङ्करश्च ॥ ४.२१ ॥
cittāntaradṛśye buddhibuddheratiprasaṅgaḥ smṛtisaṁkaraśca ॥ 4.21 ॥
[If] mind were perceived by another [mind], there would be recursion of perceptions by perceptions, and confusion of memory. *Page 242*

चितेरप्रतिसंक्रमायास्तदाकारापत्तौ स्वबुद्धिसंवेदनम् ॥ ४.२२ ॥
citerapratisaṁkramāyāstadākārāpattau svabuddhisaṁvedanam ॥ 4.22 ॥
The unchanging consciousness becomes aware of intellect when it [the intellect] takes the form of [an object]. *Page 244*

द्रष्टृदृश्योपरक्तं चित्तं सर्वार्थम् ॥ ४.२३ ॥
draṣṭṛdṛśyoparaktaṁ cittaṁ sarvārtham ॥ 4.23 ॥
Mind, colored by both the seer and the seen, has various purposes. *Page 245*

तदसंख्येयवासनाभिश्चित्रमपि परार्थं संहत्यकारित्वात् ॥ ४.२४ ॥
tadasaṁkhyeyavāsanābhiścitramapi parārthaṁ saṁhatyakāritvāt ॥ 4.24 ॥
Being imprinted with innumerable impressions, the mind is for the purpose of another [not for itself], because it works with many components. *Page 246*

विशेषदर्शिन आत्मभावभावनाविनिवृत्तिः ॥ ४.२५ ॥
viśeṣadarśina ātmabhāvabhāvanāvinivṛttiḥ ॥ 4.25 ॥
For the one who has the vision of the distinctness [of puruṣa and buddhi] contemplation on the nature of the self ceases. *Page 248*

तदा विवेकनिम्नं कैवल्यप्राग्भारञ्चित्तम् ॥ ४.२६ ॥
tadā vivekanimnaṁ kaivalyaprāgbhāraṁ cittam ॥ 4.26 ॥
Then, the mind inclined toward discrimination gravitates toward isolation. *Page 248*

तच्छिद्रेषु प्रत्ययान्तराणि संस्कारेभ्यः ॥ ४.२७ ॥
tacchidreṣu pratyayāntarāṇi saṁskārebhyaḥ ॥ 4.27 ॥
During the intervals [between discriminating wisdom], the perception of other things arises due to latent impressions. *Page 249*

हानमेषां क्लेशवदुक्तम् ॥ ४.२८ ॥
hānameṣāṁ kleśavaduktam ॥ 4.28 ॥
It is said that these [latent impressions] should be eliminated like the afflictions (kleśas). *Page 250*

प्रसंख्यानेऽप्यकुसीदस्य सर्वथा विवेकख्यातेर्धर्ममेधस्समाधिः ॥ ४.२९ ॥
prasaṁkhyāne'pyakusīdasya sarvathāvivekakhyāterdharmameghaḥ samādhiḥ ॥ 4.29 ॥
For the one who is disinterested in meditative knowledge, and [having] a complete vision of discernment, [there is] dharmamegha-samādhiḥ. *Page 250*

ततः क्लेशकर्मनिवृत्तिः ॥ ४.३० ॥
tataḥ kleśakarmanivṛttiḥ ॥ 4.30 ॥
From that [results] the cessation of afflictions and actions. *Page 251*

तदा सर्वावरणमलापेतस्य ज्ञानस्यानन्त्याज्ज्ञेयमल्पम् ॥ ४.३१ ॥
tadā sarvāvaraṇamalāpetasya jñānasyānantyājjñeyamalpam ॥ 4.31 ॥
Because the knowledge obtained when all the impurities are removed is limitless, little remains to be known. *Page 251*

ततः कृतार्थानां परिणामक्रमसमाप्तिर्गुणानाम् ॥ ४.३२ ॥
tataḥ kṛtārthānāṁ pariṇāmakramasamāptirguṇānām ॥ 4.32 ॥
From that [dharmamegha-samādhi], comes the end of the sequence of transformation of the guṇas, which have fulfilled their purpose. *Page 252*

क्षणप्रतियोगी परिणामापरान्तनिर्ग्राह्यः क्रमः ॥ ४.३३ ॥
kṣaṇapratiyogī pariṇāmāparāntanirgrāhyaḥ kramaḥ ॥ 4.33 ॥

Connected with moments, the transformation that is perceptible at their end is "sequence" (krama). *Page 252*

पुरुषार्थशून्यानां गुणानां प्रतिप्रसवः कैवल्यं स्वरूपप्रतिष्ठा वा चितिशक्तिरिति ॥ ४.३४ ॥
puruṣārthaśūnyānāṁ guṇānāṁ pratiprasavaḥ kaivalyaṁ svarūpapratiṣṭhā vā citiśaktiriti ॥ 4.34 ॥
One-ness with self or complete liberation (kaivalya) is when the guṇas are devoid of purpose for puruṣa, and are re-absorbed. Or [it is] the establishement of the power of consciousness in its own form. *Page 253*

Bibliography

Sources for Sanskrit Text

The Sanskrit verses and text used in this book are sourced from the works listed below. I have relied on my translation for the quoted verses and text. When quoting another author's text, I have cited and translated it to English (from Hindi).

Yoga Sūtras: The Sanskrit text of the sūtras is based on a comparison of the following editions.

- Āraṇya, Swāmi Hariharānanda. *Pātañjala-yogadarśan*. Delhi: Motilal Banarsidas, 1980.
- Bangali, Baba. *Yogasūtra of Patanjali*: With Commentary of Vyasa. Columbia: South Asia Books, 1990.
- Bryant, Edwin F. *The Yoga Sūtras of Patañjali*. New York: North Point Press, 2009.

Sāṅkhya-darśana:

- Acharya Ananda Prakash, *Sāṅkhya-darśanam*. Aliabad: Arsha-shodha-samsthan, 2008

Mahābhārata:

- Sukthankar, Vishnu S. and Shrimant Balasaheb Pant Pratinidhi, Critical Ed. *Mahābhārata*. Bhandarkar Oriental Research Institute: Pune, India, 1999.

Bhagavadgītā:

- Swami Chidbhavananda, *The Bhagavadgītā*. Tirupparaithurai: Sri Ramakrishna Tapovanam, 2005.

Muṇḍakopaniṣad:

- C.N. Sitaram. *Muṇḍakopaniṣad With four commentaries*. Melukote: Saṁskṛt-saṁśodhana-saṁsat, 2005.

Kaṭhopaniṣad:

- Shastri, Pandit Jagadish. *Upaniṣatsaṅgraha*. Delhi: Motilal Banarsidas, 1970.

Yajurveda:

- Yajurvedasaṁhitā. Delhi: Nāg Publishers, 2004.

Brahmavaivarta-purāṇa:

- Sharma, Pandit Shriram Acharya. *Brahmavaivarta Purāṇa*. Bareli: Saṁskriti Saṁsthān, 1970.

Other Works Consulted

- Chakrabarty, Debasish. *Vaiśeṣika-sūtra of Kaṇāda*. New Delhi: D.K. Printworld, 2003.
- Goyandka, Harikrishnadas. *Yoga-darśan*. Gorakhpur, India: Gita Press, 2008.
- Larson, G.J., and Bhattacharya, R.S. *Encyclopedia of Indian Philosophies*. New Delhi: Motilal Banarsidass, 2011.
- Leggett, Trevor. *Śaṅkara on the Yoga Sūtras*. New Delhi: Motilal Banarsidas, 1996.
- Muller Max. *The Six Systems of Indian Philosophy*. London and Bombay: Longmans, Green & Co, 2010.
- Parivrajaka, Swami Satyapati. *Yogadarśan*. Rojad, Gujarat, India: Darśana Yoga Mahāvidyālaya, 2001.
- Saraswati Swami Dayananda. *Satyārthaprakāsh*. New Delhi: Vijaykumar Govindram Hasanand, 2000.
- Shastri, Acharya Udayveer. *Sāṅkhya-siddhant*. New Delhi: Vijaykumar Govindram Hasanand, 2000.
- Shastri, Janardhana. *Sāṅkhyadarśanam: aniruddhakṛtā vṛttiḥ, vedantimahādevakṛto vṛttisāraḥ, vijñānabhikṣukṛtaṁ bhāṣyam, nāgeśabhaṭṭakṛto bhāṣyasāraśceti vyākhyācatuṣṭopetam*. New Delhi: Motilal Banarsidas, 1989.
- Swami Vivekananda. *Rāja Yoga*. New York: Ramakrishna-Vivekananda Center of New York, 1980.
- T.S. Rukmani. *Yogavārttika of Vijñānabhikṣu*. New Delhi: Munshiram Manoharlal, 1981.

Glossary

Abhiniveśā Clinging to physical life, fear of death.
Abhyāsa Practice.
Adharma Non-righteous or non-virtuous action.
Ādhibhautika Suffering caused by other beings, such as a bite from a snake or dog.
Ādhidaivika Suffering caused by a natural calamity, such as an earthquake, flood, or tornado.
Ādhyātmika Suffering caused by one's own body and mind, such as depression, trauma, or frustration.
Āgama Verbal testimony of those free from desire and ego.
Ahaṅkāra The second evolute of nature. This is also the component of the mind responsible for the feeling of "I am." *Ahaṅkāra* is translated as "ego."
Akliṣṭa Non-detrimental, leading to liberation.
A*liṅga* Non-indicatory. Something that does not have a discernible feature. A*liṅga-prakṛti* is nature in its equilibrium state which cannot be perceived.
Ānanda Bliss.
Aṅgamejayatva Trembling, tremors of the limbs of the body.
Anumāna Inference.
Apavarga Detachment and liberation from nature.
Āpūra Abundance.
Ariṣṭa A bad omen.
Artha Wealth. Also means a stage of life in which a person earns wealth, after finishing studies.
Asamprajñāta-samādhi A state of mental concentration in which all the activities of the mind are subdued.
Āsana Posture.
Asmitā The feeling of "I am"-ness (ego).
Āśrama A stage of life. Four stages of life are recognized in Indian culture: bachelorhood (*brahmacarya*), household life (*gṛhastha*), pre-renunciation (*vānaprastha*), and renunciation (*saṁnyāsa*).
Aṣṭāṅga The eight limbs of yoga.
Ātma The soul.
Bhakti-yoga A practice of Yoga that emphasizes devotion to God as the primary means to attain self-realization; *Bhakti* is devotion.
Bhoga Experience and enjoyment of nature.
Bhūmi 1) a stage of attainment (of the mind). 2) One of the five states of mind: *mūḍha*, *kṣipta*, *vikṣipta*, *ekāgra*, and *niruddha*.

Bhūtas The five gross elements of nature which are earth, water, fire, air, and space.
Brahmacarya Bachelorhood, celibacy.
Brahman The Creator, another name for God.
Brāhmanas and *Āranyakas* Works explaining Vedic hymns.
Buddhi The first evolute of the nature, the intellect — which is part of the mind.
Citta The mind, consisting of intellect (*buddhi*), ego (*ahaṅkāra*), and the coordinator of sense and motor organs (*manas*).
Citta-vṛtti Activity of the mind.
Darśanas The six sciences or systems of philosophy of ancient India. They are also called "orthodox" systems of Hindu philosophy for their belief in the existence of God and (or) the *Vedas*.
Daurmanasya Dejection, depression.
Dharma This word has two different meanings in two different contexts: 1) righteous or virtuous action, and 2) a property or form.
Dharmī Form-holder. Anything that can hold a property or form like a clay can hold the property of a pot or a plate. The pot and plate will be the properties, or *dharmas,* of the clay.
Dhāraṇā Placing attention, focusing on something.
Dhyāna Maintaining continued focus on something, meditating.
Doṣa Three combinations of the five gross elements of nature are called "doṣas," and are recognized as the basic bodily elements or humors in Ayurveda. The three *doṣas* are *vāta*, *pitta*, and *kapha* (or *śleṣma*). *Vāta* has the qualities of air, *pitta* of fire, and *kapha* of water. A balanced composition and working of the three doṣas is said to constitute good health.
Draṣṭā The seer, experiencer. This refers to the consciousness (the soul).
Dṛś The Sanskrit root word meaning "to see."
Dṛshya The seen. This refers to the mind and the universe that we come into contact with and experience.
Duḥkha Misery, sorrow, frustration.
Dveṣa Aversion, hatred.
Ekāgra One of the five states of mind in which the mind is completely focused on one thing.
Gṛhastha Household life.
Guṇa Any of the three primary constituents of natural existence: *sattva*, *rajas*, or *tamas*.
Gurukula A place of education in ancient India, usually situated in forests — away from worldly life. Rishis and yogīs perform the activities of teaching.
Haṭha-yoga A kind of Yoga that involves physical practices intended to aid in spiritual practice. *Haṭha* means forceful.

Hānam Relinquishment or elimination of misery.
Hānopāyaḥ The method of relinquishing or eliminating misery.
Heyam That which is to be abandoned or avoided (misery).
Heya-hetuḥ Cause of misery.
Indriyas Instruments. This refers to the sense and motor organs.
Īśvara Lord, God.
Īśvarapraṇidhāna Devotion to God.
Jātyantara-pariṇāma Change in class or species.
Jñānendriyas Instruments of knowledge — the instruments of hearing, touch, sight, taste, and smell.
Jñātā Knower.
Kaivalya Being by oneself, complete independence and freedom.
Kalpa Span of time equivalent to 4,320 million years.
Karmendriyas Instruments of action — the instruments of speech, grasping, locomotion, excretion, and gratification.
Kāma Desire. Also, a stage of life in a person spent in fulfilling one's physical and mental desires.
Kleśa Affliction, obstacle. There are five afflictions: incorrect knowledge, ego, attachment, aversion, and clinging to physical life.
Kliṣṭa Detrimental, producing misery.
Kṣaṇikavāda The principle stating that everything we experience is momentary and illusory.
Kūṭasthanitya Unchanging, eternal. This is used to qualify consciousness (the soul), which does not undergo transformation like our mind and the universe.
Jñāna-yoga A kind of Yoga that emphasizes study and intellectual insight to achieve self-realization. *Jñāna* means knowledge.
Karma-yoga A kind of Yoga practice that emphasizes "right action" as the means to liberation. *Karma* means action.
Krama The smallest perceptible change.
Kriyamāṇa Actions currently being performed.
Kriyā-yoga Yoga practice that consists of austerity, self-study and introspection, and devotion to God. *Kriyā* means activity.
Kṣipta One of the five states of mind dominated by distraction.
Liṅga-prakṛti Indicatory nature, the nature that is perceptible after evolution has started. *Liṅga* refers to a symbol that can be perceived.
Mahat The first evolute of primordial nature. It is also called *buddhi*. Usually the part of mahat that is used as "intellect" for an individual soul is called *buddhi*. The part of the *mahat* not used as the intellect undergoes further evolution to produce *ahaṅkāra* (ego) and other evolutes.

Manas The component of the subtle mind that coordinates the five sense and five motor organs.
Mantra A sacred incantation or hymn. It also means a secret.
Mokṣa Liberation from the cycle of birth and death. Liberation from all misery.
Mūḍha One of the five states of mind dominated by dullness, depression, and confusion.
Mūla-prakṛti The primordial matter in which the elements — *sattva*, *rajas,* and *tamas* — are in equilibrium. This is the state before the evolution of nature. This is also called *Aliṅga-prakṛti*, *Mūla-prakṛti*, or *Pradhāna*.
Nidrā Sleep.
Nimitta Cause, usually an efficient or instrumental cause.
Nirvicāra A state of mental concentration on a subtle object (like *tanmātras*) in which there is no awareness of the word, or the meaning of the word, related to the object. The awareness of time, space, and causal factors of the subtle object are eliminated — just the object shines forth.
Niruddha One of the five states of mind in which all the activities of the mind are subdued. In this state the consciousness (the soul) remains in its own state.
Nirupakrama Another name for *sañcita*.
Nirvitarka A state of mental concentration on a gross object in which there is awareness of the object, but the awareness of the word and its meaning related to the object is not present.
Niyama Observances consisting of cleanliness, contentment, austerities, self-study, and devotion to God.
Nyāya One of the six *darśanas*. It discusses methods of investigating the truth (reality), methods of proof, and the art of argumentation. Gautama is the author of the Nyāya-darśana.
Oṣadhi Medicine. Medicinal herb.
Paramātmā The great Soul, God.
Parāntakāla The span of liberation — 311,040,000 million years (311.04 trillion years).
Pariṇāma Transformation, change, consequence, result.
Pariṇāmanitya Eternal change. This is used to describe both the universe and our minds, which undergo transformations constantly.
Prabhu Lord, owner.
Pradhāna The primordial matter in which the elements — *sattva*, *rajas* and *tamas* — are in equilibrium. This is the state before the evolution of nature. It is also called *Aliṅga-prakṛti* or *Mūla-prakṛti*.
Prajñā Wisdom, insight, knowledge.
Prakṛti The primordial matter in which the three elements of *sattva*, *rajas*, and *tamas* are in equilibrium.

Pramāṇa Correct knowledge.

Prāṇāyāma Regulating, expanding vital airs.

Prārabdha Previously-performed actions, the results of which are currently being experienced.

Prasupta Dormant (describing a state of a mental affliction).

Pratipakṣabhāvanam Oppositional thinking. This consists of cultivating the attitude that transgressing thoughts, such as harming and the rest — either done, caused to be done, or approved; arising from greed, anger, or delusion; minor, moderate, or excessive — result in unending fruits of misery and ignorance.

Pratyāhāra Withdrawal of the senses.

Pratyakṣa Direct perception with one's own senses.

Puruṣa Individual consciousness (the soul).

Puruṣārtha One of the four pursuits of human life. The four *puruṣārthas* are 1) right conduct, 2) earning wealth, 3) fulfilling physical and mental desires, and 4) liberation from all misery.

Pūrva Mīmāṁsā One of the six *darśanas*. It discusses virtuous conduct and the interpretation of the *Vedas* (and associated rituals). Sage *Jaimini* was the composer of this work. It is also called *Dakṣiṇa Mīmāṁsā*.

Rāga Attachment.

Rajas One of the three *guṇas*. *Rajas* is the provoker, motivator, and that which is always moving. It imparts movement to anything that comes into contact with it.

Rāja-yoga This refers to any type of meditational practice. It usually means yogic practice as described by Patañjali. *Rāja* means royal.

Ṛtambharā The mind that only illumines or holds true knowledge.

Samādhi Absorption, perfected concentration. It is a deep state of meditation wherein the mind is completely absorbed in the object of contemplation.

Sāmānya-jñāna Common knowledge of a thing learned by reading or hearing about it.

Saṁnyāsa Renunciation, the final stage of life.

Samprajñāta-samādhi A state of mental concentration in which only one object of thinking remains, without even the awareness of the meditator.

Saṁskāra A mental impression. Every action or thought results in an impression on the mind.

Sañcita Previously performed, but the results of which are yet to be experienced.

Sāṅkhya One of the six *darśanas*. It discusses the distinction between consciousness (*puruṣa*) and nature (*prakṛti*). The great sage *Kapila* is considered the founder of this philosophy.

Santoṣa Pleasantness.

Satkārya The principle that all effects are present in the cause in an un-manifested state.

Sattva One of the three *guṇas*. *Sattva* is light (in the sense of not being heavy) and luminous.

Śauca Cleanliness.

Savicāra A state of mental concentration on a subtle object (like *tanmātras*) in which there is awareness of the word, the object denoted, and the meaning or knowledge of the word. It also contains an awareness of time, space, and causal factors of the subtle object.

Savitarka A state of mental concentration on a gross object in which there is awareness of the word, the object denoted by the word, and the meaning or knowledge of the word.

Siddhis Attainments, powers.

Smṛti Memory.

Sopakrama Another name for *prārabdha.*

Sphoṭa A mental word that is a single unit without parts, and which triggers impressions of the object in the mind of the listener.

Sthūla-bhūtas The gross elements — earth, water, fire, air, and space.

Sukha Happiness.

Sūtra A highly-condensed, succinct principle.

Svābhāsaṁ Self luminous, meaning self-knowing.

Svādhyāya The study of scriptures on one's own. This also means reciting or repeating hymns or prayers, and can also be interpreted as the study of one's own self (introspection).

Svāmi Lord, owner.

Svarūpa-pratiṣṭhā Establishment of the consciousness (the soul) in its own state.

Śvāsapraśvāsa Uncontrolled inhaling and exhalation.

Tamas One of the three *guṇas*. Tamas is heavy and functions as a stabilizer — arresting the movement of anything that comes into contact with it is its fundamental quality.

Tanmātras The five subtle elements of the nature that undergo transformation to form the five gross elements of nature.

Tanu Diminished, attenuated (a state of mental affliction).

Tapas Austerity, the behavior of bearing all hardships and dualities while performing one's duties in life. Dualities are pairs of extremes — for example, heat and cold, or praise and insult.

Udāra Magnified (a state of mental affliction).

Upaniṣads Works containing explanations of specific topics that occur in the *Vedas*. These were written to be easily understood by everyone.

Upavedas Four "sub-Vedas" — Medicine (*āyurveda*), Musicology (*gāndharvaveda*), the science of warfare (*dhanurveda*), and Economics and Commerce (*arthaveda*).

Vairāgya Detachment.

Vaiśeṣika One of the six *darśanas*. It discusses the various categories of substances and entities found in the universe, atomic theory, and proof. This work was developed by *Kaṇāda*.

Vānaprastha The pre-renunciation stage of life.

Vāsanā A mental impression. This usually refers to latent impressions that are not currently active.

Vedāṅgas The six limbs of the *Vedas*. They are Phonetics (*śikṣā*), Grammar (*vyākarana*), Etymology (*nirukta*), Poetic Rhythm (*chandas*), Manuals of Rituals and Duties (*kalpa*), and Mathematics (*jyotiśa*), which includes astronomy, algebra, trigonometry, and so on. These are essential to understanding the *Vedas*.

Vedānta One of the six *darśanas*. It discusses the nature of *God* (Brahma). This darśana is attributed to Sage *Bādarāyaṇa*. This work is also called the *Uttara Mīmāṁsā* or *Brahmasūtras*.

Vedas Ancient Indian scriptures, traditionally believed to be the source of material and spiritual knowledge in India. They are thought to be divinely inspired. There are four *Vedas*: *Ṛg*, *Yajur*, *Sāma*, and *Atharva*. In ancient times, the *Vedas* were communicated orally, and so are also called *śruti*, "that which is heard."

Vibhūti Supernatural power.

Vicchinna Interrupted (a state of mental affliction).

Vidyā Knowledge, education.

Vikalpa Imagination, conceptualization.

Vikṣipta One of the five states of mind in which one has partial ability to focus.

Viparyaya Incorrect knowledge, error.

Viśeṣa-jñāna Specific knowledge of a thing learned through direct perception with one's own sense organs, as opposed to the common knowledge that is got by reading or hearing about it.

Viveka Discernment.

Viveka-khyāti Vision of discernment.

Yama Restraints consisting of non-harming, truth, non-stealing, celibacy, and non-grasping (refraining from accumulating).

Yoga One of the six *darśanas*. It elaborates on the control of the mind that enables the distinction between consciousness and nature (and the overall goal of *Sāṅkhya*). *Patañjali* codified this body of knowledge into the *Yoga-darśana*. The word "yoga" also refers to the spiritual practice, as elaborated in the *Yoga Sūtras*.

Index

A

B

C

D

R

S

T

U

V

Y